THE BROOK KERITH

George Moore

GEORGE MOORE
THE BROOK KERITH
A SYRIAN STORY
WITH TWELVE ENGRAVINGS
BY
STEPHEN GOODEN
With a Preface by Professor **WALTER JAMES MILLER**

LIVERIGHT PUBLISHING CORPORATION
NEW YORK

THE BROOK KERITH

LIST OF ILLUSTRATIONS

FOREWORD

Time is now ripe for *The Brook Kerith* to come into its own as one of the major novels of the twentieth century.

George Moore gauged his earlier works for immediate acceptance; some—like *Esther Waters*—earned both instant and enduring popularity. His reputation thus secured, he composed his later books with more attention to the potentialities of the art than of the market. Audacious, experimental works like *The Brook Kerith*, his fictionalized study of Jesus Christ, have had to wait for public taste and public need to catch up with their pioneering creator.

These necessary revolutions have now taken place. Discovery and analyses of the Dead Sea Scrolls, and controversial speculations like Dr. Hugh Schonfield's *The Passover Plot*, have created a new and widespread secular interest in the life and times of Jesus. Growing excitement over William Faulkner's novels indicates that today's reader is eager to explore the "subjectivist" dimension in fiction. And now that every high school student knows that in *The Waste Land* "April is the cruellest month," we may assume that a larger audience exists for other modern classics of a "mythopoeic" nature.

Hence I feel that in its themes, in its methods of revealing character, and in its style, *The Brook Kerith* is today —more so than when it was first published—a work of contemporary interest.

1.

From W. B. Yeats to Shirley Jackson, modern writers have deliberately reinterpreted the ancient fertility myths that explore man's relation to the cycles of Nature and of history. With that incredible sense of the future that always puts him in the vanguard of literary adventurers, Moore was one of the first to tackle this theme in a modern manner. But instead of reworking and generalizing the mythic materials in terms of the "rough beast" that "slouches towards Bethlehem to be born," or in terms of "The Lottery" to choose this year's scapegoat, Moore went directly to that great symbolic statement of man's yearnings for purification and renewal: the story of the last days of Jesus and the early days of Christianity.

Since the New Testament is only one source of information about and interpretation of those "Days," and since he was interested in a broader reconstruction, Moore went beyond Christian Scriptures for his materials. Fascinated with the belief of some scholars that Jesus had been reared in the Essene brotherhood, Moore absorbed everything that Josephus, Philo and other writers had to say about that dissident Hebrew sect. Fascinated too with the traditional Hebrew legend that Jesus was alive when taken down from the Cross, Moore learned everything he could about the techniques of crucifixion and known survivals.

His sensitivity to hypotheses implicit in these materials is evident to us when, reading recent popular books like Edmund Wilson's *Dead Sea Scrolls* (1956) and Schonfield's *Passover Plot* (1966), we find passage after passage that bears out some insight that Moore had already used in *The Brook Kerith*. Moore, for example, partly explored a possible identification of Joseph of Arimathea with Josephus himself. And Moore, like Schonfield, saw the difficulty of reconciling the Fourth Gospel account of the centurion's spear-thrust with any belief that Jesus ultimately recovered.

But Moore's success depends least on his ingenious reworking of details and most on his tackling of this provocative question: *If Jesus did survive the Crucifixion,*
viii

what was his opinion in later years of his early ministry? of his doctrines? of his sacrifice? and of his old and new relations with God?

2.

Since Joseph of Arimathea is a major figure in the Crucifixion story about whom history tells us little, Moore seized upon him as the character he could most freely improvise. With consummate skill, Moore made Joseph a personality that serves both the historical facts, the reader's needs to know the intellectual climate of "The Last Times," and the author's needs in remaking the myth.

Moore's Joseph is the son of a rich trader with powerful political and religious connections; the young man enjoys financial means to study Hebrew and Greek with the best tutors, to dabble in philosophy and to travel post-haste wherever his commercial interests or intellectual whims take him. His quest for an ideology brings him into close contact with Pharisees, Sadducees, Essenes, Alexandrian Jews and Samaritans. Since Joseph is something of a chameleon, he is likely to assume the coloration of each succeeding environment; as a consequence, the reader comes to know the whole spectrum of Jewish thought in the time of Herod, even the ultra-violet blendings into Hellenistic concepts. A business man who is self-consciously aware of the nature of the class struggle, an inveterate hero-worshipper with conflicting loyalties, Joseph is a complex and human character. It is he, of course, who has the means to manage Jesus' survival and escape; and ironically, it is Joseph who becomes the real scapegoat.

In Moore's version of the Messiah story, Jesus' character development occurs mainly *after* the Crucifixion. Long after his body and mind have mended from his ordeal, he is able at last to review the career that led him to Golgotha. He remembers now that in his conviction that he was bringing gentle truth and love to all men, he was actually burning with cruel resolve and even malignant hate. In later life he becomes more an Oedipus than a Christ, a leader remorsefully aware now of his own *hubris*, grateful for this second life in which to atone for the arrogant errors of the first.

These "errors," though, did not "die" with him on the Cross. In what must surely be regarded as one of the great confrontations in all imaginative literature, Moore brings up the rocky path to the Essene cenoby, up to Jesus' retreat in retirement—*Paul of Tarsus, Apostle of the Lord Jesus Christ!*

What follows is subtle, poignant, and reverberative drama of ideas, reaching at times the greatness of *Antigone, Julius Caesar, The Heart of Darkness, Viva Zapata*. Paul is Jesus' double, the "other self" he has rejected, the self that once descended into the depths of evil, the proselytizing and self-righteous self that is now on the way to Rome . . . and into history. Typical of the irony in these climactic scenes is that delicious moment when the shepherd Jesus, who speaks only Aramaic, has to ask what "Christ" means.

"It's a Greek word," he is told.

Like the original twelve disciples whom he fiercely condemns, Paul is represented as unconsciously obsessed with power. Before the Crucifixion, the top members of the twelve had squabbled continually about the relative seniority they would enjoy in the coming Kingdom of God on earth. And now Paul's dramatic conversion, his superior intelligence, and his philosophical sophistication have complicated the struggle for control of the new religion.

Women, significantly, play unproductive or even destructive roles; the only sympathetically drawn woman is a mother-figure; most of the men are either on the defensive against or in full flight from sex. Nicodemus, another character whom history authorizes Moore to "create," moves through the story like a giant epicene Narcissus.

x

In his reworking of the Christ theme, then, Moore seems to be reminding us that our most noble conceptions of the fertility-and-lustration cycle are—just like the most primitive versions—shot through with ugly impotence and ignoble desires. Closely analyzed, morality and love seem admixtured of equal parts immorality and hate. Ideas can drive men as well as lead them; the baser motives can also enter the lists clad in the bright armor of abstract ideas. But these conclusions may clarify somewhat for us later on.

3.

The Brook Kerith is written in Moore's "melodic line," one of the most famous (and controversial) experiments in the history of prose style. Many factors in Moore's life seem to have blended to produce this "final manner." He was apparently the first in the English-speaking world to appreciate the possibilities suggested by Edouard Dujardin's *Les Lauriers sont Coupés* (1888), a work that employs a kind of rudimentary stream of consciousness. While much ink has been spilled in controversies over whether Dujardin really influenced James Joyce, not much has been wasted in doubting Dujardin's impact on Moore. Another factor was Moore's appreciation of the Wagnerian concept of *die unendliche Melodie;* Moore was determined to produce a prose that developed in a kind of "continuous transition." And then once when Moore tried to compose by dictating to a stenographer, he discovered that the transcribed language delivered to him was excitingly different from that of his earlier writing. Instead of revising by putting pen to paper, he then dictated from the first draft, thus composing orally his second and even his *nth* drafts, until he had refined the mellifluous prose he was seeking. And finally, as he grew older, he became more and more interested in blending all elements of the story— dialogue, unspoken thought, description—into one narrative stream; he even rewrote his earlier works to achieve this narrative unity.

In *The Brook Kerith* Moore tells his story by "tuning in" on the consciousness of his characters. While Moore may at any time be emphasizing one character's point of view—in the first half, mainly Joseph's; in the second, mainly Jesus'—he often blurs the outlines of the characters and allows their separate consciousnesses to merge. Past may blend into present, and what appears to be an abrupt jump ahead in time is often only the inner experience catching up with the outer.

Thus a dream can blend into an effort to recall the dream; contemplation of an excuse blends into the dialogue in which the excuse is offered. We may experience one character's wonderment as unspoken until we hear another character's reply to it. Often we do not know whether a sentence is narrative, dialogue, or interior monologue until we are well into the sentence. And the point of view may change even then!

This flow of disembodied and mingling consciousnesses is cast in an alternation of short and long sentences, the latter unique because their syntax is not what we expect in long sentences. Whether the action is recalled, present, or anticipated, the present participle (suffer*ing*, think*ing*) and the infinitive phrase (*to* know, *to* speak) are invoked continually to make all tenses seem more like the present.

All separate past and present experience becomes simultaneous and shared in another way: Moore uses parallels in his action. After Jesus atones for an egregious blasphemy, the *motif* of man's need for self-rehabilitation is continued in the career of his apprentice Jacob. After Jesus' action has made a mockery of his ideals, the *motif* of self-mockery through putting theory into practice is continued in the disastrous experiment of the Essenes of the Lake. And inner and outer reality blend in the symbol. Jesus' hunt for a ram that will sire a new strain in his

xii

flock of course symbolizes his intuitive return to the world of physical immortality. This leads to his realizing that God is pantheistic in nature: He inhabits the breeze, the earth, the stream. Notice that the ram is named Caesar ("Render unto Caesar . . ."), and that when Jesus is about to slip into final despair after learning of Joseph's sacrifice, the world wins Jesus back through Caesar. "What is mine" and "what is Caesar's" become one again.

This melodic line, this fugal prose, is difficult only if the reader resists it. Moore was a Symbolist even in his attempt to make the music of language carry the meaning. The reader must not mistake a certain hypnotic effect as a sign that his mind is wandering; Moore wants the reader to experience a trance-like sensation. Moore intends that the reader, slipping into the "flow" of inner and outer reality, will achieve unity with the cosmos. Like Joseph, he will "hear the stars throbbing."

4.

Relationships between Moore's many books and different styles—and even, in my opinion, the characterizations in *The Brook Kerith*—take on greater significance for the reader who knows a few crucial facts about the life and times of George Moore.

Born in Mayo County, Ireland, in 1852, Moore was descended from a long line of restless, contentious, unpredictable Irish landowners; raised amidst peasant uprisings in which his own family's views were violently opposed to their class interests, George Moore became a restless, contentious, self-opposed young landlord who turned to the creative arts to try to make sense out of life.

As soon as he reached his majority, he went to Paris to study painting. There he associated with most of the experimental writers of the day, wrote some ineffectual "decadent" poetry, and suddenly—one morning when reading an article by Émile Zola—became a Zolaist. That is to say, he embraced Zola's theory of "naturalism" and he decided to become the first naturalistic novelist in the English language.

Basic to Zola's programme was the idea of systematically studying characters as products of heredity and environment. The writer, Zola said, must approach his material with an open mind, scrap all "accepted notions," "sentimental attachments," and moral judgments, and observe and record data on the human condition. The Zolaist would also scrap the conventional "plot," which he saw as a tendentious tampering with the data of life to create a moral effect: as when novels and plays end with virtue rewarded, evil crushed. Instead of inventing a plot, the Zola disciple would set up a kind of experimental situation, trace the chain of causation in the life and circumstances of his characters, and write something akin to a laboratory report.

Maybe one reason Moore was converted to this Darwinist, positivist, free-thinking approach was that he himself, on the surface at least, was astonishingly explicable in terms of ancestry and milieu. Another is that he felt a chronic urge to experiment with the new. Not to be overlooked at all is the fact that Zolaism offered irresistible opportunities for shocking the staid, conventional-minded middle-class. *Épater le bourgeois* was the artist's favorite hobby in nineteenth-century "decadent" France as in twentieth-century "hipster" America.

Moore began systematically to observe the causes and effects of his room-mate's behavior, a study that produced his first novel, a pale and attenuated book. *A Modern Lover* was labeled "immoral" and undisplayable by the circulating libraries which, at the time, controlled English literature. Since novels were printed then in expensive three-volume editions, most readers preferred to rent their books and, consequently, circulating libraries were the real quantity buyers.

But with his second book Moore was to crash through

xiv

on every front. He designed a naturalistic "experiment" to determine a middle-class woman's reaction to an extreme change in her environment. Notebook in hand, he studied shops, homes, and pottery works of Hanley, one of the Five Towns, and then joined a light-opera comedy, a group of "mummers," that played a circuit that included Hanley. With massive documentation on hand he chronicled, in bare-as-bones style, the growth and decay of pretty, dreamy Kate Ede.

Acting on Zola's advice, Moore by-passed the circulating libraries; his publisher took the revolutionary step of printing *A Mummer's Wife* in a cheap one-volume format that the average man could—and did—buy outright. Libraries and some critics piously denounced the novel for exploring all the unmentionables, and Moore was ready with a witty pamphlet, *Literature at Nurse, or Circulating Morals*, which defended the writer's right to write and the reader's right to read whatever their impulses dictated. Many newspapers supported Moore's position and the book sold and sold.

Moore, in other words, freed English writers from dictatorship by a monopoly and opened new areas of subject-matter for them to explore.

By the time he published his most famous work, *Esther Waters* (1894), Moore was already moving steadily away from the naturalistic style but not entirely away from the naturalist's methods. He renounced Zolaism as "crude" and "unspiritual"; coming more and more under the sway of Walter Pater, he decided to develop a "lush" style. As we have seen, he became more concerned with the quality of inner rather than outer reality. He even wrote his *Hail and Farewell* (1911-1914), a three-volume memoir and one of the great books of our times, as an extended stream of recollections, selected by free association.

But all his life—and he wrote almost to the day of his death in 1933—he used the naturalist's techniques of research. For example, while working on *The Brook Kerith*, he made a trip to the Holy Land to obtain first-hand descriptions of terrain, trees, and camels; he had artist's sketches made to order to keep his memory fresh while writing; he drew heavily on the biblical scholarship of his friend Dujardin; he corresponded with friends about the validity of his characterizations of Jesus and Paul. And what had begun, in his naturalist period, as liberation from plot and concern instead with the mesh of circumstance became now, in his "subjectivist" period, a concern with continuous transition, the mesh of inner experience. Essential continuity in his ideas about novel-structure is revealed in a comparison of his own early discussion of Zola's *L'Assommoir* with his own later description of *The Brook Kerith*. In both he used a master image of a flowing current of water.

With what some people would call a "weak chin"; with what most people call "walrus moustaches"; and with what he himself called "champagne-bottle shoulders," Moore was not prepossessing in appearance. He never married and was apparently free of serious romantic attachments. He was the butt of a famous epigram in this respect; Susan Mitchell said of him that he "didn't kiss, but told." As a matter of fact, Moore was the butt of many witty jibes: he had a talent for drawing fire as well as praise from distinguished people. They became obsessed with him. T. S. Eliot, it is said, stopped visiting W. B. Yeats because all Yeats talked about was "spooks and George Moore." Yeats was the author of the most deflating criticism of the "melodic line," which he described as "toothpaste squeezed from a tube." And Moore's successive advocacy of so many distinctly different styles and movements provoked Oscar Wilde's comment that "Moore conducts his education in public." These "inner circle" criticisms confirm the obvious fact that Moore was a lone wolf; as his epitaph, carved on a rock on an island in

Lough Carra, explains it, he "deserted his family and his friends" for the sake of his art.

Family, friends, and circulating libraries suffered, perhaps, but art benefited. As Malcolm Brown wrote in his *George Moore: A Reconsideration:*

"It is owing to George Moore as much as to any artist of his time that the formlessness, the sentimentality, the tendentiousness, the evangelical piety, the compulsive dishonesty that were once all but universal in English fiction have today disappeared from the serious novels written in our language."

Perhaps, then, *The Brook Kerith* was not all naturalistic research and mythopoeic reconstruction. Perhaps it is also a profoundly personal work. George Moore, it can be said, unconsciously used the "fractionation" technique in creating his characters. The inner dynamics of Joseph the trader-philosopher is similar to the inner dynamics of Moore the landlord-artist. The Joseph who went from Pharisaism to Essenism to Christianity, hero-worshipping one teacher after another, is akin to the Moore who swung from Zolaism to Paterism, now an Ibsenite, now a Wagnerian. The Jesus who drove the money-changers from the Temple is akin to the writer who drove the monopolists out of English literature. The Jesus who in his second life looks back in dismay on his first life may derive from the older Moore who looked back on his days as a Zolaist Zealot and said: "What madness! Were we ever as mad as that?"

Yet Moore's madness seems central to his fertility. We see his influence everywhere. He staked out the Five Towns as literary territory for Arnold Bennett; *A Mummer's Wife* provided a model for *The Old Wives' Tale*. Moore's *Mike Fletcher* was a kind of rough sketch for Wilde's *Picture of Dorian Gray*. Moore's experiments in prose rhythms, I believe, influenced J. M. Synge's dialogue; in trying out musical forms in fiction, Moore anticipated Ralph Bates's experiment in *The Olive Field;* and Moore's multiple point-of-view device is certainly reflected in contemporary writers like J. P. Donleavy.

Madness—and I guess this must be the ultimate point in both *The Brook Kerith* and in Moore's own life—can be absolutely germinal.

WALTER JAMES MILLER

Professor of English
New York University
October 1969

THE BROOK KERITH

CHAPTER I.

IT was at the end of a summer evening, long after his usual bed-time, that Joseph, sitting on his grandmother's knee, heard her tell that Kish having lost his asses sent Saul, his son, to seek them in the land of the Benjamites and the land of Shalisha, whither they might have strayed. But they were not in these lands, Son, she continued, nor in Zulp, whither Saul went afterwards, and being then tired out with looking for them he said to the servant: We shall do well to forget the asses, lest my father should ask what has become of us. But the servant, being of a mind that Kish would not care to see them without the asses, said to young Saul: Let us go up into yon city, for a great seer lives there and he will be able to put us in the right way to come upon the asses. But we have little in our wallet to recompense him, Saul answered, only half a loaf and a little wine at the end of the bottle. We have more than that, the servant replied, and opening his hand he showed a quarter of a shekel of silver to Saul, who said: He will take that in payment. Whereupon they walked into Arimathea, casting their eyes about for somebody to direct them to the seer's house. And seeing some maidens at the well, come to draw water, they asked them if the seer had been in the city that day, and were answered that he had been seen and would offer sacrifice that morning, as had been announced. He must be on his way now to the high rock, one of the maidens cried after them, and they pressed through the people till none was in front of them but an old man walking alone, likewise in the direction of the rock; and overtaking him they asked if he could point out the seer's house to them, to which he answered sharply : I am the seer, and fell at once to gazing on Saul as if he saw in him the one that had been revealed to him. For hearken, Son, seers have foresight, and the seer had been warned overnight that the Lord would send a young man to him, so the moment he saw Saul he knew him to be the one the Lord had promised, and he said : Thou art he whom the Lord has promised to send me for anoint-ment, but more than that I cannot tell thee, being on my way to offer sacrifice, but afterwards we will eat together, and all that has been revealed to me I will tell. Thou understandest me, Son, the old woman crooned, the Lord had been with Samuel beforetimes and had promised to send the King of Israel to him for anointment, and the moment he laid eyes on Saul he knew him to be the king; and that was why he asked him to eat with him after sacrifice. Yes, Granny, I understand : but did the Lord set the asses astray that Saul might follow them and come to Samuel to be made a King? I daresay there was something like that in the Lord's mind, the old woman answered, and she continued her story till her knees ached under the boy's weight, telling how Samuel talked with Saul on the roof of his house, and they rose early —— The child's asleep, she said, and on the instant he awoke crying: No, Granny, I wasn't asleep. I heard all and would like to be a prophet. A prophet, Joseph, and to anoint a king? But there are no more prophets or kings in Israel. And now, Joseph, my little prophet, 'tis bedtime and past it. Come. I didn't say I wanted to anoint kings, he answered, and refused to go to bed, though manifestly he could hardly keep awake. I'll wait up for Father. Now what can the child want his father for at this hour? she muttered as she went about the room, not guessing that he was angry and resentful, that her words had wounded him deeply, and that he was asking himself in his corner, if she thought him too stupid to be a prophet. I'll tell thee no more stories, she said to him, but he answered that

2

he did not want to hear her stories, and betwixt feelings of anger and shame his head drooped, and he slept in his chair till the door opened and his father's footsteps crossed the threshold. Now, he said to himself, Granny will tell Father that I said I'd like to be a prophet. And feigning sleep he listened, determined to hear the worst that could be said of him. But they did not speak about him but of the barrels of salt fish that were to go to Beth-Shemesh on the ·morrow; which was their usual talk. So he slipped from his chair and bade his father good-night. A resentful good-night it was; and his good-night to his grandmother was still more resentful. But in saying that his head was full of sleep she found an excuse for his rudeness — a remark that vexed his pride sorely and sent him upstairs wishing that women would not talk about things they do not understand. I'll ask Father in the morning why Granny laughed at me for saying I'd like to be a prophet. But as morning seemed still a long way ahead he tried to find a reason, but could find no better one than that prophets were usually old men. But I shall be old in time to come and have a beard. Father has a beard and they can't tell that I won't have a beard, and a white one too. I can learn to play psalteries and tabrets, so why should they —— His senses were numbing, and he must have fallen asleep soon after, for when he awoke it seemed to him that he had been asleep a long time, several hours at least, so many things had happened or seemed to have happened; but as he recovered his mind all the dream happenings melted away, and he could remember only his mother. She had been dead four years, yet in his dream she looked as she had always looked, and had scolded Granny for laughing at him. He tried to remember what else she had said but her words faded out of his mind and he fell asleep again. In this second sleep an old man rose up by his bedside and told him that he was the prophet Samuel, who though he had been dead a thousand years had heard him say he would like to be a prophet. But shall I be a prophet? Joseph asked, and as Samuel did not answer he cried out as loudly as he could : Shall I? Shall I? What ails thee, Son? he heard his grandmother calling to him, and he answered : An old man, an old man. Thou'rt dreaming, she mumbled between sleeping and waking. Now, go to sleep like a good boy, and don't dream any more. I will, Granny, but do not leave thy bed; the bed-clothes need no settling; I am well tucked in, he pleaded; and

3

fell asleep praying that Granny had not heard him ask Samuel if he would be a prophet.

A memory of his dream of Samuel came upon him while she dressed him, and he hoped she had forgotten all about it; but his father mentioned at breakfast that he had been awakened by cries. It was Joseph crying out in his dream, Dan that disturbed thee last night; such cries: Shall I? Shall I? And when I asked: What ails thee, child? the only answer I got was: An old man.

Dan, Joseph's father, wondered why Joseph should seem so chapfallen and why he should mutter so shiftily that he could not remember his dream. But if he had forgotten it, why trouble him further? If we are to forget anything it were well that we should choose our dreams; at which piece of incredulity his mother shook her head, being firm in the belief that there was much sense in dreams and that they could be interpreted to the advantage of everybody. And Dan said: If that be so, let him tell thee his dream. But Joseph hung his head and pushed his plate away; and seeing him so morose they left him to his sulks and fell to talking of dreams that had come true. Joseph had never heard them speak of anything so pleasing before, and though he suspected that they were making fun of him he could not do else but listen, till becoming convinced suddenly that they were talking in good earnest without intention of befooling him he began to regret that he had said he had forgotten his dream, and rapped out: He was the prophet Samuel. What art thou saying, Joseph? his father asked. Joseph would say no more, but it flattered him to observe that neither his father nor his granny laughed at his admission, and seeing how deep they were in his dream he said: If thou wouldst know all, I saw Samuel's face burning in the dark, and he said he had heard me say that I'd like to be a prophet. But, Father, is it true that we are of his tribe? He said I was. A most wonderful dream, his father answered, for it had always been held in the family that we are descended from him. Dost mean, Joseph, that the old man thou sawest in thy dream told thee he was Samuel and that thou'rt his descendant? How should I have known if he hadn't told me? Joseph looked from one to the other and wondered why they had kept the secret of his ancestor from him. Who was laughing yesterday, Granny, when I said I'd like to be a prophet? And now what hast thou to say? Answer me that. And he con-

4

tinued to look from one to the other for an answer. But neither
had the wit to find one, so astonished were they at the news that
the prophet Samuel had visited Joseph in a dream; and satisfied at
the impression he had made and a little frightened by their silence,
Joseph stole out of the room, leaving his parents to place whatever
interpretation they pleased on his dream. Nor did he care whether
they believed he had spoken the truth. He was more concerned
with himself than with them, and conscious that something of
great importance had happened to him he ascended the stairs,
pausing at every step uncertain if he should return to ask for the
whole of the story of Saul's anointment. It seemed to him to lack
courtesy to return to the room in which he had seen the prophet
till he knew these things. But he could not go back to ask questions: later he would learn what had befallen Saul and Samuel,
and he entered the room, henceforth to him a sacred room, and
stood looking through it, having all the circumstances of his dream
well in mind: he was lying on his left side when Samuel had risen
up before him, and it was there, upon that spot, in that space, he
had seen Samuel. His ancestor had seemed to fade away from the
waist downwards, but his face was extraordinarily clear in the
darkness, and Joseph tried to recall it. But he could only remember it as a face that a spirit might wear, for it was not made up of
flesh but of some glowing matter or stuff, such as glow-worms are
made of; nor could he call it ugly or beautiful, for it was not of this
world. He had drawn the bed-clothes over his head, but — impelled he knew not why, for he was nearly dead with fright — he
had poked his head out to see if the face was still there. The lips did
not move, but he had heard a voice. The tones were not like any
heard before, but he had listened to them all the same, and if he
had not lost his wits again in an excess of fear he would have put
questions to Samuel: he would have put questions if his tongue
had not been tied back somewhere in the roof of his mouth. But
Samuel would return, and the next time he would not be frightened,
would not pull the bed-clothes over his head. And convinced of his
own courage he lay night after night thinking of all the great things
he would ask the old man and of the benefit he would derive
from his teaching. But Samuel did not appear again, perhaps
because the nights were so dark. Joseph was told the moon
would become full again, but sleep closed his eyes when he should

5

have been waking, and in the morning he was full of fear that perhaps Samuel had come and gone away disappointed at not finding him awake. But that could not be, for if the prophet had come he would have awakened him as he had done before. His ancestor had not come again : a reasonable thing to suppose, for when the dead return to the earth they do so with much pain and difficulty; and if the living, whom they come to instruct, cannot keep their eyes open, the poor dead wander back whence they came and do not try to come between their descendants and their fate again. Once more he vowed to keep awake till Samuel came, and resorted to all sorts of devices, keeping up a repetition of a little phrase : He will come to-night when the moon is full ; and lying with one leg hanging out of bed ; and these proving unavailing he strewed his bed with crumbs. But no ancestor appeared, and little by little he relinquished hope of ever being able to summon Samuel to his bedside, and accepted as an explanation of his persistent absence that Samuel had performed his duty by coming once to visit him and would not come again unless some new necessity should arise. It was then that the conviction began to mount into his brain that he must learn all that his grandmother could tell him about Saul and David, and learning from her that they had been a great trouble to Samuel he resolved never to allow a thought into his mind that the prophet would deem unworthy. To become worthy of his ancestor was now his aim, and when he heard that Samuel was the author of two sacred books he began to peep over his father's shoulder and to ask why he had not been taught to read. Another step in his advancement was the discovery that the language his father, his granny and himself spoke was not the language spoken by Samuel, and every day he pressed his grandmother to tell him why the Jews had lost their language in Babylon, till he exhausted the old woman's knowledge and she said : Well now, Son, if thou wouldst hear any more about Babylon ask thy father, for I have told thee all I know. And the long day through Joseph waited for his father to come home, and plagued him to tell him a story when he returned. But after a long day spent in the counting-house his father was often too tired to take him on his knee and instruct him, for Joseph's curiosity was unceasing and very often wearisome. Now, Joseph, his father said, thou'lt learn more about these things when thou'rt older. And why not now ? he asked, and his grand-

6

mother answered that it was change of air he wanted, not books; and they began to speak of the fierce summer that had taken the health out of all of them, and of how necessary it was for a child of that age to be sent up to the hills.

Dan looked into his son's face, and Rachel seemed to be right. A thin, wan little face, that the air of the hills will brighten, he said; and he began at once to make arrangements for Joseph's departure for a hill village, saying that the pastoral life of the hills would take his mind off Samuel, Hebrew and Babylon. Rachel was doubtful if the shepherds would absorb Joseph's mind as completely as his father thought for. She hoped, however, that they would. As soon as he hears the sound of the pipe, his father answered. A prophecy this was, for while Joseph was resting after the fatigue of the journey, he was awakened suddenly by a sound he had never heard before; one that soothed him strangely. His nurse told him that the sound he heard was a shepherd's pipe. The shepherd plays and the flock follows, she said. And when may I see the flock coming home with the shepherd? he asked. To-morrow evening, she answered, and the time seemed to him to loiter, so eager was he to see the flocks returning and to watch the she-goat milked. And in the spring as his strength came back he followed the shepherds and heard from them many stories of wolves and dogs, and from a shepherd lad, whom he had chosen as a companion, he acquired knowledge of the plumage and the cries and the habits of birds, and in what places he was to seek their nests: it had become his ambition to possess all the wild birds' eggs, one that was easily satisfied till he came to the egg of the cuckoo, which he sought in vain, hearing of it often, now here, now there, till at last he and the shepherd lad ventured into a dangerous country in search of it and were held there till news of their absence reached Magdala and Dan set out in great alarm with an armed escort to recover his son. He was very angry when he came upon him, but the trouble he had been put to and the ransom he had had to pay were very soon forgotten, so great was his pleasure at the strong healthy boy he brought back with him, and whose first question to Rachel was: Are there cuckoos in Magdala? — Father doesn't know. His grandmother could not tell him, but she was willing to make inquiries, but before any news of the egg had been gotten the hope to possess it seemed to have drifted out of Joseph's mind

7

and to be even a little foolish when he looked into his box, for many of his egg shells had been broken on the journey. See, Granny, he said, but on second thoughts he refused to show his chipped possessions. But thou wast once as eager to learn Hebrew, his grandmother said, and the chance words, spoken as she left the room, awakened his suspended interests. No sooner had she returned than she was beset with questions, and the same evening his father had to promise that the best scribe in Galilee should be engaged to teach him. A discussion began between Dan and Rachel as to the most notable and trustworthy, one that Joseph followed so eagerly that they could not help laughing; the questions he put to them regarding the different accomplishments of the scribes were very minute, and the phrase: But this one is a Greek scholar, stirred his curiosity. Why should he be denied me because he knows Greek? he asked, and his father could answer only that no one can learn two languages at the same time. But this scribe knows two languages, Joseph insisted. I cannot tell thee more, his father answered, than that the scribe I've chosen is a great Hebrew scholar. He was no doubt a great scholar, but not the man Joseph wished for: thin and tall and of gentle appearance and demeanour, he did not stir up a flame for work in Joseph, who, as soon as the novelty of learning Hebrew had worn off, began to hide himself in the garden. His father caught him one day sitting in a convenient bough, looking down upon his preceptor fairly asleep on a bench; and after this adventure he began to make a mocking stock of his preceptor, inventing all kinds of cruelties, and his truancy became so constant that his father was forced to choose another. This time a younger man was chosen, but he succeeded with Joseph not very much better than the first. After the second there came a third, and when Joseph began to complain of his ignorance his father said: Well, Joseph, thy cry was always for Hebrew; but thou hast shown no steadfastness in learning, though three of the most learned scribes in Galilee were called in to teach thee. Joseph felt the reproof without knowing how to answer it, remaining silent, grateful to his grandmother for her defence: Joseph isn't an idle boy, Dan, but his nature is such that he cannot learn from a man he doesn't like. Why dost thou not give him Azariah as an instructor? Has he been speaking to thee about Azariah? Dan asked. Maybe, she said, and Dan's face clouded.

8

CHAPTER II.

WE understand from thee, Son, Dan said, on hearing that the fourth preceptor whom he had engaged to teach his son Hebrew had failed to please him, that thou canst learn from nobody but Azariah. Now, wilt tell us what there is in Azariah more than in Shimshai, Benaiah or Zebad? He waited for his son to speak, but as Joseph did not answer he asked : Is it because he looks more like a prophet than any of the others? At this Joseph, who still dreaded any talk of prophets, turned into his corner mortified. But Rachel came forward directly and taking the child by the shoulders led him back to his father, asking Dan with a trace of anger in her voice why he should think it strange that the child should prefer to learn from Azariah rather than from a withered patriarch who never could keep his eyes open but always sat dozing in his chair like one in a dream. Isn't that so, Joseph? But it wasn't, Granny, because he went to sleep often ; I could have kept him awake by kicking him under the table. Joseph stopped suddenly and looked from one to the other. Why then? his father asked ; and on being pressed to say why he didn't want to learn Hebrew he said he had come to hate Hebrew, an admission which rendered his parents speechless for a moment. Come to hate Hebrew! they repeated one after the other, till frightened by their solemnity Joseph blurted out : Thou wouldst not like Hebrew if the scholar's fleas jumped on to thee the moment he opened the quires. And pulling up his sleeves Joseph exhibited his arms. How could I learn Hebrew with three fleas biting me and all at one time, one here, another there and a third down yonder? He always has three or four about him. No, Father, don't, don't ask me to learn Hebrew any more. But, Joseph, all Hebrew scholars haven't fleas about them. An unbelieving face confronted them, and Joseph looked as if he were uncertain whether he should laugh or cry : but seeing that his parents liked his story he began to laugh. We've tried several preceptors but thou'rt hard to please, Joseph. Now what fault didst find with — and while Dan searched his memory for the name Joseph interjected that the little fellow whose back bulged like Granny's chest wouldn't let him read the story-telling parts of the Scriptures but kept him always at the Psalms and the Proverbs. And he was always telling me about Hillel, who was a good man, but good men aren't stirring like prophets, Joseph rapped out. And wilt thou tell us what he told thee about these pious men? Dan asked, a smile playing about his long thin mouth. That the law didn't matter as long as we were virtuous, Joseph muttered, and he was always making plain stories that I understood quite well when Granny told them. So it was Hiram who confirmed thee in thy distaste for Hebrew, Dan said, and the child stood looking at his father, not quite sure if it would be in his interest to accept or repudiate the suggestion. He would have refused to give a direct answer (such is the way of children) but the servant relieved him of his embarrassment : Azariah was at the gate asking for shelter from the rain. From the rain! Dan said, rising suddenly. Hearken! it is coming down very fast, Mother, but we were so engaged in listening to Joseph that we didn't hear it. Shall we ask him in, Joseph? The child's face lighted up. Now isn't it strange, Rachel said, he should be here to-day? We haven't seen him for months, and now in the middle of a talk about tutors — thou'lt ask him in? Truly yes, Dan said, and he bade the servant ask the scribe to come upstairs. And now, Joseph, I hope thou'lt listen to all that Azariah says, giving quiet and reasonable answers. And not too many questions, mind! But if I do not understand the questions he puts to me, may I ask him to say them over again? Joseph said, and he seized on the last chance available to his tongue to tell that he had often seen Azariah in the lanes. He doesn't see us, he walks like one in a dream, his hair blowing in the wind. But when he does see us he speaks very kindly. . . . I think I'd like to learn Hebrew from him. Rachel laid her finger on her lips; the door opened and Azariah advanced into the room with a long grave Jewish stride, apologising to Dan as he came for his sudden intrusion among them, and mentioning the heavy rain in a graceful phrase. Joseph, who was on the watch for everything, could see that his father was

10

full of respect for Azariah, and hearing him say that it was some years since Azariah had been in his house he began to wonder if there had been a quarrel between them; it seemed to him that his father was a little afraid of Azariah, which was strange, for himself did not feel in the least afraid of Azariah but an almost uncontrollable desire to go and sit on his knee, and yielding to it, he slank nearer, and was about to jump on his knee when his father said: Here is my boy Joseph; he would learn Hebrew from thee. We were talking about thee and Hebrew when thy knock came. Azariah raised his thick eyebrows and waited to be told how he had come to be the subject of their talk, though he half knew the reason, for in a village like Magdala it soon gets about that four preceptors have been sent away unable to teach the rich man's son. He has made up his mind, Dan said, to learn Hebrew and Greek from none but thee. No, Father, I didn't make up my mind. But I couldn't learn from the others as I told thee truthfully. Art sure that thou canst learn from me? Azariah asked. Joseph became shy at once, but he liked to feel Azariah's friendly hand upon his shoulder, and when Dan asked the scribe to be seated Joseph followed him, and standing beside his chair asked him if he would teach him Hebrew, a question Azariah did not answer. Thou'lt teach me, he insisted, and Dan and Rachel kept silence, so that they might better observe Joseph working round Azariah with questions; and they were amused, for Joseph's curiosity had overcome his shyness; and, quite forgetful of his promise to listen and not to talk, he had begun to beg the scribe to tell him if the language they spoke had been brought back from Babylon, and how long it was since people had ceased to speak Hebrew. Azariah set himself to answer these questions; Joseph gave him close attention, and when Azariah ceased speaking he said: When may I begin my lessons? And he put the question so innocently that his father could not help laughing. But, Joseph, he said, Azariah has not yet promised to teach thee, and I wouldn't advise him to try to teach a boy that has refused to learn from four preceptors. But it will be different with thee, Master, Joseph murmured, taking Azariah's hand. Thou'lt teach me, Master? And when wilt begin? Azariah answered that it could not be this week, for he was going to Arimathea. The town we came from, Dan said. I am still

11

known as Dan of Arimathea, though I have lived here twenty years.
I too shall be known as Joseph of Arimathea, Joseph interjected.
I'd like to be Joseph of Arimathea much better than Joseph of
Magdala. No need to shake thy head at Magdala, Dan said.
Magdala has done well for us. To which Joseph answered nothing,
but it was not long, however, before he went to his father, saying:
Azariah is going to Arimathea, Father, and will take me if thou'lt
allow me to go with him. Thou'rt asking too much, Joseph, his
father answered him. No, I don't think I am, and his honour
Azariah doesn't think so, Joseph cried, for his heart was already
set upon this holiday. Azariah has perhaps promised to teach thee
Hebrew. Isn't that enough? his father remarked. Now thou
wouldst have him take thee to Arimathea. But if he likes to take
me, Joseph replied, and he cast such a winning glance at Azariah
that the scribe was moved to say that he would be glad to take
charge of the boy if his parents would confide him to his care.
Whereupon Joseph threw his arms about his father, but finding
him somewhat indifferent he went to his grandmother, who
welcomed his embrace, and in return for it pleaded that the boy
should not be denied this small pleasure. But Dan, who only half
liked to part with his son, tried to hide his feelings from his mother,
who had guessed them already, with a joke, saying to Azariah
that he was a brave man to undertake the charge of so wayward a
boy. I shall not spoil him, and if he fails to obey he'll have to
find someone else to teach him Hebrew, Azariah answered. I think
the rain is now over, he said. Some drops were still falling but the
sky was brightening, and he returned from the window to where
Joseph was standing, and laying his hand on his head promised
to come for him in the morning.

We shall hear no more about fleas preventing thee from study,
Dan said to his son, and very much offended Joseph withdrew to
his room, and stood looking at the spot in which he had seen
Samuel, asking himself if the prophet would appear to him in
Arimathea and if it would be by the fountain whither the maidens
used to come to draw water. Samuel and the maidens seemed to
jar a little, and as he could not think of them together he fell to
thinking of the rock on which the seer used to offer sacrifices. It
was still there and somebody would be about who could direct them

12

to it, and it would be under this rock that Azariah would read to him all that Samuel had said to Saul. But we shall be riding all day, he said to himself, Arimathea must be a long long way from here, and he ran downstairs to ask his father if Azariah would call for him at the head of a caravan, and if so, whether he would ride on a camel or a mule or a horse: he thought he would like to ride a camel, and awoke many times in the night, once rolling out of his bed, for in a dream the ungainly animal had jolted him from off his hump. And the old woman's patience was nigh exhausted when he cried: Granny, it is day, and bade her leave her bed and come to the window to tell him if day were not breaking; but she answered: Get thee back to thy bed, for 'tis the moon shining down the sky, simpleton. The sun won't give way an hour to the moon nor the moon an hour to the sun because thou'rt going to Arimathea. And methinks, Joseph, that to some the morrow is always better than to-day, and yesterday better than either — a remark that puzzled Joseph and kept him from his rest. Didst never hear, Joseph, that it is a clever chicken that crows in the egg? the old woman continued, and who knows but Azariah will forget to come for thee! He won't forget, Granny, Joseph uttered in so doleful a tone that Rachel repented and promised Joseph she would wake him in time; and as she had never failed to keep her promise to him he allowed sleep to close his eyelids. And once asleep he was hard to awaken. At six in the morning sleep seemed to him better than Arimathea, but when he was well awake Rachel could not hand him his clothes fast enough; he escaped from her hands, dressing himself as he ran into the lanes, and whilst lacing his sandals at the gate he forgot to tie them, and returned to the question of overnight: whether Azariah would come to fetch him on a horse or an ass or a mule or a camel, till at last the sound of hooves came through the dusk, and a moment after some three or four camels led the way; and there were horses too and asses and mules, and the mules were caparisoned gaily, the one reserved for Joseph's riding more richly than the others — a tall fine animal by which he was proud to stand, asking questions of the muleteer, while admiring the dark docile eyes, shaded with black lashes. Now why do we delay? he asked Azariah, who reminded him — and somewhat tritely — that he had not yet said good-bye to his parents.

13

But they know I'm going with thee, Master, he answered. Azariah would not, however, allow Joseph to mount his mule till he had bidden good-bye to his father and grandmother, and he brought the boy back to the house, but without earning Dan's approval, who was ashamed before Azariah of his son's eagerness to leave home; a subtlety that escaped Rachel, who chided Dan saying: Try to remember if it wasn't the same with thee, for I can remember thine eyes sparkling at the sight of a horse and thy knees all of an itch to be on to him. Well, said Dan, he'll have enough riding before the day is over, and I reckon his little backside will be sore before they halt at the gates of Arimathea: a remark that caused Rachel to turn amazed eyes on her son and to answer harshly that since he had so much foresight she hoped he had not forgotten to tell Azariah that Joseph must have a long rest at midday. Thy face tells me that no order has been taken for the care of the child on the journey. Wilt thou see to this? But Azariah cannot be far on his way; I'll send a messenger to caution him that Joseph must have his rest in the shade. Dan let her go in search of the messenger and moved around the room hoping (he knew not why) that the messenger would not overtake the caravan, which he very nearly missed doing, for while Rachel was instructing the messenger, Joseph was asking Azariah if he might have a stick to belabour his mule into a gallop. The cavalcade, he said, needed a scout that would report any signs of robbers among the rocks and bushes. But we aren't likely to meet robber bands this side of Jordan, Azariah said; they keep to the other side; and he told Joseph, who was curious about everything, that along the Jordan were great marshes into which the nomads drove their flocks and herds in the spring to feed on the young grass. So they are there now, Joseph replied meditatively, for he was thinking he would like better to ride through marshes full of reeds than through a hilly country where there was nothing to see but the barley-fields broken by an occasional olive garth. But hooves were heard galloping in the rear and when the messenger overtook the caravan and blurted out Rachel's instructions, Joseph's face flushed. Now what can a woman know, he cried, about a journey like this? Tell her, he said, turning to the messenger, that I shall ride and rest with the others. And as an earnest of his resolve he struck the messenger's horse so

14

sharply across the quarters that the animal's head went down between his knees and he plunged so violently that the messenger was cast sprawling upon the ground. The cavalcade roared with laughter and Joseph, overjoyed at the success of his prank, begged Azariah to wait a little longer, for he was curious to see if the messenger would succeed in coaxing his horse. At present the horse seemed in no humour to allow himself to be mounted. Whenever the messenger approached he whinnied so menacingly that everybody laughed again. Is there none amongst you that will help me to catch the horse? the poor messenger cried after the departing travellers. We have a long day's march in front of us, Azariah said; and he warned Joseph not to beat his mule into a gallop at the beginning of the journey or he would repent it later, words that came true sooner than Joseph had expected, for before midday he was asking how many miles would bring them to the caravansary. In about another hour, Azariah answered, and Joseph said he had begun to hate his mule for it would neither trot nor gallop, only walk. Thou'rt thinking of the nomads and would like to be after them flourishing a lance, Azariah said, and — afraid that he was being laughed at — Joseph did not answer him. And after the rest at midday it seemed to him to be his duty to see that his mule had been properly fed, and he bought some barley from the camel-driver, but while he was giving it to his mule Azariah remarked that he was only depriving other animals of their fair share of provender. It is hard, he said, to do good to one without doing wrong to another. But the present is no time for philosophy: we must start again. So the cavalcade moved on through the hills, avoiding the steep ascents and descents by circuitous paths, and Joseph, who had not seen a shepherd leading his flock for some years, was all of a sudden filled with delight by the spectacle, the sheep running forward scenting the fresh herbage with which the hills were covered as with dark velvet. They rode on, coming a little later into view of a flock of goats browsing near a wood, and Azariah sought to edify the boy by a little dissertation on the destructive nature of the goat. Of late years a sapling rarely escaped them, and still more regrettable was the carelessness of the shepherds who left the branches they had torn down to become dry like tinder. He spoke of many forest fires, and told all the sto-

15

ries he could remember in the hope of distracting Joseph's thoughts from the length of the journey. We are now about half-way, he said, disguising the truth. We shall see the city in the evening glow. The evening is still far away, Joseph complained two hours later, and I am sore on this saddle. Azariah laid his cloak under Joseph's rump. Dost thou ride easier? he asked. A little, the child answered. Then be brave a while longer. At the sight of the city on the hilltop thy heart will be lifted again and thy suffering forgotten. Art speaking truth? The truth indeed, Azariah answered. All the same, the miles seemed to Joseph everlasting, and at five o'clock he was crying: Shall we ever get to Arimathea? for I can sit on this mule no longer, nor shall I be able to stand straight upon my legs when I alight. Azariah promised they would be at the gates in a few minutes, but these few minutes seemed as if they would never pass away; yet they did pass, and at the gateway Joseph toppled from his mule and just managed to hobble into the inn at which they were to sleep that night, too tired to eat, he said, too tired, he feared, to sleep. Azariah pressed him to swallow a cup of soup and prepared a hot bath for him into which he poured a bottle of vinegar: an excellent remedy he reported this to be against stiffness, and it showed itself to be such; for next morning Joseph was quite free from stiffness and said he could walk for miles. Samuel's rock cannot be more than a few hundred yards distant, so miles are not necessary, Azariah answered, as they stepped over the threshold into a delightful morning all smiles and greetings and subtle invitations to come away into the forest and fields, full of promises of flowers and songs, but in conflict with their project, which was to inquire out their way from the maidens at the fountain, who would be sure to know the prophet's rock, and in its shade to read the story of David and Goliath first and other stories afterwards. But the gay morning drew their thoughts away from texts, and without being aware of their apostasy they had already begun to indulge in hopes that the maidens would be late at the fountain and leave them some time to loiter by the old aqueduct that brought the water in a tiny stream to fall into a marble trough: An erstwhile sarcophagus, maybe, Azariah said, as he gathered some water out of it with his hands and drank, telling Joseph to do likewise.

16

There were clouds in the sky, so the sun kept coming and going. A great lantern, Joseph said. That God holds in his hands, Azariah answered; and when tired of waiting for maidens who did not appear their beguilement was continued by shadows advancing and retreating across the roadway. The town was an enchantment in the still limpid morning, but when they rose to their feet their eyes fell on a greater enchantment — the hills clothed in moving light and shade so beautiful that the appeal to come away to the woods and fields continued in their hearts after they had lowered their eyes and would not be denied, though they prayed for strength to hold by their original project. It had died out of their hearts through no fault of theirs, as far as they could see; and wondering how they might get release from it they strode about the city, idly casting their eyes into ravines into which the walls dropped, and raising them to the crags to which the walls rose: Faithful servants, Azariah said, that have saved the city many times from robbers from the other side of Jordan. Joseph's thoughts were far away on the hillside opposite amid the woods, and Azariah's voice jarred. By this time, he said, the maidens are drawing water. But perhaps, Joseph answered, none will be able to tell us the way to the rock, and if none has heard for certain on which rock Samuel offered sacrifice we might go roaming over the hills and into forests yonder to find perhaps some wolf cubs in a cave. But a she-wolf with cubs is dangerous, Azariah replied. If we were to try to steal her cubs, Joseph interjected. But we don't want to meddle with them, only to see them. Let us go roaming to-day, Sir, and read the story of David and Goliath to-morrow. The boy's voice was full of entreaty and Azariah had very little heart to disappoint him, but he dared not break an engagement which he looked upon as almost sacred; and walked debating with himself, asking himself if the absence of a maiden at the fountain might be taken as a sign that they were free to abandon the Scriptures for the day, only for the day. And seeing the fountain deserted Joseph cried out in his heart: We are free! But as they turned aside to go their way a maiden came with a pitcher upon her head; but as she had never heard of the rock, nor indeed of Samuel, Joseph was certain that God had specially appointed her ignorant, so that they might know that the day before them was for enjoyment. Thou didst say, Master, that

17

if none could direct us we might leave the story until to-morrow. I did not say that, Azariah answered. All the same he did not propose to wait for another maiden more learned than the first, but followed Joseph to the gates of the city, nor did he raise any objection to passing through them, and they stood with their eyes fixed on the path that led over the brow down into the valley, a crooked twisting path that had seemed steep to Azariah's mule overnight and that now seemed steeper to Azariah. And will seem still steeper to me in the evening when we return home tired, he said. But we shall not be tired, Joseph interposed; we need not go very far, only a little way into the forest and —— He checked himself, not daring to say more, lest by some careless word he might provoke an elderly opposition. He dreaded to hear the words on Azariah's lips: It was under promise to thy father that some hours of the day should be given to Hebrew that I gave my consent to this journey; all of which was very true. But if he could persuade Azariah into the path he would not turn back until they reached the valley, and once in the valley he might as well ascend the opposite hill as go back and climb up the hill whence they had come. I am afraid, said Azariah, that this cool morning will pass into a very hot day: the clouds that veil the sky are dispersing. We shall not feel the heat once we are in the forest, Joseph replied, and the path up yonder hill is not so steep as the paths we go down by. Before us is the road, Master, twisting up the hillside, and it is planned so carefully to avoid a direct ascent that a man has just belaboured his ass into a trot. They have passed behind a rock, but we shall see them presently. Azariah waited a moment for the man and ass to reappear, but after all he was not much concerned with them, and began to descend unmindful of the lark which mounted the sky in circles singing trancedly. Joseph begged Azariah to hearken, but his preceptor was too much occupied with the difficulties of the descent, nor could he be persuaded to give much attention to a flight of doves flying hither and thither as if they had just discovered that they could fly, diving and wheeling and then going away in a great company, coming back and diving again, setting Joseph wondering why one bird should separate himself from the flock and alight again. Again and again this happened, the flock returning to release him from his post. Were the birds playing a sort of game?

18

MASTER AND PUPIL

Frolicking they were, for sure, and Joseph felt he would like to have wings and go away with them, and he wished Azariah would hasten, so pleasant was it in the valley.

A pleasant spacious valley it was, lying between two hills of about equal height : the hill they had come down was a little steeper than the one they were about to go up. Joseph noticed the shadows that fell from the cliffs and those that the tall feathery trees, growing out of the scrub, cast over the sunny bottom of the valley, a watercourse probably in the rainy season ; and he enjoyed the little puffing winds that came and went, and the insects that came out of their hiding-places to enjoy the morning. The dragonflies were bustling about their business : what it was was not easy to discover, but they went by in companies of small flies, with now and then a great one that rustled past on gauzy wings. And the bees were coming and going from their hive in the rocks, incited by the fragrance of the flowers, and Joseph watched them crawling over the anemones and leaving them hastily to bury their blunt noses in the pistils of the white squills that abounded everywhere in the corners, in the inlets and bays and crevices of the rocks. Butterflies, especially the white, pursued love untiringly in the air, fluttering and hovering, uniting and then separating — aerial wooings that Joseph followed with strained eyes, till at last the white bloom passed out of sight; and he turned to the dragonflies, hoping to capture one of the fearful kind, often nearly succeeding, but failing at the last moment and returning disappointed to Azariah who, seated on a convenient stone, waited till Joseph's ardour should abate a little. These stones will be too hot in another hour, he said. But it will be cool enough under the boughs, Joseph answered. Perhaps too cool, Azariah muttered, and Joseph wondered if it were reasonable to be so discontented with the world, especially on a morning like this, he said to himself; and to hearten Azariah he mentioned again that the path up the hillside zigzagged. Thou'lt not feel the ascent, Master. To which encouragement Azariah made no answer but drew Joseph's attention to the industry of the people of Arimathea. The eager boy could spare only a few moments for the beauty of the fig and mulberry leaves showing against the dark rocks, but he snuffed the scent the breeze bore and said it was the same that had followed them yesterday. The scent of the

19

vine-flower, Azariah rejoined. The hillsides were covered with the pale yellow clusters, Joseph replied. But I thought, Joseph, that thou wast too tired yesterday to notice anything. Only towards the end of the journey, Joseph muttered. What wouldst thou, Master? he asked. I am going to run up the hill. If it please thee to run, run, the preceptor answered, and as he followed the boy at a more leisurely pace he wondered at Joseph's spindle shanks struggling manfully against the ascent. He'll stop before the road turns, he said, but Joseph ran on. He is anxious to reach the top, Azariah pondered. There's some pleasant flowering turf a-top of yon hill: he'll like to roll like a young donkey, his heels in the air, Azariah said to himself as he ascended the steep path, stopping from time to time that he might better ponder on the moral of this spring morning. He'll roll among the grass and flowers like a young donkey, and then run hither and thither after insects and birds, desiring so many things that he'll know not what he desires, only that he desires. Whereas I can but remember that once I was as he is to-day. So the spring is sad for the young as well as for the old. But old as he was he was glad to feel himself still liable to the season's thrill in retrospect at least, and he asked himself questions: How many years ago is it since Miriam died? But he did not get further with his recollections. The ascent is too steep, he said, and he continued the ascent thinking of his breath rather than of her, while Joseph stood waiting on the edge of the rocks and cried out in the fullness of his joy on seeing his preceptor appear above the cliff. At once he fell to rolling himself over and over. Just as I expected he would, Azariah remarked to himself. And then, starting to his feet, Joseph began gathering flowers, but in a little while he stood still, his nosegay dropping flower by flower, for his thoughts had taken flight. The doves, the doves! he cried, looking into the blue and white sky. The doves have their nests in the woods, the larks build in the grass, he said, and asked Azariah to come with him. The nest was in a tuft. But I've not touched it, he said. Three years ago I used to rob all the nests and blow the eggs, for I was making a collection. Azariah asked him if the lark would grieve for her eggs, and Joseph answered that he supposed she would soon forget them. Hark to his singing! and he ran on into the outskirts of the woods, coming back a few minutes afterwards

20

to ask Azariah to hasten, for the wood was more beautiful than any wood he had ever seen. And if thou knowest the trees in which the doves build I will climb and get the nest. Doves build in taller trees than these, in fir-trees, Azariah answered. But this is a pretty wood, Joseph. And he looked round the quiet sunny oak wood and began to tell that this wood was probably the remains of the ancient forests that had covered the country when the Israelites came out of the north of Arabia. How long ago was that, Master? Joseph asked, and Azariah hazarded the answer that it might be as many as fifteen hundred years ago. How old is the oldest oak-tree? Joseph inquired, and Azariah had again to hazard the answer that a thousand years would make an old tree. And when will these trees be in leaf, Master, and may we come to Arimathea when they are in leaf? And look! somebody has been felling trees here. Azariah looked round. The forest must have been supplying the city with firewood for many years, he said. All these trees are young and they are too regularly spaced for a natural growth. But higher up the hills the woods are denser and darker, and there we may find some old trees. Any badgers and foxes? Joseph asked, and shall we see any wolves?

The sunny woods were threaded with little paths, and Joseph cast curious eyes upon them all. The first led him into bracken so deep that he did not venture farther, and the second took him to the verge of a dark hollow so dismal that he came running back to ask if there were crocodiles in the waters he had discovered. He did not give his preceptor time to answer the difficult question, but laid his hand upon his arm and whispered that he was to look between two rocks, for a jackal was there, slinking away — turning his pointed muzzle to them now and then. To see he isn't followed, Azariah added: and the observation endeared him so to Joseph that the boy walked for a moment content and pensive in the path they were following. It turned into the forest, and they had not gone very far before they became aware of a strange silence, if silence it could be called, for when they listened the silence was full of sound, innumerable little sounds, some of which they recognised; but it was not the hum of the insects or the chirp of a bird or the snapping of a rotten twig that filled Joseph with awe, but something that he could neither see, nor hear, nor smell, nor touch.

The life of the trees — is that it? he asked himself. A remote and mysterious life was certainly breathing about him, and he regretted he was without a sense to apprehend this life. Again and again it seemed that the forest was about to whisper its secret, but something aways happened to interrupt. Once it was certainly Azariah's fault, for just as the trees were about to speak he picked up a leaf and began to explain how the shape of an oak leaf differed from that of the leaf of the chestnut and the ash. A patter was heard among the leaves. There she goes — a hare! Joseph said, and a moment afterwards a white thing appeared. A white weasel, Azariah said. Shall we follow him? Joseph asked, and Azariah answered that it would be useless to follow. We should soon miss them in the thickets. And he continued his discourse upon trees, hoping that Joseph would never again mistake a sycamore for a chestnut. And what is that tree so dark and gloomy rising up through all the other trees, Joseph asked, so much higher than any of them? That is a cedar, Azariah said. Do doves build in cedars? Azariah did not know, and the tree did not inspire a climb: it seemed to forbid any attempt on its privacy. Do trees talk when they are alone? Joseph asked Azariah, and his preceptor gave the very sensible answer that the life of trees is unknown to us, but that trees had always awakened religious emotions in men. The earliest tribes were tree-worshippers, which was very foolish, for we can fell trees and put them to our usage.

They had come to a part of the forest in which there seemed to be neither birds nor beasts and Joseph had begun to feel the forest a little wearisome and to wish for a change, when the trees suddenly stopped, and before them lay a sunny interspace full of tall grass with here and there a fallen tree, and on these trees prone great lizards sunned themselves, nodding their heads in a motion ever the same. Something had died in that beautiful interspace, for a vulture rose sullenly and went away over the top of the trees, and Azariah begged Joseph not to pursue his search but to hasten out of the smell of the carrion that a little breeze had just carried towards them. Besides, this thick grass is full of snakes, he said, and the words were no sooner out of his mouth than a snake issued from a thick tuft, stopped and hissed. Snakes feed on mice and rats? Joseph asked, and come out of their holes to catch them,

22

isn't that so, Sir? Everything is out this sunny morning, seeking its food, Azariah answered: snakes after mice, vultures after carrion. This way, Joseph — yonder we may rest awhile, but we must be careful not to sit upon a snake; that knoll yonder is free from vermin, for the trees that grow about it are fir-trees and snakes do not like any place where they can easily be detected. And they sat on the fibrous ground and looked up into the darkness of the withered pines — withered everywhere except in the topmost branches that alone caught the light. A sad place to sit in, Joseph said. Azariah answered that it was. But sadness is preferable to snakebites, he added. At that moment slowly flapping wings were heard overhead. It is the vulture returning, Azariah whispered to Joseph, and he is bringing a comrade back to dinner. To a very smelly dinner, Joseph rejoined, for the breeze had veered suddenly and they found themselves again in the smell of carrion. We must go on farther, Azariah said, and after passing into many quiet hollows and ascending many crests the path to which they had remained faithful came out at last on broken ground with the tail end of the forest straggling up the opposite hillside in groups and single trees. I know where we are now! Joseph cried. Dost remember, Master —— Joseph's explanation was cut short by the sight of some shepherds sitting at their midday meal, and hunger falling suddenly upon Azariah and Joseph, both began to regret they had not brought food with them. But Azariah had some shekels tied in his garment, and for one of these pieces of silver the shepherds were glad to share their bread and figs with them and to draw milk for them from one of the she-goats. From which shall I draw milk? the shepherd asked his mate, and the mate answered: White-nose looks as if her udder is paining her. She lost her kid yesterday. He mentioned two others: Speckled and Long-ears. Whichever would like her milk drawn off will answer to thy call, the shepherd answered, and the goat came running to him as if glad to hear her name. White-nose, isn't it? Joseph asked, and he broke off a branch for her, and while she nibbled he watched the milk drawn off and drank it foaming and warm from the jug, believing it to be the sweetest he had ever drunk, though he had often drunk goat's milk before. Azariah, too, vowed that he had never drunk better milk and persuaded the shepherds into discourse of their trade, learning much

23

thereby, for these men knew everything that men may know about flocks, having been engaged in leading them from pasture to pasture all their lives and their fathers before them. After telling of many famous rams they related the courage and fidelity of their dogs, none of which feared a wolf, and they mentioned that two had been lost in an encounter with a leopard — but the flock had been saved. As much as wolves the shepherds feared the eagles. There are a dozen nests in yon mountain if there be one. Take the strangers up the hillside, mate, so that they may get a sight of the birds. And Azariah and Joseph followed the shepherd up to the crags and were shown some birds wheeling above rocks so steep that there was no foothold for man. Or else we should have had their nests long ago, the shepherd said. Now this is a bear's trail. He's been seeking water here, but he didn't get any; he came by here, and my troth, he's been climbing after wild bees. The shepherd showed scratches among the dropping resin, saying: It was here that he clawed his way up. But did he get the honey? Joseph asked, a question the shepherd could not answer; and talking about bears and honey and eagles and lambs and wolves and lions, the afternoon passed away without their feeling it, till one of the shepherds said: It is folding-time now; and answering to different calls the flocks separated, and the shepherds went their different ways followed by their flocks.

The sunset had begun to redden the sky, and the shadows of the trees drew out as they crossed the hillside and descended by the steep path into the valley. The ascent that faced them was steep indeed, and Azariah had to rest several times, but at last they reached the slope on which the city was built : they did not however enter the gates yet awhile but stood looking back, thinking of the day that had gone by. We shall remember this day always, Joseph said, if we live to be as old as the patriarchs. Was it then so wonder-ful? Azariah asked, and Joseph could only answer: Yes, very wonderful, and if thou hadst not lived so many days thou too wouldst think it wonderful. But, Master, tell me, he added, is it true that God is going to destroy the world and very soon? Why dost thou ask, Joseph? Azariah replied, and Joseph answered: Because the world is so very beautiful. I never saw the world until to-day. My eyes are opened, and I shall be sorry if God destroys the world, for I should like to see more of it. But why should he

24

make a beautiful world and then destroy it? Will not God relent when the time comes, if the day be as beautiful as it was this morning? Azariah answered him that God does not relent, for he knows the past and future as well as the present, and that the world was not as beautiful as it seems to be, for man is sinning always, though certainly God said all things are beautiful. But perhaps we sinned this morning in the sight of God. We sinned? Joseph repeated. How did we sin? Hast forgotten, Azariah answered, that it was arranged that we should spend the day reading the Scriptures, and we've spent it talking to shepherds? Was that a sin? Joseph asked. We can read the Scriptures to-morrow; if the day be clouded and rain come we can read them indoors. If the day be clouded, Azariah replied, smiling. But was not thy life dedicated to Samuel? Thou hast forgotten him. But the world is God's world. Joseph answered that he had forgotten his vow, and all that evening, in spite of Azariah's gentleness with him, he was pursued by the memory of the sin he had committed. In Samuel's own city he had broken his vow! And Azariah heard the boy blubbering in the darkness that night.

CHAPTER III.

HE should not have interrupted the manifestations of joy at his return with : When may I go to Arimathea again ? And his second question was hardly less indiscreet : Why did we leave Arimathea ? His father answered : Because it suited us to do so ; and Joseph withdrew to Rachel who was never gruff with him. But despite her bias in favour of all he said and did she reproved him, saying that he should not ask as soon as he returned home when he was going away again. I am glad in a way, Granny, but there's no forest here. Dan left the room, and the boy would tell no more but burst into tears, asking what he had done to make Father so angry. Rachel could not tell him with safety, and Joseph, thinking that perhaps something unpleasant had happened to his father in the forest (a wolf might have bitten him there), spoke of the high rock on the next occasion and of the story of Jonathan and David that Azariah had read to him. Thou'lt ask him to come here one night, Father, and translate it to thee ? Promise me that. But I can read Hebrew, Dan replied, and there is no reason for those wondering eyes. Thy granny will tell thee. But, Father —— Joseph stopped suddenly. It had come into his mind to ask his father how it was that he had never read the story of Jonathan and David to him, but his interest in the matter dying suddenly, he said : To-morrow I begin my lessons, and Azariah tells me that I must have a copy of the Scriptures for my very own use. Now where are thy thoughts ? In a barrel of salt fish ? Father, do listen. I'd like to learn Hebrew from bottom to top and from top to bottom and then sideways, so as to put the Scribes in Jerusalem to shame when thou sendest me thither for the Feast of the Passover. And thou'lt mind that my Scriptures be made by the best Scribe in Galilee and on the best parchment, promise me, Father !

Dan promised his son that no finer manuscript should be procurable in Galilee. But the making of this magnificent copy would delay for many months Joseph's instruction in Hebrew, and Joseph was so impatient to begin that he lay awake that night and in the morning ransacked his father's rooms, laying hands on some quires of his father's Scriptures; and no sooner out of the house than a great fear fell upon him that he might be robbed; the quires were hidden in his vest suddenly and he walked on in confidence, also in a great seriousness, going his way melancholy as a camel, his head turned from the many temptations that the way offered to him — the flower in the cactus hedge was one. He passed it without picking it, and farther on allowed a strange crawling insect to go by without molestation, and then feeling his mood to be an odd one, fell to thinking that his granny would laugh were she to see him, but unafraid or almost of her laughter he wandered on muttering softly to himself: Women have no sense of the Word of God, his eyes bent on the ground lest a nest might entice him to climb, which he could not do with several quires of Scriptures under his arm. He would lose his grip and fall, or else the Scriptures would fall, and if a thief happened to be going by at the time it would be easy for him to pick up the quires and away with them before it would be possible for Joseph to slide down the tree and raise a hue and cry.

The lanes through which his way took him were frequented by boys, ball-players every one of them, and at this time ball-playing was a passion with Joseph and he would steal away whenever he got a chance and spend a whole day in an alley with a number of little ragamuffins. And if he were to meet the tribe, which was as likely as not at the next turning, he must tell them that he was going to school and dared not stop. But they would jeer at him. He might give them his ball and in return they might not mock at him. He walked very quietly, hoping to pass unobserved, but a boy was looking over the cactus hedge and called to him, asking if he had brought a ball with him, for they had lost theirs. He threw his ball to him. But thou'rt coming to play with us? Not to-day, Joseph answered. I'm on my way to school. Well, to-morrow? Not to-morrow. I may not play truant from learning, Joseph answered sententiously, walking away, leaving his former playmates staring after him without a word in their mouths. But by the next day they had recovered their speech and cried out : The fishmonger's son is going by to his lessons and dare not play at ball. Azariah would whip him if he did. One a little bolder than the rest dangled a piece of rope in his face saying : This is what thou wouldst get for staying with us. He was moved to run after the boy and cuff him, but the quires under his arms restrained him and he passed on, keeping a dignified silence. Soon thou'lt be reading to us in the synagogues! was the last jeer cried after him that day, and the way became so hateful to him that his grandmother asked him if he were already weary of Greek and Hebrew. But Joseph kept his own counsel; he went forth restraining his tears, and as he showed no sign of anger the persecution grew wearisome to the persecutors, and soon after he discovered another way to Azariah. But this way was beset with women, whose sex impelled a yearning for this tall lithe boy with the gazelle-like eyes. Joseph was more inclined to the welcome of the Greek poets and sculptors who stopped their mules and leaning from high saddles spoke to him, for he was now beginning to speak Greek and it was pleasant to avail himself of the hazards of the road to chatter his Greek and to acquire new turns of phrase. Why not? since it seemed to be the wish of these men to instruct him. My very model! a bearded man cried out one morning, and stopping his mule he bent from the saddle towards Joseph and asked him many questions. Joseph told him that he was on his way to his lessons and that he passed through this lane every morning. At these words the sculptor's eyes lighted up, for he had accepted Joseph's answer as a tryst, and when Joseph came through the lane next day he caught sight of the sculptor waiting for him and — flattered — Joseph entered into conversation with him, resisting, however, the sculptor's repeated invitation that Joseph should come to sit to him — if not for a statue, for a bust at least. But a bust is a graven image, Joseph answered, and as the point was being debated a rich merchant came by, riding a white horse that curveted splendidly, and Joseph, who was interested in the horse, referred the difficulty to the merchant. After some consideration of it he asked the meaning of the scrolls that Joseph carried in his hand, feigning an interest in them and in Azariah. Who is he? he asked, and Joseph answered : A very learned man, my tutor, to whom I

28

must be on my way. And with a pretty bow he left merchant and sculptor exchanging angry looks. But the sculptor knowing more of Joseph than the merchant — that he would be passing through the lane on the morrow at the same time — and as the boy's beauty was of great importance to him, kept another tryst, waiting impatiently, and as soon as Joseph appeared he besought him to come to Tiberias and pose in his studio for a statue he was carving, offering presents that would have shaken many determinations. But Joseph was as firm to-day as he was yesterday. I must be going on to my Hebrew, he said, and he left the sculptor cast away in dreams. He had not gone very far, however, before he met the merchant, who happened to be passing through the lane again, and seeing Joseph his eyes lighted up with pleasure, and after speaking to him he dismounted from his mule and showed him a beautiful engraved dagger which Joseph desired ardently; but a present so rich he did not care to accept, and hurried away, nor did he look back, so busy was he inventing reasons as he went for the delay.

I do not deny, Master, that I'm past my time, but not by an hour; at most by half-an-hour. Playing at ball again, and in the purlieus of the neighbourhood, against thy father's orders! Azariah said, his face full of storm. No, Master, I have put ball-playing out of my mind; or Hebrew has put it out of my mind, and Greek too has turned my thoughts aside. The delay was caused by meeting a sculptor who asked me to pose before him for a statue. And what was thy answer to him? That we were forbidden by our laws to look upon graven images. And what answer did he give to that very proper answer? Azariah asked, somewhat softened. Many answers, Master, and among them was this one: that there was no need for me to look upon the statue he was carving. The answer that one might expect from a Greek, Azariah rapped out, one that sets me thinking that there is more to be said against the Greek language than I cared to admit to thy father when last in argument with him on the subject. But, Master, thou'lt not forbid me the reading of Menander for no better reason than that a Greek asked that he might carve a statue after me, for how am I to blame, since thyself said my answer was commendable? And in these words there was so plaintive an accent that Azariah's heart was touched, for he guessed that the diverting scene in which the slave

arranges for a meeting between the lovers was in the boy's mind.
At that moment their eyes went together to the tally on the wall,
and pointing to it Joseph said it bore witness to the earnestness
with which he had pursued his studies for the last six months, and
Azariah could not do else than admit there was little to complain
of in the past, but he had noticed that once a boy came late for his
lessons his truancy became common. Moreover, my time is of importance, Azariah declared, his hairy nostrils swelling at the
thought of the half hour he had been kept waiting. But may we
finish Menander's comedy? Joseph asked, for he was curious to
learn if Moschion succeeded in obtaining his father's leave to marry
the girl he had gotten with child. The lovers' plan was to ingratiate
themselves with the father's concubine and to persuade her to get
permission to rear and adopt the child. Yes, Joseph, the father
relents. But it would please me to learn why he relents. And
Joseph promised that he would be for a whole year in advance of
his time rather than behind it. He did not doubt that he would
be able to keep his promise, for he had found a new way to Tiberias ;
a deserted way it seemed to be at first, and most propitious, without
the temptations of ball-players, but as the season advanced the lane
became infested by showmen on their way to Tiberias : mummers,
acrobats, jugglers, fortune-tellers, star-mongers, dealers in charms
and amulets, and Joseph was tempted more than once to stop and
speak with these random folk, but the promise he had given Azariah
was sufficiently powerful to inspire a dread and a dislike of these,
and to avoid them he sought for a third way to Tiberias and found
one : a path through an orchard belonging to a neighbour, who
gladly gave him permission to pass through it every morning, which
he did, thereby making progress in his studies till one day, by the
stile over which his custom was to vault into the quiet lane, he
came suddenly upon what seemed to him like a small encampment :
wayfarers of some sort he judged them to be, but of what sort he
could not tell at first, there being some distance and the branches of
an apple-tree between him and them. He drew back the branch,
and as he came through the trees he decided in his mind that they
were the servitude of some great man : varlets, hirelings or slaves.
But his eyes fell on their baskets and — deceived by the number
and size of these — the thought crossed his mind that they might
30

be poulterers on their way to Tiberias. But whatever their trade they had no right to encamp in the orchard, and he informed them politely that the orchard belonged to friends of his, and that large and fierce dogs were loose about the place. For his warning they thanked him, saying they'd make off at once; remarking as they made their preparations for going that they did not think they were doing any harm by coming into the orchard, having crossed the stile only to rest themselves.

Going with poultry to Tiberias? Joseph asked. Not with poultry, Sir, the varlets answered. We are not poulterers, but cockers. Cockers! Joseph repeated, and on reading the blank look in his face they told him they were the servants of a great Roman who had sent them in search of fighting cocks, for a great main was going to be fought that day in Tiberias. We are his cockers, a man said (he spoke with some slight authority, the others seemed to be in his charge), and have been far in search of these birds. He pointed to the baskets and asked Joseph if he would care to see the cocks, and as if to awaken Joseph's curiosity he began to tell their pedigrees. That one, he said, is a Cilician and of a breed that has won thousands of shekels, and a bird in the basket next him is a Bithynian brown-red, the victor in many a main, and the birds in the next three baskets are Cappadocian Duns, all of celebrated ancestry, for our master will have none but the finest birds; and if thou shouldst know of any good birds, price will not stand in the way of our purchasing them. Joseph answered that he had not heard of any, but if he should —— Thou'lt not forget us, said a small meagre woman with black shining eyes in a colourless face, drab as the long desert road she had come by. Joseph promised; and then a short thick-set man with matted hair, and sore eyes that were always fixed on the ground, opened one of the baskets and took out a long lean bird, which he held up for Joseph's admiration. Listen to him! cried the woman in a high thin voice. Listen to him! for no one can set a cock a-sparring like him. The servants consulted among themselves in a language Joseph did not understand, and then, as if they had come to an agreement among themselves, the foreman said, approaching Joseph and cringing a little before him, that if the little master could assure them they would not be disturbed by dogs, they would like to show him the cocks. A little exercise, the man said, would be of advantage to the birds — to those that were not fighting that morning — he added, and the man whom the woman nicknamed the Heeler, a nickname acquired from the dexterity with which he fitted the cocks' heels with soft leather pads, said: As thou seest, Master, they may fight and buffet one another for a space without injury.

Joseph watched the birds advance and retire and pursue each other, and after this exhibition they were put back into their baskets and covered with hay. So thou'rt the Heeler? Joseph asked. The man grinned vacantly, and the woman answering for him said: None in this country equals him in the craft of fixing a pair of spurs, cutting the tail and wings and shortening the hackle and the rump feathers. Give thine eyes, young Master, to this bird. His comb is cut so close that there is no mark for t'other bird's bill, and it is but natural that thou wouldst like to see the spurs with which they fight. And she showed him spurs of two kinds, for there are cocks that fight better with long spurs and cocks that fight better with short. And how many days does it take to train a cock? Joseph asked, and they began to tell him that a fighting cock must be fed with bread and spring water, and have his exercise — running and sparring — every day. It was the woman that kept Joseph in chat, for the men were busy carrying the baskets over the stile and placing them in mule cars waiting in the lane. But, young Master, she said, if thou hast not seen a cock-fight, come with us, for a better one thou'lt never live to see. The best birds in Western Asia will be in Tiberias to-day. Joseph did not answer this invitation at once, for he did not altogether like this woman nor her manner of standing near to him, her black shining eyes fixed upon him. But he was like one infected, and could not escape from his desire to see a cock-fight. He knew that Azariah would never forgive him for keeping him waiting . . . waiting for how long? he asked himself. Till he cares to wait no longer, his conscience answered him. He was going to get into great trouble, but he could not say no to the cockers, and he followed them, asking himself when he should escape from the evil spirit which — at their instigation, perhaps — had taken possession of him. A moment after he was assuring himself that the folk he had fallen in with were ignorant of everything but cockering, without knowledge of

32

witchcraft, star-mongering or sortilege — the servants of some
great Roman, without doubt, which was sufficient assurance that
though they might be cock stealers on occasion they were not kid-
nappers. Besides, in frequented lanes and in Tiberias the stealing
of a boy was out of the question, and after seeing one or two cocks
killed he could return home, for he need not wait till the end. He
could not help himself, he must see the great red and yellow bird
strike his spur through the head of his adversary, as the Heeler
told him he had never failed to do in many combats. And he would
not fail now, though he was two years old, which is old for a fighting
cock. 'Tis for thee to see, little Master, the woman said, that they
are not as quick on their legs as they get older, nor are they as
eager to fight. To-day's battle will be his last — win or lose — and
if he come out alive at the end he'll go to the hens, which will be
more frolicsome than having spurs driven into his neck, as happened
three months gone by; but it didn't check his spirit, she continued;
he killed his bird and let off one great crowing before he toppled
over. We thought he was gone, but I sucked his wound, bathed
it with salt and water, and he's none the worse to-day; game he is
as ever. Come with us to Tiberias. At every turning of the lane
the demon seemed to thrust Joseph on more violently, till at last he
put Azariah out of his head and began to ask himself if he would be
guilty of any great sin in going to see the cock-fight. Of any sin
greater than that of following the custom of the heathen? His
father might be angry, but there'd be no particular atonement:
a fast day, or some study of the law, no more, for he'd be careful
not to raise his eyes to the gods and goddesses that beset the streets
and public places in Tiberias. And on this resolve he followed the
cockers into the city. The statues on the roofs of the buildings were
so far away that no faces or limbs were visible, for which he was
glad, but it was difficult to avoid seeing the statues in the streets;
and worst of all, the cock-fight that he had looked forward to seeing
in the open air was to be fought in a great building — a theatre or
circus — he did not know which. Joseph had never seen so great a
crowd before, and the servants he had come with pointed out to
him their master among a group of Romans. The Jews from Alexandria, he was told, came to these games, and this caused his
conscience to quicken, for he had heard his father speak of the Alex-

33

andrian Jews as heretics. Azariah did not hold such orthodox views, but what his tutor's views were about cock-fighting Joseph did not know; and when he asked if he might approach the ring he was told that the circle about the ring was for the Romans and those whom they might invite, but he'd be able to see very well from where he was.

The Romans seemed to him an arrogant and proud people; and, conscious of an innate hostility, he watched them as they leaned over the railing that enclosed the fighting ring, talking among themselves, sometimes, however, deigning to call a Jew to join them. The Jews came to them obsequiously, hoping that the honour bestowed upon them did not escape notice; and Joseph's ear caught servile phrases: A bird of thine, young Sir, is well reported, one that will smite down all comers, and, Sir, we can offer thee but a poor show of birds. Those at Rome —— An unexpected silence fell, broken by the clattering of dice, and Joseph was told that the throw would decide which seven birds were to begin. . . . We have won the throw, was whispered in his ear. We've the advantage. But why it was an advantage to fight from the right rather than from the left Joseph was too excited to inquire, for the cocks had just been put into the ring or pit, and Joseph recognised the tall lank bird that the Heeler had taken out of his basket in the orchard. He's fighting to-day with long spurs, he was told. But why does he fight the other bird — a yearling? he heard the woman ask; and he saw a black cock crouch to meet the red in deadly fight. Must one die? he asked, but the cockers were too intent on the battle to answer his question. The birds sparred and leapt aside, avoiding each other's rushes, and before long it became clear even to Joseph that their bird, though stronger than the younger bird, did not spring as high or as easily. A good bird, he heard the servants say: there'll be a battle for it; my word, there will, and our bird will win if the young one doesn't get his stroke in quickly; an old bird will tire out a young bird. . . . As these words were spoken the black cock dashed in, and with a quick stroke sent his spur through the red bird's head. He's gone this time beyond thy care! Tears came into Lydia's eyes. I am sorry to see thee, friend, in the dust — victor in many mains; I'd liefer see thee end thy days happily among the hens, a-treading of them.

34

Joseph felt he had not rightly understood her, and when he inquired out her meaning from her she told it with so repulsive a leer that he could not conquer a sudden dislike. He moved away from her immediately and asked her no more questions. More cocks were set to fight, and they fought to the death always : only once did a cock turn tail and refuse to continue the combat. To persuade him to be brave, the slave in charge placed him breast to breast with his adversary, but despite all encouragement he turned tail and hid himself in the netting. Now what will happen to him? Joseph asked. First he'll be cut and then fattened for the spit or the grid-iron, the Heeler answered. Look, young Master, and turning his eyes whither the Heeler's finger pointed, Joseph saw the bird's owner sign to the slave that he was to twist the bird's neck; which was done, and the poltroon went into a basket by himself — he did not deserve to be with those that had been slain in combat.

The ring was now covered with blood and feathers, and two slaves came with buckets of water and brushes to clean it, and while this office was being performed many fell to drinking from flasks which their slaves handed to them. The man who had told his slave to wring his cock's neck regretted that he had done so. The merited punishment would have been to hand the bird over to a large ape, that would have plucked the bird feather by feather, examining each feather curiously before selecting the next one; and he swore a great oath by Jupiter and then, as if to annoy the Jews, by Jehovah, that the next of his birds that refused combat should be served this way. Our master will not put us on the cross for so misjudging a bird's courage, Joseph heard the Heeler say; and Lydia sidled up against Joseph, and it was her thigh as much as the memory of the oaths he had heard and that were being uttered and that would be uttered again as soon as the fighting commenced that set him thinking of Azariah scanning the tally on the wall — vowing that he would teach him no more; but the tally, which Joseph knew well, showed that he had not missed an hour for many months. Still a whole day's absence was something more than any truancy he had ever indulged in before, and the only reason he could give for it would be the inacceptable one that the cockers had bidden a demon take possession of him. Another pair of cocks was already in the ring : two young birds trained to the finest pitch,

35

and they sparred so lustily that even the experts could not predict the victor. But there was no heart in Joseph for more cock-fighting, and he viewed with disgust the mean vile faces that leered at him while he thanked them for the occasion which he owed them of overlooking so much fine sport. But they were a scurvy lot, viler than he had supposed, though he had suspected from the first that they were nursing up some trick against him. And he searched himself, for he would willingly give them money to be rid of them. But how much will they accept? he asked himself, as he searched his pockets . . . his money was gone! Stolen, no doubt, but by whom? By the cockers standing around him, quarrelling and railing at each other, levelling accusations right and left — the Heeler wrangling with Lydia, saying it was she who had asked the young penniless to come with them. A mercy it was he didn't call me a ragamuffin, Joseph said to himself, and he was not without some apprehension that they might detain him till a ransom was paid, and right glad he was to perceive himself free to go; having gotten his money they wished to be rid of him quietly; and he too wishing to avoid attracting attention, slunk out of Tiberias without laying complaint before the magistrate.

It was unlikely that his money would be found upon the thieves, and his father would be very angry indeed if he were obliged to go to Tiberias to bear witness to the truth of his story that his son, while on his way to his tutor's —— Joseph stopped to consider the eventualities, and he heard in imagination the tale unfolding. Azariah might be called! And if he were he would tell he had been kept waiting all day, and the jealous neighbours would be glad to send round to commiserate his father. It seemed to Joseph that he had escaped lightly with the loss of a few shekels. But what reason should he give for coming home so late? He'd have to say where he had spent the day. Azariah would tell of his absence from his lessons. Ah, if he had foreseen all these worries, he wouldn't have gone to Tiberias. . . . Should he say he had been out fishing on the lake? The fishers would not betray him, but they might; and he could not bring himself to tell his father a lie. So did he argue with himself as he walked, saying that he had not done worse than —— But what had happened at home? Something must have happened, for the gates were open. The gate-keeper, where was he?

His wonder increased as he reached the house, for all the servants seemed to be running to and fro. And the Lord be praised for sending thee back to us! they exclaimed. Your thought then was that the Lord had taken me from you? Joseph asked, and the man replied that they had been searching for him all day — sending messengers hither and thither, and that in the afternoon a boat had hoisted sail and put out for the fishing fleet, thinking that Simon Peter might be able to give tidings of Master Joseph. But why all this fuss? Joseph said, because I come home a little later than usual. Thy father, Master Joseph, is beside himself, and thy grandmother —— Joseph left the man with the end of the sentence on his tongue.

So thou'st returned at last! his father cried on seeing him, and began at once to tell the anxiety he had suffered. Nor was Rachel without her word, and between their reproofs it was some time before Joseph began to apprehend the cause of the tumult: Azariah had laid a long complaint of truancy! As to that, Joseph answered tartly, he has little to complain of. And he spoke of the pact between them, relating that seven or eight months before he had promised Azariah not to be past his time by five minutes. Look to his tally, Father: it will tell that I have kept my word for eight months and more and would have kept it for the year if —— Be mindful of what he is saying to thee, Dan. Look well to the tally before condemning, Rachel cried. Wouldst have it then, woman, Azariah lied to me? Not lied, but was carried beyond himself in a great heat of passion at being kept waiting, Rachel answered. He said that he enjoyed teaching thee, Joseph, God having granted thee good intelligence and ways of comprehension. But he couldn't abide seeing thee waste thy time and his. We're willing and ready to hear about this absence and the cause of it, Dan interposed. So get on with the story: where hast thou been? Out with it, boy. Where hast thou been, and with whom? a question that could be met only by the bare answer: Watching a cock-fight in Tiberias; and to save his parents from much misunderstanding he said he must begin at the beginning. Dan would have liked a straight answer, but Rachel said the boy should be suffered to tell his story his own way; and Joseph told a fine tale, the purport of which was that he had sought for a byway to Tiberias, the long lanes being

37

beset by acrobats, zanies, circus riders and the like, and had found
one through Argob orchard and had followed it daily without meeting anyone for many months, but this morning as he came through
the trees he had caught sight of an encampment; some cockers on
their way to Tiberias, where a great main was to be fought. And it
was the cocks of Pamphylia that had —— He stopped, for the great
change that had come over his parents' faces set him wondering
if his conduct was as shameful as their faces seemed to affirm.
He could not see that he had sinned against the law by going to
Tiberias, though he had associated himself with Gentiles and for a
whole day . . . he had eaten in their company, but not of any
forbidden meat. And whilst Joseph sought to minimise his offence
to himself, his father sat immersed in woe, his head in his hands.
What calamity, he cried, has fallen on my house, and how have I
sinned, O Lord, that punishment should fall upon me, and that my
own son should be chosen to mete out my punishment? My house
is riven from rafter to foundation stone. But, Father, at most ——
It seemed useless to plead. He stood apart; his grandmother stood
silent and grave, not understanding fully, and Joseph foresaw that
he could not count upon her to side with him against his father.
But if his father would only tell him if he had sinned against the
law, instead of rending his garments, he would do all the law commanded to obtain forgiveness. Was there, he asked, anything in
the law against cock-fighting? or in the traditions? It was a pastime of the heathen: he knew that, and had hoped a day of fasting
might be suggested to him; but if this offence was more serious
than he had supposed he besought his father to say so. Tell me,
Father, have I sinned against the law? The question seemed to
exasperate his father, who at last cried out: Of what value may be
thy Hebrew studies and a knowledge of the language if thou study
not the law with Azariah? Does not the Book of Leviticus ever
lie open before thee? How has the law been affronted? — the law
given by the Lord unto Moses. My own son asks me this! And if a
soul sin and hear the voice swearing and is a witness whether he
has sinned or known of it, if he did not utter it, then he shall bear
his iniquity. Was there no swearing at thy cock-fight? Plenty, I
reckon. All day was spent listening to swearing, hearing the name
of the Lord taken in vain: a name we don't dare to pronounce our-
38

selves. Joseph sat dumbfounded. So Azariah never taught thee the law? All the time goes by wasted in the reading of Greek plays. We read Hebrew and speak it, Joseph answered, and it was thy wish that I should learn Greek. And, Father, is there any reason to worry over a loss of good name? For my sin will be known to nobody but God, unless told by thee, and thou'lt keep it secret. Or told by Azariah, Dan answered moodily, who never teaches the law, but likes Greek plays better. Well, thou shalt hear the law from me to-night, for I can read Hebrew, not, belike, as well as Azariah, but I can read Hebrew all the same. Mother, hand me down the Scriptures from the shelf.

CHAPTER IV.

WELL, Dan, thou must make up thy mind whether thou art
going to look out for one who will teach him better, or let him remain with Azariah, who likes teaching him, for he is a clever but
oft-times an idle boy. I don't know that I should have said idle,
she added, and sat thinking of what word would describe Joseph's
truancy better than idle, without, however, finding the word she
needed, and her thoughts floated away into a long consideration of
her son's anger, for she could see he was angry with Azariah.
But the cause of his anger she could not discover. It could not be
that he was annoyed with Azariah for coming to complain that he
was often kept waiting; and it was on her tongue to ask him why
he was so gloomy, why he knitted his brows and bit his lips. But
she held back the question, for it would not be long before Dan
would let out his secret: he could not keep one. And Dan, knowing
well his own weakness and his mother's shrewdness (she would
soon be guessing what was passing in his mind), began to cast
blame on Azariah for his residence in Tiberias, a pagan city — his
plan for leading her on a false trail. Others, he said, spoke more un-
favourably than he did; and he continued in this strain until Rachel,
losing patience, interrupted him suddenly saying that Azariah
did not live in Tiberias. If not in Tiberias, he answered, in a sub-
urb, and within a stone's throw of the city walls. But what has that
got to do with Joseph? Rachel asked. What has it got to do with
Joseph! Dan growled, when to reach the scribe's house he has to
pass through lanes infested with the off-scourings of the pagan
world: mummers, zanies, jugglers, dancers, whores from Babylon.
Didst thou not hear him, woman, describe these lanes, saying that
he had to change his course three times so that he might keep his
promise to Azariah? and art thou unmindful that he told me, and
thou sitting there listening on that very stool, that the showmen
40

he met in Argob orchard put a spell upon him, and that it was the demon that had obtained temporary lodgment in him that had bidden him to Tiberias to see the cock-fight? Jews from Alexandria, heretics, adventurers, beggars, aliens! Nay, but think, Dan, Rachel said, he is a proud boy and may thank thee little for —— There are others to teach him, Dan interrupted, and continued to walk up and down the room, for he wished to make an end of this talk with his mother. But he hadn't crossed the room twice when he was brought to a full stop, having remembered suddenly that it is always by such acts as he was now meditating that fathers lose the affections of their sons. If he were to drag Joseph away from Azariah, from whom he was learning Hebrew and Greek, Joseph might begin to look upon him as a tyrant. His mother was a sharp-witted woman, and very little was needed to set her thinking. She had an irritating way of looking as it were into his mind, and if she were to suspect him of jealousy of Azariah he would never have a moment's peace again. But what may we understand from all this thy raging up and down the room? asked Rachel. Make thy mind if thou'rt going to withdraw the boy from his schooling or leave him. Dan cast an angry glance at his mother and hated her; and then his heart misgave him, for he knew that he lacked courage to take Joseph out of his present schooling, and dared not divide his house against himself, or do anything that might lose him his son's love and little by little cause himself to be looked upon as a tyrant. He knew himself to be a weak man, except in the counting-house; he knew it, and must needs stifle his jealousy of Azariah, who had forgiven Joseph his truancy and was the only one that knew of the excursion into Tiberias. But Azariah's indulgence did not altogether please him. He began to suspect it and to doubt if he had acted wisely in not ordering Joseph away from Azariah: for Azariah was robbing him, robbing him of all that he valued in this world, his son! And it seemed to him a little later in the day, as he closed his ledger, that he had come to be disregarded in his own house; and he thought he would have liked much better to stay away, to dine in the counting-house, urging a press of business. The first thing he would hear would be: Azariah. The hated name was never off the boy's lips: he talked of nothing else but Azariah and Hebrew and Greek and the learned Jews whom he met at

41

Azariah's house. And feeling like one on whom a robbery was being committed, Dan sat asking himself if his bargain were not that his son should learn the Greek language but not Greek literature : Which is full of heresy, he said to himself; and he returned home determined to raise the point; but Joseph told him, and he thought rather abruptly, that it was only through Greek literature that one could learn Greek in Tiberias — the spoken language was a dialect.

It may have been that Joseph perceived that praise of Azariah caused his father to writhe a little, and — curious to observe the effect — he spoke more of Azariah than he would have done otherwise, and laid an accent on his master's learning, and related incidents in which his master appeared to great advantage, causing his father much perplexity and pain of mind, till at last, unable to bear the torture any longer, he said — the words slipped from him incontinently —— Thou'rt no better than a little Azariah! and, unable to contain himself, he rushed from the room, leaving Joseph and Rachel to discuss his vehemence and discover motives which he hoped would not include the right one. But afraid that he had betrayed his jealousy of Azariah he returned, and to mislead his mother and son he began to speak of the duty of the pupil to the master, telling Joseph he must submit himself to Azariah in everything; by representing Azariah as one in full authority he hoped to overcome his influence, and before many months had passed over a different accent was notable in Joseph's voice when he spoke of Azariah; but he continued his lessons with him for some time longer, and Dan's annoyance slumbered and awoke, till he could bear it no longer and began to devise plans to end his son's studies in Hebrew and Greek. Joseph knows now all that Azariah can teach him, and it is high time that I took him in hand and taught him his trade. But though determined to rid himself of Azariah he felt he must proceed gently (if possible, in conjunction with his mother) : he must wait for an occasion; and while he was watching for one it fell out that Joseph wearied of Azariah and went to his father saying that he had learnt Hebrew and could speak Greek, so there was no use in his returning to Azariah any more. At first his parents could only think that he had quarrelled with Azariah, but it was not so; they soon discovered that he had merely become

42

tired of him — a change that betokened a capricious mind. A growing boy is full of fancies, Rachel said: an explanation that Dan deemed sufficient, and he was careful not to speak against Azariah lest he should turn his son's thoughts back on Greek literature, or Greek philosophy, which is more pernicious even than the literature. He did not dare to ask Joseph to come down to the counting-house, afraid lest by trying to influence him in one direction he might influence him in the opposite direction. He deemed it better to leave everything to fate, and while putting his trust in God, Dan applied himself to meditate on the young man's character and his tastes, which seemed to have taken a sudden turn; for, to his father's surprise, Joseph had begun to put questions to him about the sale of fish, and to speak of visiting Tyre and Sidon with a view to establishing branch houses — extensions of their business. His father, while approving of this plan, pointed out that Tyre and Sidon being themselves on the coast of the sea could never be as good customers as inland cities, sea fish being considered, he thought mistakenly, preferable to lake. He had been doing, it is true, a fair trade with Damascus, but whereas it was impossible to reckon on Damascus it seemed to him that their industry might be extended in many other directions. And delighted with the change that had come over his son he said that he would have tried long ago to extend his business, if he had had knowledge of the Greek language. He spoke of Heliopolis, and proposed to Joseph that he should go there and establish a mart for salt fish as soon as he had mastered all the details of the trade, which would be soon: a very little application in the counting-house would be enough for a clever fellow like Joseph. As he said these words his eyes met Rachel's, and as soon as Joseph had left the room she asked Dan if he believed that Joseph was likely to settle down to the selling of salt fish: a question which was not agreeable to Dan, who was at that moment settling himself into the conviction that Joseph had begun to evince an aptitude for trade that he himself did not acquire till many years older, causing him to flame up as might be expected against his mother, telling her that her remarks were most mischievous, whether she meant them or not. He hoped Joseph was not the young man that she saw in him. Before he could say any more Joseph returned and linked his arm into his father's,

43

and the twain went away together to the counting-house, Dan enamoured of his son, but just a little afraid all the same that Joseph might weary of trade in the end, just as he had wearied of learning. He was moved to speak his fear to Joseph, but on consideration he resolved that no good could come of such confidences, and on the evening of the first day in the counting-house he whispered to Rachel that Joseph had taken to trade as a duck to the water, as the saying is.

Day after day he watched his son's progress in administration, saying nothing, waiting for the head clerk to endorse his opinion that there were the makings of a first-rate man in Joseph. He was careful not to question him directly, but every now and then he would shape the conversation so that the clerk might say that Master Joseph had a head for trade. But the clerk made no remark : it might as well have been that Joseph was not in the counting-house ; Dan had begun to hate his clerk, who had been with him for thirty years. He had brought him from Arimathea and could never dismiss him ; he could only look into his eyes appealingly. At last the clerk spoke, and his words were like manna in the desert ; and, overjoyed, Dan wondered how it was that he could have refrained so long. It was concerning a certain falling off in an order : If Master Joseph were to make a round through the Greek cities—— Dan could have thrown his arms about his clerk for these words, but it were better to dissimulate. Thy thought is that Joseph understands the business sufficiently ? The clerk acquiesced, and it was a great day, of course, the day Joseph went forth ; and in a few weeks Dan had proof that his confidence in his son's wits was not misplaced. For very soon Joseph showed himself to be suited to the enterprise by his engaging manner as well as by his knowledge of Hebrew and Greek, the two languages procuring him admission into the confidences of Jew and Gentile alike. The length of these excursions was from three to four weeks, and when Joseph returned home for an interval his parents disputed as to whether he should spend his holiday in the counting-house or the dwelling-house. So to avoid giving offence to either, and for his own pleasure, Joseph often spent these days on the boats with the fishers, learning their craft from them, losing himself often in meditations how the draught of fishes might be increased by a superior kind of net :

44

interested in his trade far too much, Rachel said. His mind seemed bent on it always; whereas she would have liked to have heard him tell of all the countries he had been to and of all the people he had seen, but it was always about salt fish that he was talking: how many barrels had gone to this town, and how many barrels to another, and the new opening he had discovered for salt fish in a village the name of which he had never heard before. And I would that thou hadst never heard of it! Rachel exclaimed, for Joseph had put her past her patience. I shall be glad when the last barrel of salt fish comes out of the lake, for it will not be till then that we shall have time to live our lives in peace and comfort. She gathered up her knitting and was going to bed, but Joseph would not suffer her to go. He said he had stories to tell her, and he fell to telling of the several preachers he had heard in the synagogues, and his voice beguiled the evening away so pleasantly that Rachel let her knitting drop into her lap and sat looking at her grandson, stupefied and transported with love.

Dan's love for his son was more tender in these days than it had ever been before, but Rachel looked back, thinking the old days were better, when Joseph came back from Azariah thinking only of his lessons. It may be that Dan, forgetful of his jealousy, looked back to those days gone over with a certain wistfulness. A boy is, if not more interesting, at least more unexpected, than a young man. In the old days Dan did not know what sort of son God had given him, but now he knew that God had given him the son he always desired, and that Azariah's tending of the boy's character had been kind, wise and salutary, as the flower and fruit showed. But in the deepest peace there is disquiet, and in the relation of his adventures Joseph had begun to display interest in various interpretations of Scripture which he had heard in the synagogues — true that he laughed at these, but he had met learned heretics from Alexandria in Azariah's house. Dan often wondered if these had not tried to impregnate his mind with their religious theories and doctrines, for being without religious interests, Dan was strictly orthodox, a hard and fast follower of Ezra. He did not suspect Azariah, whom he knew to be withal orthodox, as much as Azariah's friend, Apollonius, the Alexandrian Jew. But though he kept his ears open for the slightest word he could not discover any trace of

45

his influence. If his discourse had had any effect, it was to make Joseph more than ever a Pharisee. He was sometimes even inclined to think that Joseph was a little too particular, laying too much stress upon the practice of minute observances, and he began to apprehend that there was something of the Scribe in Joseph after all. The significance of his mother's words becoming suddenly clear to Dan, he asked himself if it were not yet within the width of a finger that Joseph would tire of trade and retire to Jerusalem and expound the law and the traditions in the Temple. His vocation, Dan was of opinion, could not yet be predicted with any certainty : he might go either way — to trade or to religious learning — and in the midst of these meditations on his son's character Dan remembered that some friends had come to see Joseph at the counting-house yesterday. Joseph had taken them out into the yard and they had talked together, but it was not of the export of salt fish they had spoken, but of the observances of the Sabbath. Dan had listened, pen in hand, his thoughts suspended, and had heard them devote many minutes to the question whether a man should dip himself in the nearest brook if he had accidentally touched a pig. He had heard them discuss at length the grace that should be used before eating fruit from a tree, and whether it were necessary to say three graces after eating three kinds of fruit at one meal. He had heard one ask if a sheep that had been killed with a Greek knife could be eaten, and he had heard Joseph ask him if he knew the sheep had been killed with a Greek knife and the man confess that he had not made inquiry. If he had known —— Dan did not hear the end of the sentence, but imagined that it ended in a gesture of abhorrence. In his day religion was limited to the law of Moses, a skein well combed out, but the Scribes in Jerusalem had knotted and twisted the skein. He had heard Joseph maintain, and stiffly too, that an egg laid on the day after the Sabbath could not be eaten, because it had been prepared by the hen on the Sabbath. But one can't always be watching hens, he said to himself, and the discussion of such points seeming to him unmanly, he drew back the window-curtain and fell into admiration of his son's slim loins and great shoulders. Joseph was laughing with his companions at that moment and his teeth glistened, every one white and shapely. Why do such discussions interest him?

46

Dan asked, for his eyes are soft as flowers; and he thought her a lucky woman that Joseph would resort unto in the night. But very often men like Joseph did not marry, and a new disquietude arose in his mind: he wanted children, grandchildren. In a few years Joseph should begin to look round. . . . Meanwhile it might be well to tell him that men like Hillel had always held that it is after the spirit rather than the letter we should strive, and that in running after the latter we are apt to lose the former, and he accepted the first opportunity to admonish Joseph, who listened in amazement, wondering what had befallen his father, whom he had never heard speak like this before. All the same he hearkened to these warnings and laid them in his memory, and fell to considering his father as one who had just jogged along the road that he and his ancestors had come by, without much question. But if his father had set himself to consider religions, and with that seriousness they deserved, he would not keep back any more the matter on which he had long desired to speak to him. The young men to whom he had just bidden good-bye were all going to Jerusalem, whither Dan was accustomed to go every year for the Feast of the Passover, but last year the journey thither had fatigued him unduly, and it seemed to Joseph that this year he should go to Jerusalem in his father's place; and when he broached the subject, Dan, who had been thinking for some time that he was not feeling strong enough for this journey, welcomed Joseph's proposal — a most proper presence Joseph's would be at the Feast. Joseph had come to the age when he should visit Jerusalem, but he did not readily understand this sudden enthusiasm. If he wanted to go to Jerusalem to the Feast of the Passover, why had he not said so before? And Dan, whose thoughts reached back to the discussion overheard in the yard, was compelled to ask Joseph if it were for the purpose of discussing the value of certain minute points of law that he wished to go to Jerusalem. At which Joseph was astonished that his father should have asked him such a thing. . . . Yet why not? For a while back he was discussing such very points with some young gossips. His tongue wagged as was its wont on all occasions, though his mind was away and he suddenly stopped speaking; and when the stirring of his father's feet on the floor awakened him, he saw his father sitting pen in hand watching him and no doubt asking himself of what great and wonderful thing his son was thinking. And once again actuality disappeared. He stood engulfed in memories of things heard in Azariah's house : or things only half heard, for he had never thought of them since. The words of the Jews he met there had fallen dead at the time, but now he remembered things that had passed over his mind. The heresies of the Jews in Alexandria awoke in him, and a marvellous longing awoke to see the world. First of all he must begin with Jerusalem, and he bade his father good-bye with an eagerness not too pleasant to the old man.

CHAPTER V.

GONE to the study of the law! Dan said, as he walked up and down the room, glancing often into Joseph's letter, for it figured to him the Temple with the Scribes meditating on the law, or discussing it with each other while their wives remained at home doing the work. So do their lives pass over, he said, in the study of the law. Nothing else is to them of any worth. . . . My poor boy hopes that I shall forgive him for not returning home after the Feast of the Passover! Does he suspect that I would prefer him indifferent to the law in Magdala, rather than immersed in it at Jerusalem? A little surprised and shocked at the licentiousness of his thoughts, he drew them into order with the admission that it is better in every way that a young man should go to Jerusalem early in his life and acquire reverence for the ritual and traditions of his race, else he might drift later on into heresy, or maybe go to live in cities like Tiberias, amongst statues. But why do I trouble myself like this? For there was a time before I had a son, and the time is getting very close now when I shall lose him. Dan stood swallowed up in the thought of the great gulf into which precarious health would soon pitch him out of sight of Joseph for ever, and it was Rachel coming into the room that awoke him. She too! he muttered, and once more he began to fuss about, seeking for parchments, for he was now intent on sending Joseph a letter of recommendation to the High Priest, having already forgotten the gulf that awaited him, in the pleasurable recollection of the courtesy and consideration he received from the most distinguished men the last time he was in Jerusalem — from Hanan the son of Seth and father-in-law of Kaiaphas: Kaiaphas was now High Priest, the High Priest of that year; but in truth, Hanan, who had been High Priest before him, retained all the power and importance of the office and was even called the High Priest. Dan remembered that he had been received

49

with all the homage due to a man of wealth. He liked his wealth to be acknowledged, for it was part of himself : he had created it ; and it was with pride that he continued his letter to Hanan recommending his son to him, saying that anything that was done to further Joseph's interests would be a greater favour than any that could be conferred on himself.

The letter was sent off by special messenger and Joseph was enjoined to carry it himself at once to Hanan, which he did, since it was his father's pleasure that he should do so. He would have preferred to be allowed to pick his friends from among the people he met casually, but since this was not to be, he assumed the necessary reverence and came forward in the proper spirit to meet Hanan, who expressed himself as entirely gratified by Joseph's presence in Jerusalem and promised to support his election for the Sanhedrin. But if the councillors reject me? For as thou seest, I am still a young man. The innocency of Joseph's remark pleased Hanan, who smiled over it, expressing a muttered hope that the Sanhedrin would not take upon itself the task of discussing the merits and qualifications of those whom he should deem worthy to present for election. The great man purred out these sentences, Joseph's remark having reminded him of his exalted position. But thinking his remark had nettled Hanan, Joseph said : I have been barely a week as yet in Jerusalem ; and this remark continued the flattery, and with an impulsive movement Hanan took Joseph's hands and spoke to him about his father in terms that made Joseph feel very proud of Dan, and also of being in Jerusalem, which had already begun to seem to him more wonderful than he had imagined it to be, and he had imagined it very wonderful indeed. But there was a certain native shrewdness in Joseph; and after leaving the High Priest's place he had not taken many steps before he began to see through Hanan's plans : Which no doubt are laid with the view to overawe me with the magnificence of Jerusalem and its temple. He walked a few yards farther, and remembered that there are always dissensions among the Jews, and that the son of a rich man (one of first-rate importance in Galilee) would be a valuable acquisition to the priestly caste. But though he suspected deceit in Hanan's courtesy, he was still the dupe of Hanan, who was a clever man and a learned man : his importance loomed up very large, and Joseph could not be without a hero, true or false; so it could not be otherwise than that Hanan and Kaiaphas and the Sadducees, whom Joseph met in the Sanhedrin and whose houses he frequented, commanded his admiration for several months and would have held it for many months more, had it not been that he happened to be a genuinely religious man, concerned much more with an intimate sense of God than with the slaying of bullocks and rams. He had accepted the sacrifices as part of a ritual which ought not to be questioned and which he had never questioned : yet, without discussion, without argument, they fell in his estimation without pain, as naturally as a leaf falls. A friend quoted to him a certain well-known passage in Isaiah, and not the whole of it : only a few words; and from that moment the Temple, the priest and the sacrifices became every day more distasteful to him than they were the day before, setting him pondering on the mind of the man who lives upon religion while laughing in his beard at his dupe; he contrasted him with the fellow that drives in his beast for slaughter and pays his yearly dole; he remembered how he loved the prophets instinctively though the priests always seemed a little alien, even before he knew them. Yet he never imagined them to be as far from true religion (which is the love of God) as he found them; for they did not try to conceal their scepticism from him : knowing him to be a friend of the High Priest, it had seemed to them that they might indulge their wit as they pleased, and once he had even been moved to rebuke some priests, so blasphemous did their jests appear to him. An unusually fat bullock caused them to speak of the fine regalement he would be to Jahveh's nose, and one sacristan, mentioning the sacred name, figured Jahveh as pressing forward with dilated nostrils. There is no belly in heaven, he said : its joys are entirely olfactory, and when this beast is smoking, Jahveh will call down the angels Michael and Gabriel. As if not satisfied with this blasphemy, as if it were not enough, he turned to the sacristans by him, to ask them if they could not hear the angels sniffing as they leaned forward out of their clouds. My priests are doing splendidly : the fat of this beast is delicious in our nostrils, were the words he attributed to Jahveh. Michael and Gabriel, he said, would reply : It is indeed as thou sayest, Sire — a most enjoyable reek !

Joseph marvelled that priests could speak like this, and tried to forget the vile things they said, but they were unforgettable: he retained them in his heart, for he could not do else, and when he did speak, it was at first cautiously, though there was little need for caution; for he found to his surprise that everybody knew that the Sadducees did not believe in a future life and very little in the dogma that the Jews were the sect chosen by God, Jahveh. He was their God and had upheld the Jewish race, but for all practical purposes it was better to put their faith henceforth in the Romans, who would defend Jerusalem against all barbarians. It was necessary to observe the Sabbath and to preach its observances and to punish those who violated it, for on the Sabbath rested the entire superstructure of the Temple itself, and all belief might topple if the Sabbath was not maintained, and rigorously. In the houses of the Sadducees Joseph heard these very words, and their crude scepticism revolted his tender soul: he was drawn back to his own sect, the Pharisees, for however narrow-minded and fanatical they might be he could not deny to them the virtue of sincerity. But would this sincerity allow him to witness in all gravity observances that he had repudiated long ago in Galilee? As he put the question to himself a sudden recollection of the discussion that had once arisen in the yard behind the counting-house: whether an egg could be eaten if it had been laid the day after the Sabbath, brought a smile to his face, but a different smile from that of yore, for he understood now better than he had understood then that this (in itself a ridiculous question) was no more serious than a bramble that might for a moment entangle the garment of a wayfarer: of little account was the delay if the feet were on the right road. Now the scruple of conscience that the question had awakened might be considered as a desire to live according to a law which, observed for generations, had become part of the national sense and spirit. On this he fell to thinking that it is only by laws and traditions that we may know ourselves — whence we have come and whither we are going. He attributed to these laws and traditions the love of the Jewish race for their God, and their desire to love God, and to form their lives in obedience to what they believed to be God's will. Without these rites and observances their love of God would not have survived. It was not by exaggeration of these laws but by the scepticism of the Sadducees that the Temple was polluted. If the priests degraded religion and made a vile thing of it, there were others that

52

ennobled the Temple by their piety. And as these thoughts passed through Joseph's mind, his eyes went to the simple folk who never asked themselves whether they were Sadducees or Pharisees, but were content to pray around the Temple that the Lord would not take them away till they witnessed the triumph of Israel, never asking if the promised resurrection would be obtained in this world — if not in each individual case, by the race itself — or whether they would all be lifted by angels out of their graves and carried away by them into a happy immortality.

The simple folk on whom Joseph's eyes rested favourably, prayed, untroubled by difficult questions: they were content to love God; and, captured by their simple unquestioning faith, which he felt to be the only spiritual value in this world, he was glad to turn away from both Sadducees and Pharisees and mix with them. Sometimes, and to his great regret, he brought about involuntarily the very religious disputations that it was his object to be rid of for ever when he withdrew himself from the society of the Pharisees. A chance word was enough to set some of them by the ears, asking each other whether the soul may or can descend again into the corruptible body; and it was one day when this question was being disputed that a disputant, pressing forward, announced his belief that the soul, being alone immortal, does not attempt to regain the temple of the body. A doctrine which astonished Joseph, so simple did it seem and so reasonable; and as he stood wondering why he had not thought of it himself, his eyes telling his perplexity, he was awakened from his dream, and his awakening was caused by the word Essene. He asked for a meaning to be put upon it, to the great astonishment of the people, who were not aware that the fame of this third sect of the Jews was not yet spread into Galilee. There were many willing to instruct him, and almost the first thing he learnt about them was that they were not viewed with favour in Jerusalem, for they did not send animals to the Temple for sacrifice, deeming the shedding of blood a crime. A still more fundamental tenet of this sect was its denial of private property: all they had belonged to one brother as much as to another, and they lived in various places, avoiding cities, and setting up villages of their own accord; notably one on the eastern bank of the Jordan, from whence recruiting missionaries sometimes came forth, for the Essenes disdained marriage, and relied on proselytism for the maintenance of the order. The rule of the Essenes, however, did not exclude marriage because they believed the end of the world was drawing nigh, but because they wished to exclude all pleasure from life. To do this, to conceive the duty of man to be a cheerful exclusion of all pleasure, seemed to Joseph wonderful, an exaltation of the spirit that he had not hitherto believed man to be capable of : and one night, while thinking of these things, he fell on a resolve that he would go to Jericho on the morrow to see for himself if all the tales he heard about the brethren were true. At the same time he looked forward to getting away from the seven windy hills where the sun had not been seen for days, only grey vapour coiling and uncoiling and going out, and where, with a patter of rain in his ears, he was for many days crouching up to a fire for warmth. But in Jericho he would be as it were back in Galilee : a pleasant winter resort, to be reached easily in a day by a path through the hills, so plainly traced by frequent usage that a guide was not needed. A servant he could not bring with him, for none was permitted in the cenoby, a different mode and colour of life prevailing there from any he ever heard of, but he hoped to range himself to it, and — thinking how this might be done — he rode round the hillside, coming soon into view of Bethany over against the desert. From thence he proceeded by long descents into a land tossed into numberless hills and torn up into such deep valleys that it seemed to him to be a symbol of God's anger in a moment of great provocation. Or maybe, he said to himself, these valleys are the ruts of the celestial chariot that passed this way to take Elijah up to heaven? Or maybe . . . His mind was wandering, and — forgetful of the subject of his meditation — he looked round and could see little else but strange shapes of cliffs and boulders, rocks and lofty scarps enwrapped in mist so thick that he fell to thinking whence came the fume? For rocks are breathless, he said, and there are only rocks here, only rocks and patches of earth in which the peasants sow patches of barley. At that moment his mule slid in the slime of the path to within a few inches of a precipice, and Joseph uttered a cry before the gulf which startled a few rain-drenched crows that went away cawing, making the silence more melancholy than before. A few more inches, Joseph thought, and we should have been over, though a mule has

54

never been known to walk or to slide over a precipice. A moment after his mule was climbing up a heap of rubble; and when they were at the top Joseph looked over the misted gulf, thinking that if the animal had crossed his legs mule and rider would both be at the bottom of a ravine by now. And the crows that my cry startled, he said, would soon return, scenting blood. He rode on, thinking of the three crows, and when he returned to himself the mule was about to pass under a projecting rock, regardless, he thought, of the man on his back; but the sagacious animal had taken his rider's height into his consideration, so it seemed, for at least three inches were to spare between Joseph's head and the rock. Nor did the mule's sagacity end here; for finding no trace of the path on the other side he started to climb the steep hill as a goat might, frightening Joseph into a tug or two at the bridle, to which the mule gave no heed but continued the ascent with conviction, and after a little circuit among intricate rocks turned down the hill again and slid into the path almost on his haunches. A wonderful animal truly! Joseph said; guessing that the path lay under the mass of rubble come away in some landslip, he knew he would meet it farther on. He may have been this way before. However this may be, a wonderful animal; a perfect animal, if he can be persuaded not to walk within ten inches of the brink! and Joseph drew the mule away to the right, under the hillside; but a few minutes after, divining his rider's thoughts to be lost in those strange argumentations common to human beings, the mule returned to the brink, out of reach of any projecting rocks, content to follow the twisting road, giving no thought to the hills always falling into steep valleys and always rising out of steep valleys, as round and humped as the hills that were left behind. Joseph noticed the hills, but the mule did not: he only knew the beginning and the end of his journey, whereas Joseph began very soon to be concerned to learn how far they were come, and as there was nobody about who could tell him he reined up his mule, which began to seek herbage — a dandelion, an anemone, a tuft of wild rosemary — while his rider meditated on the whereabouts of the inn. The road, he said, winds round the highest of these hills, reaching at last a tableland halfway between Jerusalem and Jericho, and on the top of it is the inn. We shall see it as soon as yon cloud lifts.

CHAPTER VI.

A FEW wanderers loitered about the inn. Come from Mount Sinai,
so the innkeeper said; and descrying thieves and rogues in them,
he mentioned a camel and an ass in the paddock — stolen no doubt
on the way hither, he added, and called to the wanderers that
they waited in vain for water — he had none to give them. A
strange and fierce lot, remote like the desert, whence they had come,
and Joseph was afraid of them like the innkeeper, but began to
pity them when he heard that they had not tasted food for a fort-
night, only a little camel's milk. They're waiting for me to give
them the rinsings, the innkeeper said, if any should remain at the
bottom of the barrel. My ox-cart plies daily, bringing two barrels
of water to the inn, and we sell it to those who have money to pay
for it. Then let the man drink his fill, Joseph answered, and his
wife too. And standing monumental beside her, he examined the
woman curiously, for he had never seen so mean a thing before :
her small beady eyes were like a rat's, and her skin nearly as brown.
Twenty years of desert wandering leave them like mummies, he
reflected ; and the girl, whom the mother enjoined to come forward
and to speak winningly to the rich man, was already shrivelled,
crinkled and brown, ugly and mean as her mother. Marauders they
sometimes were, but now they seemed so poor that Joseph thought
he could never have seen poverty before, and took pleasure in distributing figs amongst them. I would have thee pay me for the
figs within the house, the innkeeper said ; for half a shekel they
would have my life, and many's the time they'd have had it if
Pilate, our governor, had not sent me a guard ; and he spoke of the
new procurator till Joseph mounted his mule. I'll see that none of
them follows thee, the innkeeper whispered ; and Joseph rode away
down the lower hills, alongside of precipices and through narrow

56

defiles, following the path, which issued at last on to a shallow valley full of loose stones and rocks. I suppose the mule knows best, Joseph said, and he held the bridle loosely and watched the rain, regretting that the downpour should have begun in so exposed a place : but so convinced did the animal seem that the conduct of the journey should be left entirely to his judgment that it was vain to ask him to hasten his pace, and he continued to clamber down loose heaps of stones, seeking every byway unnecessarily, Joseph could not help thinking, but bringing his rider and himself safely, he was forced to admit, at the foot of the hills over against Jericho. Another toiling ascent was begun, and Joseph felt a trickle of rain down his spine, while the mule seemed to debate with himself whether shelter was to be sought, and spying a rock a little way up the hillside he trotted straight to it and entered the cave — the rock projected so far beyond a hill that it might be called a cave, and better shelter from the rain they could not have found. A wonderful animal thou'rt surely, knowing everything, Joseph said, and the mule shook the rain out of his long ears, and Joseph stood at the mouth of the cave, watching the rain falling and gathering into pools among the rocks, wondering the while if this land was cast away into desert by the power of the Almighty God because of the worship of the Golden Calf; and then remembering that it was cast into desert for the sins of the cities of the plain, he said : How could I have thought else? As soon as this rain ceases we will go up the defile and at the end of it the lake will lie before us deep down under the Moab mountains. He remembered too that he would have to reach the cenoby before the day was over, or else sleep in Jericho. The sky seemed to be brightening — at that moment he heard footsteps. He was unarmed and the hills were infested by robbers. The steps continued to approach. . . . His hope was that the man might be some innocent shepherd in search of a lost yoe; if he were a robber, that he might pass on, unsuspicious of a traveller seeking shelter from the rain in a cave a little way up the hillside. The man came into view of the cave and stood for some time in front of it, his back turned to Joseph, looking round the sky, and then, like one who has lost hope in the weather, he hastened on his way. As soon as he was out of sight Joseph led out his mule, clambered into the saddle, and digging his heels into the mule's sides galloped the best part of a mile till he reached the Roman fort overlooking the valley. If a robber was to emerge, a Roman soldier would speedily come to his assistance; but behind him and the fort were some excellent lurking-places, Joseph thought, for robbers, and again his heels went into his mule. But this time, as if he knew that haste was no longer necessary, the mule hitched up his back and jangled his bells so loudly that again Joseph's heart stood still. He was within sight of Jericho, but half-way down the descent a group of men were waiting, as if for travellers. His best chance was to take them for harmless passengers, so he rode on, and the beggars — for they were no more — held up maimed leprous limbs to excite his pity.

He was now within two miles of Jericho, and he rode across the sandy plain thinking of the Essenes and the cenoby on the other side of Jordan. He rode in full meditation, and it was not till he was nigh the town of Jericho that he attempted to think by which ford he should cross Jordan : whether by ferry, in which case he must leave his mule in Jericho, or by a ford higher up the stream, if there was a ford practicable at this season — Which is doubtful. he said to himself, as he came within view of the swollen river. And he hearkened to one who declared the river to be dangerous to man and beast : but another told him differently, and being eager to reach the cenoby he determined to test the ford, saying to himself : If the water prove too strong I will return to Jericho. But the mule plunged forward, and at one moment it was as like as not that the flood would carry them away into the lake beyond, but Joseph's weight enabled the animal to keep on his hooves, and the water shallowing suddenly, the mule reached the opposite bank. It was my weight that saved us, Joseph said; and dismounting, he waited for the panting animal to recover breath. We only just did it. The way to the cenoby? he called out to a passenger along the bank, and was told he must hasten, for the Essenes did not receive anybody after sunset : Which may or may not be true, he muttered, as he pursued his way, his eyes attracted and amused by the long shadow that himself and his mule projected over the wintry earth. He was tempted to tickle the animal's long ears with a view to altering the silhouette, and then his thoughts ran on into the cenoby and what might befall him yonder : For that must be it, he

58

said, looking forward and discovering a small village on the lower slopes of the hills, on the ground shelving down towards the river. His mule, scenting food and rest, began to trot, though very tired, and half-an-hour afterwards Joseph rode into a collection of huts, grouped — but without design — round a central building which he judged to be an assembly hall whither the curators, of whom he had heard, met to carry on the business of the community. And no doubt, he said, it serves for a refectory, for the midday meal which gathers all the brethren for the breaking of bread. As he was thinking of these things one of the brethren laid hands on the bridle and asked him whom he might be wishing to see; to which question Joseph answered: The Head. The brother replied: So be it; and after tethering the mule to a post at the corner of the central hut, he begged Joseph to enter and seat himself on one of the benches, of which there were many; and it was whilst awaiting the coming of the president that Joseph recognised from the long table that he was in the refectory, where the rite of the breaking of bread was accomplished. To-morrow I shall witness it, he said, and felt like dancing and singing in his childish eagerness. But the severity of the hall soon quieted his mood, and he remembered he must collect his thoughts and prepare his story for recital, for he would be asked to give an account of himself. As he was preparing his story, the president entered: a tall man of bulk, with the pallor of age in his face and in the hand that lifted the black taffeta cap from his head. The courteousness of the greeting did more than to put Joseph at his ease, as the saying is. In a few moments he was confiding himself to this man of kindly dignity, whose voice was low, who seemed to speak always from the heart, and it was wholly delightful to tell the great Essene that he was come from Galilee to attend the Feast of the Passover in his father's place, and that after having allied himself in turn to the Sadducees and the Pharisees he came to hear of the Essenes: I have come hither, hoping to find the truth. Thou hast truthful eyes, said the president; and, thus encouraged, Joseph told that there were some in the Temple, the poor who worship God daily with a whole heart. It was from them, he said, that I heard of your doctrines. Of which thou canst have only the merest outline, the president answered; and perhaps when thou knowest us better our rule may seem too hard for thee to follow, or it may be that thou'lt feel that thou'rt called to worship God differently from us. But it matters naught how we worship, if our worship come from the heart. Now the word: heart, startled Joseph out of himself, and his eyes falling at that moment on the Essene he was moved to speak these words: Father, I could never disobey thee. Let me stay, put me to the tests. But the tests are long, the president answered; we would not suffer thee to return to Jericho to-night, even if thou wished it. Thy mule is tired and would be swept away by the descending flood. Be guest with us for to-night and for as long after it as pleases thee — to the end of thy probationship and after, if thou shouldst prove worthy of admission. Meanwhile thou'lt be given a girdle, a white garment and a little axe. Thou'lt sleep in one of the outlying huts. Come with me. On our way round our village we shall meet some of the brethren returning from their daily tasks, for we all have a craft: many of us are husbandmen; the two coming towards us carrying spades are from the fields, and that one turning down the lane is a shepherd; he has just folded his flock, but he will return to them with his dogs, for we suffer a great deal from the ravages of wild beasts with which the woods are thronged, wolves especially. In our community there are healers, and these study the medicinal properties of herbs. If thou desirest to remain with us, thou'lt choose a craft. Joseph mentioned that the only craft he knew was drysalting, and it was disappointing to hear that there were no fish in the lake. There is a long time of probation before one is admitted, the president continued, and when that is concluded another long time must pass over before the proselyte is called to join us at the common repasts. Before he breaks bread with us he must bind himself by oath to be always pious towards the Divinity, to observe justice towards men, and to injure no one voluntarily or by command: to hate always the unjust and never to shrink from taking part in the conflict on the side of the just; to show fidelity to all and especially to those who rule. Thou'lt soon begin to understand that rule doesn't fall to anyone except by the will of God. I have never deserved to rule, but headship came to me, he added half sadly, as if he feared he had not been sufficiently exacting. After asking Joseph whether he felt himself strong enough to obey so severe a rule, he passed from father to teacher. Every

60

one of us must love truth and make it his purpose to confute those who speak falsehood; to keep his hands from stealing and his soul from unjust gain. He must never conceal anything from a member of the order, nor reveal its secrets to others, even if he should have to suffer death by withholding them; and above all, while trying to engage proselytes he must speak the doctrines only as he has heard them from us. Thou'lt return perhaps to Jerusalem. . . .

He broke off to speak to the brothers who were passing into the village from their daily work, and presented Joseph as one who, shocked by the service of the Sadducees in the Temple, had come desiring admission to their order. At the news of a new adherent the faces of the brothers became joyous: For though the rule seems hard when related, they said, in practice, even at first, it seems light enough, and soon we do not feel it at all. They were now on the outskirts of the village, and pointing to a cabin the Essene told Joseph that he was to sleep there and on the morrow enter upon his probation. But, Father, may I not hear more? If a brother be found guilty of sin, will he be cast out of the order? The president answered that if one having been admitted to their community committed sins deserving of death, he was cast out and often perished by a most wretched fate, for being bound by oath and customs he could not even receive food from others but must eat grass, and with his body worn by famine he perished. Unless, the president added, we have pity on him at the last breath and think he has suffered enough for his sins.

CHAPTER VII.

THE hut that Joseph was bidden to enter was the only one left in the cenoby for allotment, four proselytes having arrived two months ago. No better commodity have we for the moment, the curator said, struck by the precarious shelter the hut offered — a crazy door and a roof that let the starlight through at one end of the wall. But the rains are over, he added, and the coverlet is a warm one. On this he left Joseph, whom the bell would call to orison, too tired to sleep, turning vaguely from side to side, trying to hush the thoughts that hurtled through his clear brain — that stars endure for ever, but the life of the palm-tree was as the life of the man who fed on its fruit. The tree lived one hundred years, and among the Essenes a centenarian was no rare thing, but of what value to live a hundred years in the monotonous life of the cenoby? And in his imagination, heightened by insomnia, the Essenes seemed to him like the sleeping trees. If he remained he would become like them, while his father lived alone in Galilee! Dan rose up before him in his thought and he could find no sense in the assurances he had given the president that he wished to be admitted into the order. He seemed no longer to desire admission, and if he did desire it he could not, for his father's sake, accept the admission. Then why had he talked as he had done to the president? He could not tell: and it must have been while lying on his right side, trying to understand himself, what he was and why he was in the cenoby, that he fell into that deep and dreamless sleep from which he was awakened by a bell, and so suddenly that it seemed to him that he had not been asleep more than a few minutes. It was no doubt the bell for morning prayer: and only half awake he repaired with the other proselytes to the part of the village open to the sunrise. All the Essenes were assembled there, and he learnt

62

that they looked upon this prayer of thanksgiving for the return of light as the important event of the day. He joined in it, though he suspected a certain idolatry in the prayer. It seemed to him that the Essenes were praying for the sun to rise; but to do this would be to worship the sun in some measure, and to look upon the sun as in some degree a God, he feared; yet the Essenes were certainly very pious Jews. What else they were, time would reveal to him: a few days would be enough; and long before the prayer was finished he was thinking of his father in Galilee, and what his face would tell, were he to see his son bowing before the sun. But the Essenes were not really worshipping the sun but praying to God that the sun might rise and give them light again to continue their daily work. One whole day at least he must spend in the cenoby, and — feeling that he was becoming interested again in the Essenes — he began to form a plan to stay some time with them.

On rising from his knees he thought he might stay for some weeks. But if the Essene brotherhood succeeded in persuading him that his fate was to abandon his father and the trade that awaited him in Galilee and the wife who awaited him somewhere? His father often said: Joseph, thou'rt the last of our race. I hope to see a good wife with thee, one who will bear thee children, for I should like to bless my grandchildren before I die. The Essenes would at least free him from the necessity of telling his father that there was no heart in him for a wife; and if he did not take a wife he might become —— One of the curators whispered to him the use he should make of the little axe, and he followed the other proselytes; and having found a place where the earth was soft, each dug a hole about a foot deep, into which they eased themselves, afterwards filling up the hole with the earth that had been taken out. Joseph then went down with them to a spring for purifications, and these being finished the proselytes grouped themselves round Joseph, anxious to become acquainted with the last recruit, and asking all together what provision of food he had made for himself for that day: if he had made none, he would have to go without food, for only those who were admitted into the order were suffered to the common repasts. A serious announcement, he said, to make to a man at break of day who knew nothing of these things yesterday, and he asked how his omission might be repaired. He must ask

63

for permission to go to Jericho to buy food. As he was going there on a mule, he might bring back food not only for himself but for all of them: enough lentils to last a week; and he inquired what else they were permitted to eat — if eggs were forbidden? At which the proselytes clapped their hands. A basket of eggs! A basket of eggs! And some honey! cried another. Figs! cried a third; we haven't tasted any for a month. But my mule's back will not bear all that you require, Joseph answered. Our mule! cried the proselytes; all property is held in common. Even the fact of my mule having become common property, Joseph said, will not enable him to carry more than his customary burden, and the goods will embarrass me. If the mule belongs to the community, then I am the mule-driver, the provider of the community. Constituted such by thy knowledge of the aptitudes and temper and strength of the animal! cried a proselyte after him, and he went away to seek out one of the curators; for it is not permissible for an Essene to go to Jericho without having gotten permission. Of course the permission was at once granted, and while saddling his mule for the journey the memory of the river overnight now caused Joseph to hesitate and to think that he might find himself return empty-handed to the group of proselytes now waiting to see him start. Said one of them: If thou didst cross the river in safety yesterday, there is no reason why thou shouldst not cross it in safety now. But forget not the basket of eggs, said a second. Nor the honey, mentioned a third, and a fourth called after him the quality of lentils he liked the best. The mind of the fifth regarding food was not expressed, for a curator came by and after reproving them, saying they were mere belly-worshippers, he walked to the head of the mule and told Joseph that there would be less water in the river than there was overnight; whereat Joseph was pleased, for it would be a harsh and disagreeable death to drown in a lake so salt that fish could not live in it. True, he would escape being eaten by fishes: But if the mule be carried away, he said to himself, drown I shall, long before I reach the lake, unless indeed I strike out and swim — which, it seemed to him, might be the best way to save his life — and if there be no current in the lake I can gain the shore easily. But the first sight of the river proved the vanity of his foreboding, for during the night it had emptied a great part of its flood into the lake and the struggle in getting his mule across was slight; still slighter when he returned with a sack of lentils, a basket of eggs, some pounds of honey and many misgivings as to whether he should announce this last commodity to the curator or introduce it surreptitiously. To begin his probationship with a surreptitious act would prove him unworthy of the good opinion that the prior had formed of him, setting at naught his pleasure; and Joseph was glad when he met a curator, who told him that sometimes, on the first day of probation, honey and figs were allowed.

The cooking of the food and the eating of it in the only cabin in which there were conveniences for eating helped the time away, and Joseph began to ask himself how long his cloistral life was going to endure, for he seemed to have lost all desire to leave it, and had begun to turn the different crafts over in his mind and to debate which he should choose to put his hand to. Of husbandry he was as ignorant as a crow, nor could he tell poisonous pastures from wholesome, nor could he help in the bakery. At first venture there seemed to be no craft for him to follow, since fish did not thrive in the Salt Lake and the fisherman's art could not be practised, he was told, in the Jordan, for the Essenes were not permitted to kill any living thing. Whilst laying emphasis on this rule, the curator cracked a flea under his robe, but Joseph did not call his attention to his disobedience, but bowed his head and left him to the scruple of conscience which he hoped would awaken in him later. Before this had time to come to pass, the curator called after him and suggested that he might teach Hebrew to the four proselytes, whose knowledge of that language had seemed to Mathias, their instructor, disgracefully weak. They were all from Alexandria, like their teacher, and read the Scriptures in Greek; but the Essenes, so said the curator, must read the Scriptures in Hebrew. And the teaching of Hebrew, Mathias said to Joseph, takes me away from my important work. But our father may accept thee as a sufficient teacher: go to him for examination. I have heard from Mathias of thy learning in Hebrew, said the president; and a few passages read from the Scriptures satisfied him that Joseph was the assistant teacher that had been so long desired in the community, and he spoke to Joseph soothingly of Mathias, whose life work was the true interpretation of the Scriptures. But did the Scriptures need interpretation? Joseph asked himself, not daring to put questions to the president; and on an early occasion he asked Mathias what the president meant when he spoke of a true interpretation of the Scriptures, and was told that the true meaning of the Scriptures lay below the literal meaning. There can be no doubt, he said, that the Scriptures must be regarded as allegories; and he explained to Joseph that he devoted all his intellect to discovering and explaining these allegories, a task demanding extraordinary assiduity, for they lay concealed in what seemed to the vulgar eye mere statements of fact: As if, he added scornfully, God chose the prophets for no better end than a mere relation of facts! We read that Adam and Eve hid themselves from the eyes of God; but can anybody hide himself from God? he asked Joseph, wherefore the story is an allegory. There is no doubt that the story of Adam and Eve is an allegory, said Joseph. Mathias smiled encouragingly: Now let me lead thee into the lecture-room. And to the end of his life Joseph kept in his memory the moment when he sat in the corner of the hall, his eyes fixed upon Mathias' young and beautiful profile, clear cut, hard and decisive as the profiles of the young gods that decorated the Greek coins which shocked him in Cæsarea. His memory of Mathias was as partial; but he knew the president's full face, and while pondering on it he remembered that he had never seen him in profile. Nor was this all that set the two men apart in Joseph's consciousness. The president's simple, homely language came from the heart, entered the heart and was remembered, whereas Mathias spoke from his brain. The heart is simple and always the same, but the brain is complex and various; and therefore it was natural that Mathias should hold, as if in fee, a great store of verbal felicities, that he should translate all shades of thought at once into words, and that his mind, moving in a rich, erudite and complex syntax, should obtain great power over the young and turn all opposition into admiration. Even the president, who had been listening to theology all his life and had much business to attend to, must fain neglect some of it for the pleasure of listening to Mathias when he lectured. Even Saddoc, the most orthodox Jew in the cenoby, Mathias could keep as it were chained to his seat. He resented and spurned the allegory, but the beautiful voice that brought out sentence after sentence, like silk from off a

66

spool, enticed his thoughts away from it. The language used in the cenoby was Aramaic, and never did Joseph hear that language spoken so beautifully. It seemed to him that he was listening to a new language, and on leaving the hall he told Mathias that it had seemed to him that he was listening to Aramaic for the first time. Mathias answered him — blushing a little, Joseph thought — that he hoped one of these days, in Egypt perhaps, if Joseph ever went there, to lecture to him in Greek. He liked Aramaic for other purposes, but for philosophy there was but one language. But let us speak it when we are together, Mathias said, and if I detect any incorrectness I will warn thee against it. That Mathias should choose to speak to him in Greek was flattering indeed, and Joseph, who had not spoken Greek for many months, began to prattle, but he had not said many words before Mathias interrupted him and said : Thou must have spoken Greek from childhood. This remark turned the talk on to Azariah ; and Mathias listened to Joseph's account of his tutor carelessly, interrupting him when he had heard enough with a remark anent the advancement of the spring, to which Joseph did not know how to reply, so suddenly had his thoughts been jerked away from the subject he was pursuing. Thou hast the full Jewish mind, Mathias continued ; interested in moral ideas rather than philosophy, led from thought by the sight of a village. I was thinking, Sir, of the near season, when the fields will be green and the lintels running over with flowers. Mathias waited for a better defence from Joseph, but Joseph did not know for certain that Mathias was not right — perhaps he was more interested in moral ideas than in beauty. However this might be, he began to experience an aversion, and might have taken leave of Mathias, if they had not come upon the president, who stopped to speak to them, for he was minded to congratulate Mathias on having fortuned at last on an efficient teacher of Hebrew and Greek, and having addressed a few kindly words directly to Joseph, and taken his hand in his, the head of the community bade them both good-bye, saying that important business needed his presence. He sped away on his business, seeming, however, to leave so much of himself behind, that even Mathias was perforce distracted from his search of a philosophic point of view and indulged himself in the luxury of a simple remark. His goodness, he said, is so natural, like the air we breathe and the bread we eat, and that is why we all love him, and why all dissension vanishes at the approach of our president; a remarkable man. The most wonderful I have ever seen, Joseph answered: a remark that did not altogether please Mathias, for he added: His power is in himself, for he is altogether without philosophy.

Mathias' words: for he is altogether without philosophy, startled Joseph, and he was moved to ask Mathias if the pleasure that the president brought to all was not due to this very absence of philosophy. But he curbed his desire to provoke Mathias into argument, and yielded himself instead to the spell of the Greek voice and the music that Mathias sounded out of the wonderful Greek language, till the sight of threescore sheep lying by a well recalled Rachel; and the old peasant and his two sons were so plainly Isaac, Jacob, and Esau, that he continued to discover the Bible everywhere he looked, his heart seeming to stand still when a tall, well-favoured girl came with some sheep. Her father's sheep! Joseph said to himself, and when the taller of the two lithe lads rolled the stone from the mouth of the well and the several flocks were watered, he added: Only Leah is lacking. Her name carried his thoughts back into the old story of Jacob's disappointment when in the darkness of the tent he had accepted the elder for the younger sister, and he was considering the long years of toil Jacob had endured for Rachel's sake when a stern voice asked: Are thy thoughts with me, or with what is passing about that well-head? Joseph answered: With thee, Master, and bethought himself of a return to the cenoby, though were he to return thither it would be to give a lesson in Hebrew. Even at this cost he would escape from Mathias; but as the words: God be with thee, rose to his lips, Mathias began to deplore that the Essenes were content with mere piety, saying: God has given to man a mind, and therefore desires man to meditate, not on his own nature, which is trivial and passing, but on God's nature, which is important and eternal — a remark that revealed a new scope for inquiry to Joseph, who was interested in the Essenes. But his search was for miracles and prophets rather than for ideas, and if he tarried among the Essenes it was because he had come upon two great men; and forgetful of Mathias' admonitions that the business of man is to meditate

68

on the nature of God, he said: The Essenes perform no miracles and do not prophesy — an interruption to Mathias' loquacity which the other took with a better grace than Joseph had expected, for no one had ever dared before to interrupt Mathias. Joseph had done so accidentally and expected a very fine reproof, but Mathias checked his indignation and told Joseph that Manahem, an Essene, had foreknowledge of future events given to him by God: For when he was a child and going to school, Manahem saw Herod and saluted him as king of the Jews; and Herod, thinking the boy was in jest or did not know him, told him he was but a private citizen; whereat Manahem smiled to himself, and clapping Herod on the backside with his hand said: Thou wilt be king and wilt begin thy reign happily, for God finds thee worthy. And then, as if enough was said on this subject, Mathias began to diverge from it, mixing up the story with many admonitions and philosophical reflections, very wise and salutary, but not what Joseph cared to hear at that moment. He was in no wise interested at that moment to hear that he had done well in testing all the different sects of the Jews, and though the Essenes were certainly the most learned, they did not possess the whole truth. With a determination that was impossible to oppose, Mathias said: The whole truth is not to be found, even among the Essenes, and, my good friend, I would not encourage in thee a hope that thou mayst be permitted ever during thy mortal life to discover the whole truth. It exists not in any created thing: but glimpses of the light are often detected, now here, now there, shining through a clouded vase. But the likeness, he added, of the clouded vase gives rise to the thought that the light resides within the vase: the very contrary of which is the case. For there is no light in the vase itself: the light shines from beyond the skies, and I should therefore have compared man to a crystal itself, that catches the light so well that it seems to our eyes to be the source of light, which is not true in principle or in fact, for in the darkness a crystal is as dark as any other stone. In such part do I explain the meaning that the wicked man, having no divine irradiation, is without instruction of God and knowledge of God's creations; he is as a fugitive from the divine company, and cannot do else than hold that everything is created from the world to be again dissolved into the world. And being no better than a follower of Heraclitus ——

69

But who is Heraclitus? Joseph asked. A clouded face was turned upon Joseph, and for some moments the sage could not collect his thoughts sufficiently to answer him. Who is Heraclitus? he repeated, and then, with a general interest in his pupil, he ran off a concise exposition of that philosopher's doctrine — a mistake on his part, as he was quick enough to admit to himself, — for it awakened in Joseph an enthusiasm so real that he felt himself obliged to expose Heraclitus' fallacies more thoroughly; but in doing this he became embarrassed, his refutation of Heraclitus seeming to him suddenly to imperil his own doctrine : that we must not hope to discover the whole truth of things in this life, and unable to foresee how he might disentangle himself from Heraclitus, he warned Joseph that he must not press him with further questions, the hour being nigh when the Essenes would retire to their cells for meditation. To press would be presumptuous, Joseph answered, but if I do not ask at once, my chance is gone for ever; for thy discourse is like the clouds, always taking new shapes. In dread lest all be forgotten, I repeat to myself what has been said, and so lose a great deal for a certain remembrance.

Joseph's manifest delight in his statement of the doctrines of Heraclitus and his subsequent refutation of the heathen philosopher caused Mathias to forget temporarily certain ideas that he had been fostering for some days — that God, being the designer and maker of all things, and their governor, is likewise the creator of time itself, for he is the father of its father, and the father of time is the world, which made its own mother — the creation. So that time stands towards God in the relation of a grandson; for this world is a younger son of God inasmuch as it is known only through the outward sense. On these things the sage's thoughts had been running for some days past, and he would have liked to have expounded his theory to Joseph : that nothing is future to God : creations and the very boundaries of time are subject. He began to speak, but Joseph did not hear, being too busy memorising what he had already heard, and during long hours he strove to come to terms with what he remembered, but in vain. The more he thought, the less clear did it seem to him that in eternity there is neither past nor future, that in eternity everything is present — Mathias' very words; but when he said them, there seemed to be something

70

behind the words; while listening, it seemed to Joseph that sight had been given to him, but his eyes proved too weak to bear the too great illumination, and he had been obliged to cover them with his hands, shutting out a great deal so that he might see just a little . . . as it were between his fingers. As we think of God only under the form of light, it seemed to him that the revelation entered into him by his eyes rather than by his ears. He would return to the sage every day, but what if he were not able to remember, if it were all to end in words with nothing behind the words? The sage said that in a little while the discourses would not seem so elusive and evanescent. At present they seemed to Joseph like the mist on the edge of a stream, and he strove against the belief that a philosopher is like a man who sets out to walk after the clouds. Such a belief being detestable, he resolved to rid himself of it, and Mathias would help him, he was sure, and in this hope he confided his life to him, going back to the night when Samuel appeared to him, and recounting his father's business and character, introducing the different tutors that were chosen for him, and his own choice of Azariah, to whom he owed his knowledge of Greek. To all of which the philosopher listened complacently enough, merely asking if Azariah shared the belief prevalent in Galilee that the world was drawing to a close. On hearing that he did, he seemed to lose interest in Joseph's story of Azariah's relations to his neighbours, nor did he seem unduly afflicted at hearing that only the most orthodox views were acceptable in Galilee. His indifference was disheartening, but being now deep in his biography, Joseph related perforce the years he spent doing his father's business in northern Syria, hoping as he told his story to awaken the sage's interest in his visit to Jerusalem. The Sadducees did not believe that Jahveh had resolved to end the world and might be expected to appear in his chariot surrounded by angels blowing trumpets, bidding the dead to rise. But the Pharisees did believe in the resurrection — unfortunately including that of the corruptible body, which seemed to present many difficulties. He was about to enter on an examination of these difficulties, but the philosopher moved them aside contemptuously, and Joseph understood that he could not demean himself to the point of discussing the fallacies of the Pharisees — Who, Joseph said, hope to stem the just anger of God on the last day by minute observances of the Sabbath. Mathias raised his eyes. And it was a revulsion of feeling, Joseph continued, against hypocrisy and fornication, that put me astride my mule as soon as I heard of the Essenes, the most enlightened sect of the Jews in Palestine. That thou shouldst be among them is testimony of their enlightenment. . . . Mathias raised his hand, and Joseph's face dropped into an expression of attention. Mathias was willing to concede that much, but certain circumlocutions in his language led Joseph to suspect that Mathias was not altogether satisfied with the Essenes. He seemed to think that they were too prone to place mere piety above philosophy — a mistake; for our intellect being the highest gift we have received from God, it follows that we shall please him best by using it assiduously. He spoke about the prayers before sunrise and asked Joseph if they did not seem to him somewhat trite and trivial and if he did not think that the moment would be more profitably spent by instituting a comparison between the light of the intellect and that of the sun?

Mathias turned to Joseph, and waited for him to confess his thought. But it was hard to confess to Mathias that philosophy was useless if the day of judgment were at hand! He dared not speak against philosophy and it was a long time before Mathias guessed his trouble, but as soon as it dawned on him that Joseph was in doubt as to the utility of philosophy, his face assumed so stern an expression that Joseph began to feel that Mathias looked upon him as a fool. It may have been that Joseph's consternation, so apparent on his face, restored Mathias into a kindly humour. Be that as it may, Mathias pointed out, and with less contempt than Joseph expected, that the day of judgment and philosophy nad nothing in common. We should never cease to seek after wisdom, he said. Joseph concurred. It was not, however, pleasing to Joseph to hear prophecy spoken of as the outpourings of madmen, but — having in mind the contemptuous glance that would fall upon him if he dared to put prophecy above philosophy — he held his peace, venturing only to remark that no prophets were found in Judea for some hundreds of years. Except Manahem, he added hurriedly. But his remembrance of Manahem did not appease the philosopher, who dropped his eyes on Joseph and fixed them on him. The moment was one of agony for Joseph. And as if

72

he remembered suddenly that Joseph was only just come into the district of the Jordan, Mathias told with some ironical laughter that the neighbourhood was full of prophets, as ignorant and as ugly as hyenas. They live, he said, in the caves along the western coasts of the Salt Lake, growling and snarling over the world, which they seem to think rotten and ready for them to devour. Or else they issue forth and entice the ignorant multitude into the Jordan, so that they may the more easily plunge them under the flood. But of what use to speak of these crazed folk, when there are so many subjects of which philosophy may gracefully treat? Are they less, then, than the birds of the air and the beasts of the field? These live by signs and auguries, as we do. But thou'rt not going in search of these wretched men? Mathias asked, and his eyes filled with contempt, and Joseph felt that Mathias had already decided that all intellectual companionship was henceforth impossible between them. It behoved him to propitiate the learned man, and to do so he said that it was not to discuss the resurrection that he desired to see these men, but for curiosity; and during the long walk he would meditate on Mathias' doctrines. . . . Mathias did not answer him, and Joseph, seeing him cast away in philosophy and unable to advise him further, went to the president to ask for permission to absent himself for two days from the cenoby, a permission that was granted willingly when the object of the absence was duly related.

CHAPTER VIII.

THERE was one John preaching in the country about the Jordan; the Baptist, they call him, the president said. But go, Joseph, and see the prophets for thyself. I shall be right glad to hear what thou hast to say! And he pressed Joseph's hand, sending him off in good cheer. Banu, ask for Banu! were the last words he called after him, and Joseph hoped the ferryman would be able to point out the way to him. Oh yes, I know the prophet; the ferryman answered: a disciple of John, that all the people are following. But there be a bit of a walk before thee, and one that'll last thee till dark, for Banu has been that bothered by visits these times, that he has gone up the desert out of the way, for he be preparing himself these whiles. For what? Joseph asked. The ferryman did not know; he told that John was not baptizing that morning, but for why he did not know. As like as not he be waiting for the river to lower, he said. At which Joseph had half a mind to leave Banu for John; but a passenger was calling the ferryman from the opposite bank and he was left in uncertain mind, and wandered on in doubt whether to return in quest of the Baptist or make shift with the disciple. The way pointed out to him lay through the desert, and to find Banu's cave without guidance would not be easy, and after having found and interrogated him the way would seem longer to return than to come. But, having gone so far, he could not do else than attempt the hot weary search. And it will be one! he said, as he picked his way through the bushes and brambles that contrive to subsist somehow in the flat sandy waste lying at the head of the lake. But as he proceeded through them into the desert these signs of life vanished, and he came upon a region of craggy and intricate rocks rising sometimes into hills and sometimes breaking away and littering the plain with rubble. The desert is never com-
74

pletely desert for long, and on turning westward as he was directed, Joseph caught sight of the hill which he had been told to look out for — he could not miss it, for the evening sun lit up a high scarp, and on coming to the end of a third mile the desert began to look a little less desert; brambles began again. Banu could not be far away. But Joseph did not dare to go farther. He had been walking for many hours, and even if he were to meet Banu he could not speak to him, so closely did his tongue cleave to the sides of his mouth. But these brambles betoken water, he said; and on coming round a certain rock bulging uncouth from the hillside, he discovered a trickle, and a few paces distant, Banu, ugly as a hyena and more ridiculous than the animal, for — having no shirt to cover his nakedness — he had tressed a garland of leaves about his waist! Yet not so ugly at second sight as at first, for God is by him always, Joseph said to himself; and he waited for Banu to rise from his knees.

Even hither do they pursue me, Banu's eyes seemed to say, while his fingers modestly rearranged his garland; and Joseph, who began to dread the hermit, begged to have the spring pointed out to him that he might drink. Banu pointed to it, and Joseph knelt and drank, and after drinking he was in better humour to tell Banu that Mathias, the great philosopher from Alexandria, scorned the prophecies that the end of the world could not be delayed much longer. And, as John is not baptizing these days, I thought I'd come and ask if we had better begin to prepare for the resurrection and the judgment. On hearing Joseph's reasons for his visit, the hermit stood with dilated eyes, as if about to speak. But he did not speak; and Joseph asked him what would become of the world after God destroyed it. Before answering, Banu stooped down, and having filled his hand with sand and gravel he said: God will fill his hand with earth, but not this time to make a man and woman, but out of each of his hands will come a full nation, and these he will put into full possession of the earth, for his chosen people will not repent. . . . But the ferryman told me that John gathered many together and was baptizing in Jordan, Joseph said. To which Banu answered naught, but stood looking at Joseph, who could scarce bring himself to look at Banu, though he felt himself to be in sore need of some prophetic confirmation of the date of the judgment.

Is John the Messiah, come to preach that God is near and that we must repent in time? he asked; to which the hermit replied that the Messiah would have many forerunners, and one of these would give his earthly life as a peace-offering, but enraged Jahveh would not accept it as sufficient and would return with the Messiah and destroy the world. I am waiting here till God bids me arise and preach to men, and the call will be soon, Banu said, for God's wrath is even now at its height. But do thou go hence to John, who has been called to the Jordan, and get baptism from him. But John is not baptizing these days, the river being in flood, Joseph cried after him. That flood will pass away, Banu answered, before the great and overwhelming flood arises. Will the world be destroyed by water? At this question Banu turned towards the hillside, like one that deemed his last exhortation to be enough, and who desired an undisturbed possession of the solitude. But at the entrance of the cave he stopped: The track is easy to lose after nightfall, he said, and panthers will be about in search of gazelles. Thou wouldst do well to remain with me: my cave is secure against wild beasts. Look behind thee: how dark are the rocks and hills! Joseph cast his eyes in the direction of Jericho and thanked God for having put a kind thought into the hermit's mind, for the landscape was gloomy enough already, and an hour hence he would be stumbling over a panther in the dark, and the sensation of teeth clutching at his throat and of hind claws tearing out his belly banished from his mind all thoughts of the unpleasantness of passing a night in a narrow cave with Banu, whom he helped to close the entrance with a big stone and to pile up other stones about the big stone, making themselves safe, so Banu said, from everything except perhaps a bear.

The thought of the bear that might scrape aside the stone kept Joseph awake listening to Banu snoring, and to the jackals that barked all night long. They are quarrelling among themselves, Banu said, turning over, for the jackals succeeded in waking him, quarrelling over some gazelle they've caught. A moment after he was asleep again, and Joseph, despite his fear of the wild beasts, must have dozed for a little while, for he started up, his hair on end. A bear! a bear! he cried, without awakening Banu, and he listened to a scratching and a sniffling round the stones with which

BANU

they had blocked the entrance to the cave. Or a panther, he said
to himself. Whichever he was, the animal moved away, and then
Joseph lay awake hour after hour, dropping to sleep, awakening
again and again, until Banu awakened him about an hour after
sunrise, and asked him to help him to roll the stones aside; which
Joseph did, and as soon as they were in the dusk he turned out of
his pockets a few crusts and some cheese made out of yoe's milk,
and offered to share the food with his host; but Banu, pointing to
a store of locusts, put some of the insects into his mouth and told
Joseph that his vow was not to eat any other food till God called
him forth to preach; which would be, he thought, a few days
before the judgment: a view that Joseph did not try to combat, nor
did he eat his bread and cheese before him, lest the sight of it should
turn the prophet's stomach from the locusts. It was distressing to
watch him chewing them; they were not easy to swallow, but he
got them down at last with the aid of some water obtained from the
spring, and during breakfast his talk was all the while of the day of
judgment and the anger of God, who would destroy Israel and build
up another nation that would obey him. It would be three or four
days before the judgment that God would call him out to preach,
he repeated; and Joseph was waiting to hear how far distant were
these days? A month, a year, belike some years, for God's patience
is great. He stopped speaking suddenly, and throwing out his
arms he cried out: He has come, he has come! He whom the world
is waiting for. Baptize him! Baptize him! He whom the world is
waiting for has come.

But for whom is the world waiting? Joseph asked; and Banu
answered: Hasten to the Jordan, and find him whom thou seekest.

CHAPTER IX.

I SHALL pray that the Lord call thee out of the desert to join thy voice with those already preaching, Joseph cried; and the hermit answered him : Let us praise the Lord for having sent us the new prophet ! But do thou hasten to John, he called after Joseph, who ran and walked alternately, striving up every hillock for sight of the ferryman's boat which might well be waiting on this side for him to step on board; Joseph being in a hurry, the boat would certainly be lying under the opposite bank, the ferryman asleep in it, and so soundly that no cries would awaken him.

But Joseph's fortune was kinder than he anticipated, for on arriving at the Jordan he found himself at the very spot where the ferryman had tied his boat and — napping — awaited a passenger. So rousing him with a great shout, Joseph leaped on board and told the old fellow to pull his hardest; but having been pulling across the Jordan for nigh fifty years, the ferryman was little disposed to alter his stroke for the pleasure of the young man, who, he remembered, had not paid him over-liberally yester-evening; and in the mid-stream he rested on his oars, so that he might the better discern the great multitude gathered on yon bank. For baptism, he said; or making ready to go home after baptism, he added; and letting his boat drift, sat discoursing on the cold of the water, which he said was colder than he ever knew it before at this season of the year : remarks that Joseph considered well enough in themselves, but out of his humour. So thou'rt craving for baptism, the ferryman said, and looked as if he did not care a wild fig whether Joseph got it that morning or missed it. But there was no use arguing with the ferryman, who after a long stare fell to his oars, but so leisurely that Joseph seized one of them and — putting his full strength upon it — turned the boat's head up-
78

stream. There be no landing up-stream anywhere, so loose my oars or I'll leave them to thee, the ferryman growled, and we shall be twirling about stream till midday and after. But I can row, Joseph said. Then row! and the ferryman put the other oar into his hand. But we shall be quicker across if thou'lt leave them to me. And as this seemed to Joseph the truth, he fell back into his seat, and did not get out of it till the boat touched the bank. But he jumped too soon and fell into the mud, causing much laughter along the bank, and not a few ribald remarks, some saying that he needed baptism more than those that had gotten it. But a hand was reached out to him, and that he should ask for the Baptist before thinking of his clothes showed the multitude that he must be another prophet, which he denied, calling on heaven to witness that he was not one: whereupon he was mistaken for a great sinner, and heard that however great his repentance it would avail him nothing, for the Baptist was gone away with his disciple. Joseph, thinking that he had left the Baptist's disciple in the desert, began to argue that this could not be, and raved incontinently at the man, bringing others round him, till he was hemmed into a circle of ridicule. Among the multitude many were of the same faith as Joseph himself, and these drew him out of the circle and explained to him that the Baptist baptized in the river for several hours till — unable to bear the cold any longer — he had gone away, his teeth chattering, with Jesus the Essene. Jesus the Essene! Joseph repeated, but before he could inquire further, men came running along the bank, saying they had sins to repent, and on hearing that the Baptist was gone, and would not return that day, they began to tell each other stories of the great cloud that was seen in the east, bearing within it a chariot; and from the chariot angels were seen descending all the morning with flaming swords in their hands. Get thee baptized! they shouted, and clamoured, and pushed to and fro — a thronging gesticulating multitude of brown faces and hooked noses, of bony shoulders and striped shirts. Get thee baptized before sunset! everybody was crying. And Joseph watched the veils floating from their turbans as they fled southwards. On what errand? he asked; in search of the Baptist or the new disciple Jesus? Not the new disciple, was the answer he got back; for Jesus leaves baptism to John. But why

79

doesn't Jesus baptize, Joseph asked, since he is a disciple of the Baptist? If baptism be good for him, it is good enough for another. And so the multitude seemed to think, and were confounded till one amongst them said that Jesus might not be endowed with the gift of baptism; or belike had accepted baptism from John for a purpose, it having been prophesied that the Messiah would have a forerunner. But who, asked many voices together, has said that Jesus is the Messiah? some maintaining that Jesus was the lesser prophet. But this contention was not agreeable to all, some having, for reasons unknown to Joseph, ranged themselves already alongside of Jesus, believing him to be greater than John, yet not the final prophet promised to Israel. And these came to blows with the others, who looked upon John as the Messiah, and Jesus as the one whom John had called to his standard: a recruit — a nothing. Skinny fists were striving in the air and — thrusting himself between two disputants — Joseph begged them to tell him if Jesus, John's disciple, was from the cenoby? Yea, yea, he heard from all sides; the shepherd of the brotherhood — that one who follows their flocks over the hills; but not being sure of his mission, he has gone into the desert to wait for a sign. An Essene, but one that was seldom in the cenoby, more often to be met on the hills with his flocks. A shepherd? Joseph asked. Yea, and it was among the hills that John met him, and seeing a prophet in him spoke to him, and Jesus, seeing that another prophet was risen up in Israel, had thrown his flute away and gone to the president to ask for leave to preach the baptism of repentance unto men, for the grand day is at hand. Joseph having heard this before, heeded only tidings of the new prophet, when a woman pressing forward shouted: A pleasant voice to hear on the mountain-side; and another added: The hills will seem lonely without his gait. A great slinger, cried a third. But why did he come to John for baptism, knowing himself to be the greater prophet? A question that started them all wrangling again, and crying one against the other that repentance was necessary, or else the Lord would desert them or choose another race. These are irksome gossips, a man said to Joseph, but stand aside with me and I'll tell thee much about him. A better shepherd never ranged the hills, and his cure for scab is a wonder. Thou hast heard tell of it? The word scab

80

falling on the ears of another shepherd, he said: I am with my mate in all that he says about the cure, but I wouldn't have him forget that Jesus is gone, taking the brief with him. True for thee, mate, the first answered; he might have left it with us, and would have if a great forgetfulness were not upon him this time past. A third shepherd, attracted by Joseph's appearance, was drawn to listen. He would have left it right enough, but daren't, it belonging to the monks, come down to them from Abraham.

Abraham was a great man; I'll have no gainsaying of it, were the last words that came to Joseph's ears, and feeling that the shepherds could tell him no more of their old comrade, he took leave of them, certain that Jesus must have been among the Essenes for many years before God called him to leave his dogs and to follow John, whom he had begun to recognise as greater than himself, but whom he was destined to supersede. Had not Banu seen John in a vision plunging Jesus into Jordan? and the men along the banks had testified to Jesus baptized. The Jesus that had come to John for baptism was of a certainty none other than the young shepherd whom Joseph had seen, at the beginning of his novitiate, walking with the president in deep converse. He had wondered at the time how a mere shepherd from the hills could talk on an equality with the president, and his memory continuing to unfold, he recalled with singular distinctness and pleasure the fine brow curving upwards —— A noble arch, he said to himself — eyes mysterious as stars, and a certain underlying sadness in the voice, oftentimes soft and low but with a cry in it occasionally. He remembered, too, that their eyes had met, and it seemed to him now as he walked from Jordan to the cenoby that he had read in the shepherd's eyes a look of recognition and amity. But was the young shepherd that Banu saw John baptize in Jordan an Essene? he asked himself, stopping suddenly, and if he were, whither had he gone? Did the brethren know? Questions were against the rule. . . . The president could tell him, but he dared not go to the president; yet consult somebody he must. A few days afterwards he got leave again to visit Banu, whom he found lying in his cave. Fetch me water from the rock, he said. And having drunk, the hermit revived a little, and Joseph told him that he had missed Jesus on the bank and had no tidings of him except that he was gone into the desert

81

to meditate. But the desert is large, and I know not which side of the lake he has chosen. To which Banu answered : John is baptizing in the Jordan ; get thee baptized and repent! On these words he reached out his hand to his store of locusts, and whilst munching a few he added : The Baptist is greater than Jesus, and he is still baptizing. Get thee to Jordan! At this Joseph took offence, and returned to the cenoby with the intention of resuming his teaching. But so possessed was he of Jesus that he could not keep his mind on the lesson before him, and when a pupil's question broke his sick reverie he showed a face so full of pain that the classroom began to pity him and kept up a fire of questions to save him from what they had come to call his doldrums. Of the cause of his vacancy they could have no exact knowledge, but he was not sure that their thoughts might not be running on Jesus absent, and every moment except those in which he sat immersed in dreams was a penance. At last he pleaded illness, and Mathias took his class, leaving him free to wander from the cenoby into Jericho, where he often spent the day in the public gardens, watching the people crossing up and down, each intent on his own business, till he could bear the spectacle of human life no longer and began to meditate on death as a means of escape from the power of the demon whom he could not keep out of his thoughts as he sat drawing patterns on the gravel with his staff. Whether he looked north or south, east or west, he espied a shadow always moving behind his life, disturbing every project, and very often he heard a ghostly whisper : Thy sorrow is my joy ; death alone can lift my power from thee! But he had no will to die, only to believe that he had come within the power of a demon.

One day it seemed to Joseph that the demon had cast a net over him and that he was being drawn down —— Whither? he asked aloud. Somebody spoke to him, and he awoke so bewildered that the would-be gossip laughed outright and passed on (no sooner gone than forgotten), leaving Joseph to his tears and a hope of getting baptism from John, and through baptism freedom. But it was not till it came to be rumoured in Jericho that a prophet had gone to Egypt to learn Greek that he roused sufficiently to ask why a Jewish prophet needed Greek. The answer he got was that the new doctrine required a knowledge of Greek, Greek being a world-wide language and the doctrine being also world-wide. As there was but one God for all the world, it was reasonable to suppose that every man might hope for salvation, be he Jew or Gentile. And it seeming to Joseph that such a doctrine could emanate only from the young shepherd he had met in the cenoby, he joined a caravan, and for fifteen days dreamed of the meeting that awaited him at the end of the journey, and of the delightful instruction in Greek that he was going to impart to Jesus.

He had dreamed of meeting him somewhere in the city, sure that he would recognise the lean jaws and thoughtful eyes in any crowd, and if he did not meet him in the streets he would get news of him in the synagogues; and day after day he wandered seeking Jesus, getting tidings of another of the same name, for the camel-drivers at Mount Sinai had not informed him wrongly: a young Jew had passed through the city on his way to Athens. But the Jew did not correspond to Joseph's remembrances of Jesus, and he did not deem it worth his while to follow him to Athens, but remained in Alexandria, seeking his Jesus in the Jewish quarters, returning again to the synagogues, this time to be met with incredulous looks and smiles, and the rather when he confessed everything: that he was seeking a young prophet discovered by John in the hills of Judea tending sheep. Now, what tale is this he is telling us? the Jews asked apart; but finding Joseph well instructed, and of agreeable presence and manner, they made much of him, saying: If Galilee can produce such a man as Joseph, Galilee is beginning to take a place in the world. We will receive thee and gladly, but speak no more to us of thy shepherd prophet; betake thyself to our schools of philosophy, which thou'lt enjoy, for thy Greek is excellent. But who taught thee Greek? And while Joseph was telling of Azariah, little smiles played about his eyes and mouth, for the incredulity of the Alexandrian Jews had begotten incredulity in him, and he had come to see how much absurdity his adventure made show for.

The Alexandrian Jews liked him better for submitting himself so cheerfully to their learning and their ideas; he became a notable and welcome person among them, almost without himself perceiving the change, and it was not till he had moulded himself, or been moulded, into a new shape that he began to think that he might

83

have done better to have left the moulding to God. His conscience told him this, whilst reminding him that he had vowed himself to Jesus. All the same he remained unaffectedly a young man enticed by the charm of the Greek language, and the science of the Alexandrian philosophers, who were every one possessed of Mathias's skill in dialectics. They all knew Mathias and were imbued with much respect for him as a teacher, and were willing to instruct Joseph in psychology, taking up the lesson where Mathias closed the book. And putting his conscience behind him, Joseph listened, his ears wide open and his mind alert to understand that it was a child's story — the report in Jerusalem that the end of the world was approaching, and that God would remould it afresh — as if God were human like ourselves, animated with like business and desires! He heard for the first time that to arrive at any clear notion of divinity we must begin by stripping divinity of all human attributes, and when every one is sloughed, what remains? Divinity, Joseph answered; and his instructor bowed his head, saying: Here is no matter for reflection. At which all the philosophers concurred, and were surprised to learn that in Jerusalem many still retained the belief that God was no more than a man of colossal stature, angry, revengeful, and desirous of burnt offerings, of prayers which were little better, and that the corruptible body could be raised from the dead and given back to the soul for a dwelling. That Jerusalem had fallen so low in intellect was not known to them; and Joseph, feeling he was making a noise in the world, admitted that despite the knowledge of the Greek language he accepted the theory that the soul was created before the body and waited in a sort of dim hall, hanging like a bat, for the shaping of the body into which it was predestined to descend, there to sojourn till the death of the body released it. He was, however, now willing to believe that the souls of all the wise men mentioned in the books of Moses were sent down to earth as to a colony; great souls could not abide like bats in the darkness, but are ever desirous of contemplation and learning. And on pursuing this thought in the Greek language, which lends itself to subtle shades of thought, he discovered that there are three zones: the first zone is reason, the second passion and the third appetite. And that his first psychological discovery was approved by his teacher,

84

so that many months were passed over in agreeable exercises of the mind of like nature, interrupted only by letters from his father, asking him when he proposed to return home.

After reading one of these letters, his unhappiness lasted sometimes for a whole day, and was revived many times in the days that followed; but philosophy enabled him to resist the voice of conscience still a little while, and even a letter relating the death of his grandmother did not decide his departure. It seemed at first to have decided him, and he told all his friends that he was leaving with the next caravan. But of what use, he asked himself, for me to return to Galilee? Granny is in her grave: could I bring her back to life I would return. But as I cannot, I shall remain here a little while longer in the hope that Jesus may come back from Lower Egypt — in vain hope, maybe, watching oxen draw a plough up and down a long plain day after day whilst the shadow of the palm shortens and lengthens. . . . But the days went by without bringing Jesus. He may be with the Essenes at Kerith, he said, or with the Essenes beyond Jordan. By the next caravan I return; and before the camels were relieved of their packs he was hastening through the desert towards Banu's cave. But of Jesus Banu could only tell him that he was doing the work that our Father had given him to do. Which is more than thou art doing. Go and get baptism from John! Go back to Jericho and wait for a sign, leaving me in peace, for I need it, having been troubled by many, eager and anxious about things that do not matter. I will indeed, Joseph replied, for nothing matters to me since I cannot find him. And he returned to Jericho, saying to himself that Jesus must be known to every shepherd: Perhaps to that one, he said, running to head back his flock, which has been tempted by a patch of young corn. Joseph stood at gaze, for the shepherd wore the same garb as Jesus had done: a turban fixed on the head with two tiring-rings of camel's hair, with veils floating to the shoulders to save the neck from the sun. Jesus, too, wore a striped shirt, and over it was buckled a dressed sheepskin; and Joseph pondered on the shepherd's shoon, on his leathern water-bottle, on his long slender fingers twitching the thongs of the sling. He had been told that no better slinger had been known in these hills than Jesus. But he had left the hills and had gone, whither none could tell! He was

85

gone, whither no man knew, not even Banu. He is about his Father's work, was all Banu could say; and Joseph wandered on from shepherd to shepherd, questioning them all, and when none was in sight he cried again Jesus's name to the winds, and never passed a cave without looking into it, though he had lost hope of finding him. But he continued his search, for it whiled the time away, though it did nothing else, and one day as he lay under a rock, watching a shepherd passing across the opposite hillside, he tried to summon courage to call him; but judging him to be one of those whom he had already asked for tidings of Jesus, he let him go, and fell to thinking of the look that would come into the shepherd's face on hearing the same question put to him again. A poor demented man, he would mutter to himself as he went away. Nor was Joseph sure that his mind was not estranged from him. He could no longer fix it upon anything: it wandered as much at random as the wind among the hills, and very often he seemed to have come back to himself after a long absence, but without any memory. Yet he must have been thinking of something; and he was trying to recall his thoughts, when the shepherd came back into view again and Joseph remarked to himself that he was without a flock. He seemed to be seeking something, for from a sheer edge he peered down into the valley. A yoe that has fallen over, no doubt, Joseph thought; but what concern of mine is that shepherd who has lost a yoe, and whether he will find his yoe or will fail to find it? Of no concern whatever, he said to himself, and — forgetful of the shepherd — he began to watch the evening gathering in the sky. Very soon, he said, the hills will be folded in a dim blue veil, and sleep will perchance blot out the misery that has brooded in me all this livelong day. May I never see another, he muttered, but close my eyes for ever on the broad ruthless light. Of what avail to witness another day? All days are alike to me.

It seemed to Joseph that he was in a sort dead already, for he could detach himself from himself, and consider himself as indifferently as he might a blade of grass. My life, he said, is like these bare hills, and the one thing left for me to desire is death. A footstep aroused him a little. The man whom he had seen on the hill yonder had come up the valley to ask for news of some straying camels — a rough, bearded man in a sheepskin, describing his beasts so garrulously that Joseph failed to understand him. Camels, camels, he repeated aimlessly, as if he had not heard the word before or had forgotten it. One of the brotherhood or a prophet in meditation, the man said to himself, and bowing reverently he would have taken his leave if Joseph had not called him back, saying:, I will come to thy help, and together we cannot miss the camels. In a valley close by the camels were found, staring into emptiness. And since I have found thy camels for thee, who knows but that thou mayst tell me of one Jesus, an Essene from the cenoby on the eastern bank of the Jordan? A shepherd of these hills? the man asked, and Joseph replied: Yes, indeed. To which the camel-driver answered: If I hear of him, I'll send him a message that thou'rt looking for him, and I'll send thee word that he has been found. But thou'lt never find him, Joseph answered. Thou hadst no thought to find my camels, the driver replied; but so it fell out, and had I but a few more camels, or the money to buy them, I could lay down a great trade in figs between Jericho and Jerusalem; and he talked on, telling that figs ripen earlier in Jericho, and the rather if the trees have the advantage of high rocks behind them. It pleased Joseph to listen to his patter, and so plunged was he in misery that the deed was signed that evening, and within a month a caravan laden with figs went forth and wended its way safely to Jerusalem. Another caravan followed a few weeks after, and still larger profits were made, and this becoming known to certain thieves, the next caravan was waylaid and driven away to the coast, and the figs shipped to some foreign part or sold to unscrupulous dealers, who knew them to be stolen. The loss was so great that Gaddi said to Joseph: If we lose a second caravan we shall be worse off than we were when we began, and we shall lose a third and a fourth, unless the robbers be driven out of their caves. Let us then go to the Roman governor, Pilate, and lay our case before him. Joseph had no fault to find with Gaddi's words, and he said: It may be that I shall go to Pilate myself, for I am known to him through my father, who trades largely between Tiberias and Antioch with salt fish. It so happened that Pilate had received instructions from Rome to give every protection to trade, the hope of Rome being to win the Jews from religious disputations, which always ended in riots. Joseph had now brought him the pretext he needed, for the ridding of the road between Jerusalem and Jericho would prove his ability as administrator; and with his hand in his beard, his fine eyes bent favourably upon Joseph, he promised that all the forces of the Roman Empire would be employed to smoke out these nests of robbers. From the account given by Joseph of the caves, he did not deem it worth while to send soldiers groping through the darkness of rocks; he was of opinion that bundles of damp straw would serve the purpose admirably; and turning to the captain of the guard he appealed to him, and got for answer that a few trusses of damp straw would send forth such a reek that all within the cave would be choked, or reel out half blinded. Whereupon Joseph reminded Pilate and the captain of the guard that as long as the caves were left open the robbers who managed to escape from the reek by outlets unknown to any except themselves (many caves, he said, had two outlets) would return, and the plundering of caravans begin again. The only way to make the road from Moab to Jerusalem safe for all time would be to close the caves with rocks and mortised stones, which could be done by letting soldiers down the cliffs with baskets. He also advised that the shepherds that fed their flocks in the neighbourhood of the caves should be forced by torture, if necessary, to betray the robbers. And Joseph's words seeming good to Pilate, he gave orders that all that Joseph said should be done. Within six months the larger dens were betrayed, and whilst the robbers writhed on crosses, long trains of camels and asses pursued their way from Jericho to Jerusalem and back again, without fear of molestation, the remnant of robbers never daring to do more than draw away a single camel or ass found astray from the encampment. Figs were no longer scarce in Jerusalem; and when a delay in bringing wheat from Moab was announced to Pilate, he sent a messenger to Joseph, that the carrying service so well ordered by him might be doubled. A hundred camels, Joseph answered, needs a great sum, but perhaps Gaddi, my partner, may have some savings, or my father may give me the money. And with Pilate's eyes full upon him, Joseph sat thinking of the lake, recalling every bight and promontory, and asking himself how it was that he had not thought of Galilee for so long a time. He longed to set eyes on Magdala, and he would have ridden away at once, but an escort would have

88

to be ordered, for a single horseman could not ride through Samaria without a certainty of being robbed before he got to the end of his journey. Pilate's voice roused Joseph from his reverie, and after apologising to the Roman magistrate for absentmindedness he went away to consult hurriedly with Gaddi, and then to make preparations for the journey — a journey of three days on horseback, he was told, but of two days only on camel-back, a camel walking three miles an hour for eighteen hours. But can I last on a camel's back for eighteen hours? Joseph asked, and the driver showed Joseph how with his legs strapped on either side of the beast he could lie back in the pack and sleep away many hours. Thy head, Sir, will soon get accustomed to the rocking. But I shall have to leave my horse behind, Joseph said. He was fain to see his father and the lake; he was already there in spirit, and would like to transport his cumbersome body there in the least possible time; but he could not separate himself from Xerxes, a beautiful horse that he had brought with him from Egypt — a dark grey — a sagacious animal that would neigh at the sound of his voice and follow him like a dog, and when they encamped for the night, wander in search of herbage and come back when he was called, or wait for him like a wooden horse at an inn door.

Horse and horseman seemed a match the morning they went away to Galilee together, Xerxes all bits and bridles, stirrups and trappings; and Joseph, equipped for the journey not less elaborately than his horse, wore a striped shirt and an embroidered vest, with two veils falling from his turban over his shoulders, and as he was not going to visit the Essenes, he did not forget to provide himself with weapons: a curved scimitar hung by his side and the jewelled hilt of a dagger showed above his girdle. His escort not having arrived yet, he waited; taking pleasure in the arch of Xerxes' neck when the horse turned his head towards him, and in the dark courageous eyes and the beautifully turned hoof that pawed the earth so prettily. At last the five spearmen and their captain appeared, and Xerxes, who seemed to recognise the escort as a sign for departure, presented his left side for Joseph to mount him. As soon as his master was in the saddle he shook his accoutrements and sprang forward at the head of the cavalcade, Joseph crying back: He must have the sound of hoofs behind him. He could

89

refuse his horse nothing, and suffered him to canter some few hundred yards up the road, though it was not customary to leave the escort behind, and when Joseph returned, the captain told him, as he expected he would, that it would be well not to tire his horse by galloping him at the beginning of the journey, for a matter of thirty miles lay in front of them. Thirty miles the first day, he said, and fifty the second day; for by this division he would leave twenty-five miles for the third day; and Joseph learnt that the captain had arranged the journey in this wise for the sake of the inns, for though they would meet an inn every twenty miles, there were but three good inns between Jerusalem and Tiberias. He had reckoned too with a view to the rest at midday. Our way lies, he said, through the large shallow valley, and that is why I started at six. It is about four hours hence, so we shall be through it well before noon. But why must we pass through it before noon? Joseph asked. Because, the captain answered, the rocks on either side are heated after noon like the walls of an oven, and man and beast choke in it. But once we get out of the valley we shall have pleasant country. You know the hills, Sir, and Joseph remembered the rounded hills and Azariah's condemnation of the felling of the forests, a condemnation that the captain agreed with; for though it was true that the woods afforded cover for wolves, still it was not wise to fell the trees: For when the woods go, the captain said, the country will lose its fertility. He was a loquacious fellow, over-flowing with stories of the country, wherefore a pleasant riding companion, and Joseph noticed that the hours passed quickly in his company. And when after two days' riding Joseph wearied of his captain's many various relations, his eyes admired the slopes, now greener than they would be again till another year passed. The fig-trees were sending out shoots, the vines were in little leaf, and the fragrance of the vineyards and fig gardens was sweet in the cool morning when dusk melted away and rose-coloured clouds appeared above the hills; and as Joseph rode he liked to think that the spectacle of the cavalcade faring through the vine-clad hills would abide in his memory, and that in years to come he would be able to recall it exactly as he now saw it — all the faces of the spearmen and their odd horses; even his captain's discourses would be a pleasure to remember when time had redeemed them of trite-

90

ness and commonplace; the weariness he now experienced in listening would, too, become a memory, part of his life which he would not forgo even if he could. But at noon he was resentful of the man's intrusions on the privacy of his thought, and made no answer to tiresome lore about the great acacia-tree into whose shade he had withdrawn himself. He was content to enjoy the shelter of the tree that flourished among rocks where no one would expect a tree to flourish, and did not need to be told that the roots of a tree seek water instinctively, and that the roots of the acacia find it, about three feet down. The tree gave the captain a chance to air his knowledge, and Joseph remembered suddenly that he would be returning to Jerusalem with him in three days, for not more than three days would his escort remain in Galilee, resting their horses, unless they were paid a large sum of money; and with that escort idle in the village the thought would never be out of his mind that in a few days he would be listening to this captain all the way back to Jerusalem. Impossible! He couldn't go back to Jerusalem in three days, nor in three weeks. His father would be mortally grieved if he did; and Pilate himself would be surprised to see him back so soon and think him lacking altogether in filial affection if, after an absence of more than two years, he could stay only three days with his father. He must, however, send a letter to Pilate, and one that would accord with all the circumstances, and the barely stirring foliage of the acacia inspiring a desire of composition (a more favourable moment than the present, or a more inspiring spot, he did not think he would be likely to find), he called for his tablets and fell to thinking, but had hardly filled in the first dozen lines when his captain — this time apologising for the intrusion — came to tell him that if he wished to reach Magdala that evening they must start at once. He could not but acquiesce, and — as if contemptuous of the protection of his escort — he rode on in front, wishing to be left alone so that he might seek out the terms of his letter, his mood of irritated perplexity, however, not passing away till he came within sight of the great upland, rising so gently that he did not think Xerxes would mind ascending it at a gallop. As soon as he reached the last crest he would see the lake alone, having — thanks to the speed of Xerxes — escaped from his companions for at least five minutes — minutes to which he had looked forward

91

eagerly, and from the beginning of the journey. The lake had always seemed to him a sort of sign, symbol or hieroglyphic, in which he read a warning addressed especially, if not wholly, to himself. But the message the lake held out to him had always eluded him, and never more completely than now.

At the end of a windless spring evening it came into view a moment sooner than he had expected, and in an altogether different aspect — bluer than he had ever seen it in memory or reality — and, he confessed to himself, more beautiful. Like a great harp it lay below him, and his eyes followed the coast-lines widening out in an indenture of the hills : on one side desert, on the other richly cultivated ascents, with villages and one great city, Tiberias — its domes, cupolas, towers and the high cliffs abutting on the lake between Tiberias and Magdala bathed in a purple glow as the sun went down. My own village ! he said, and it was a pleasure to him to imagine his father sipping sherbet on his balcony, in good humour, no doubt, the weather being so favourable to fish-taking. Now which are Peter's boats among these ? he asked himself, his eyes returning to the fishing fleet. And which are John's and James's boats ? He could tell that all the nets were down by the reefed sails crossed over, for the boats were before the wind. A long pull back it will be to Capernaum, he was thinking, a matter of thirteen or fourteen miles, for the leading boat is not more than a mile from the mouth of the Jordan. Then, raising his eyes from the fishing-boats, he followed the coast-lines again, seeking the shapes of the wooded hills, rising in gently cadenced ascents. A more limpid evening never breathed upon a lake ! he said ; and when he raised his eyes a second time they rested on the ravines of Hermon far away in the north, still full of the winter's snow ; and — being a Galilean — he knew they would keep their snow for another month at least. The eagerness of the spring will then be well out of the air, he said, and I shall be thinking of returning to Jerusalem and concerning myself once more with Pilate's business. But what a beautiful evening ! still and pure as a crystal, beautiful as the mind of God.

A bird floated past, his black eyes always watchful. The bird turned away to join his mates, and Joseph bade his escort watch the flock : a bird here and a bird there swooping and missing and getting no doubt sometimes a fish that had ventured too near the surface —— That one leaving his mates, flying high towards Magdala, to be there, he said, in a few minutes, by my father's house; and in another hour thou shalt be in thy stable, thy muzzle in the corn, he whispered into his horse's ear; and calling upon his comrades to put their heels into their tired steeds, he turned Xerxes into the great road leading to Tiberias. But there were some Jews among the escort who shrank from entering a pagan city. Their prejudices might be overcome with argument, but it were simpler to turn their horses' heads to the west and then to the north as soon as the city was passed. The detour would be a long one, yet shorter than argument: none the less argument he did not escape from, for as they rode through the open country behind Tiberias, some declared that Herod was not a pure Jew; and to make their points clearer they often reined up their horses, to the annoyance of Joseph, who could not bring the discussion to an end without seeming indifferent to the law and the traditions. But, happily, it had to end before long, for within three miles of Magdala they were riding in single file down deep lanes along whose low dykes the cactus crawled, hooking itself along. One lane led into another. A network of deep lanes wound round Magdala, which, judging by the number of new dwellings, seemed to have prospered since Joseph had last seen it. Humble dwellings no doubt, Joseph said to himself, but bread is not lacking, nor fish. Then he thought of the wharves his father had built for the boats, and the work-shops for the making of the barrels into which the fish was packed. Magdala owed its existence to Dan's forethought, and he had earned his right, Joseph thought, to live in the high house which he had built for his pleasure in a garden amid tall acacia-trees that every breeze that blew up from the lake set in motion. If ever a man had earned his right to a peaceable old age amid pleasant surroundings, that man was his father; and in imagination he saw him returning from his counting-house to his spacious verandah, thinking of the barrels of salt fish that he would send away the following week, if the fishers were letting down their nets with fortunate enterprise.

CHAPTER X.

A VERY good guessing of his father's wonts and thoughts was that of Joseph whilst riding from Tiberias, for as the horseman came up the lane at a canter the old man was wending homeward from his counting-house, wishing Peter and Andrew, James and John and the rest good fortune with their nets, or else, he had begun to think, the order from Damascus could not be executed; but the sound of the hooves of Joseph's horse checked the words on his lips and he had to squeeze himself against the ditch, to escape being trodden upon. Joseph sprang from the saddle. Father, I haven't hurt thee? No hurt to speak of, Joseph, only the prick of a cactus thorn, already forgotten in the pleasure of seeing thee. But look to thy horse, for up and down these lanes he would give us a fine chase. He will be at my heels as we walk, Joseph answered, and Xerxes followed, pushing his head against Joseph's shoulder from time to time; but Joseph was too deep in talk with his father to give heed to his horse, and feeling himself neglected Xerxes fell to browsing.

My thoughts figured thee drinking sherbet in the verandah as we rode past Tiberias, Father. We shall sip some later, Dan said, and Joseph began to ask after the monkeys and parrots. Much the same as afore, Dan answered, his hand on the latch of the gate. Xerxes returned, and his reins were thrown to a servant. A monkey came hopping across the sward and jumped on Joseph's shoulder; another came and then a third, which was well for the monkeys: Dan would have been displeased with them if they had forgotten Joseph, it seeming to him that all things should love his son. Hast no eyes, Joseph, for the parrots, all dancing on their perches, waiting for thy fingers to scratch their polls? But, Joseph, I'd hear thee say that thou art glad to be back in Galilee, by God's own lake. Jerusalem has its temple —— Father, it is of thee I'm thinking and

94

not of temples or lakes, Joseph answered, and for a moment Dan could not speak, so deep was his happiness. Joseph, too, was overcome, and he followed his father up the tall stairs to the balcony, where he drew the curtains to shut out the sun; and when they had drunk some sherbet and Joseph had vowed he had not tasted any like it, Dan interposed suddenly : But thou hast not told me, Joseph, how thou camest by thy beautiful horse. He came from Egypt, Joseph answered casually, and was about to add that he was an Egyptian horse, but on second thoughts it seemed to him that it would be well not to speak the word Egypt again, for to do so might put another question into his father's mouth, and to begin to tell of Egypt could not do else than lead him into an intricate story which would indispose his father to listen to Pilate's projects, or at least estrange Dan's mind from a calm judgment of them; so he resolved to omit all mention of Banu, Jesus and Egypt and to begin his narrative with an account of his meeting with the camel-driver Gaddi. But the camel-driver seemed to be the last person that Dan was interested in. But he's my partner! Joseph exclaimed, and it was he who sent me to Pilate. I'll tell thee about the Essenes afterwards. And feeling that he had at last succeeded in fixing his father's attention on that part of the story which he wished to tell him, Joseph said : An excellent governor, one who is ready to listen to all schemes for the furtherance of commercial enterprise in Judea : he has ridded the hills of the robbers; and his account of the summer in the desert with the Roman soldiers, smoking out nest after nest and putting on crosses those that were taken alive, pleased the old man. I wish he would start on Samaria, said Dan, raising his eyes. Joseph replied : He will as soon as he is certain that he can rely on the help of men like thee. Pilate's favour is worth winning, Father, and it can be won. I doubt thee not, but wilt tell how it may be won, my boy? By falling in with his projects, Joseph answered, and began his argument. And when he had finished, Dan sat meditating, casting up the account. Pilate's good will is profitable, he said, but a large sum of money will have to be put out. But, Father, the carrying trade is doing well. Well, let us go into figures, Joseph; and they balanced the profits against the losses. Without doubt thou hast done well this last half-year, Dan said, and if business don't fall away —— But,

Father, Joseph interrupted, think of the profit my account would have shown if we had not lost two convoys. The loss has already been made good. The robbers are no more and the demand for figs is steady in Jerusalem. Figs ripen much earlier —— Say no more, Joseph. My money is thy money, and if fifty camels be wanted, thou shalt have them. 'Tis the least I can do for thee, for thou hast ever been a frugal son, Joseph, and art deserving of all I have. So Pilate has heard of my fish-salting and maybe that was why he met thee on such fair terms. That has much to do with it, Joseph replied, and he watched the look of satisfaction that came into his father's face. But tell me, Joseph, has all this long time been spent smoking out robbers? Tell me again of their caves. Well, Father, the caves often opened on to ledges, and we had to lower the soldiers in baskets. And the tale how one great cavern was besieged amused the old man till he was nigh to clapping his hands with delight and to reminding Joseph of the time when he used to ask his grandmother to tell him stories. Were she here she'd like to hear thee telling thy stories. Thou wast in her thoughts to the last and now we shall never see her any more, however great our trouble may be; and in the midst of a great silence they fell to thinking how the same black curtain would drop between them and the world. She has gone away to Arimathea, Joseph, whence we came and whither I shall follow her. We go forward a little way but to go back again. But I can't talk of deaths and graves. Go on telling me about Pilate and the robbers, for I've been busy all day in the counting-house adding up figures, and to listen to a good tale is a rare distraction. Yet I wouldn't talk of them either, Joseph, but of thyself and thy horse that all the country will be talking about the day after to-morrow, when thou'lt ride him into the town. And now say it, Joseph: thou'rt a wee bit tired, isn't that so? Nay, Father, not a bit. We have come but twenty miles from the last halt, and as for the telling of my story, maybe the loose ends that I've forgotten for the moment will unravel themselves while we're talking of fish-salting — of the many extra barrels thou hast sent out. Now, Father, say how many? At it, Joseph, as beforetimes, rallying thy old father! Well, I've not done so badly, but a drop in the year's trading is never a pleasant thought, though it be but a barrel. And he began again his complaint

96

FATHER AND SON

against the government of Antipas, who had never encouraged trade as he should have done. Now, if we had a man here such as thy friend Pilate, I'd not be saying too much were I to say that my trade could be doubled. But Pilate has no authority in Galilee. Joseph thought that Pilate's authority should be extended. But how can that be done? Dan inquired, and being embarrassed for an answer, Joseph pressed Dan to confide in him, a thing which Dan showed no wish to do; but at last his reluctance was overcome, and shyly he admitted that his despondency had nothing to do with Antipas nor with a casual drop in the order from Damascus, but with a prophet that was troubling the neighbourhood. A very dangerous prophet, too, is this one; but I am afraid, Joseph, we don't view prophets in exactly the same light. Joseph was about to laugh, but seeing the smile coming into his eyes, his father begged him to wait till he heard the whole story.

He called up all his attention into his face, and the story he heard was that the new prophet, who came up from Jordan about a year ago, was preaching that the Lord was so outraged at the conduct of his chosen people that he had determined to destroy the world, and might begin the wrecking of it any day of the week. But before the world ends there'll be wars. Joseph said: But there has been none, nor have I heard rumours of any. We don't hear much what's going on up here in Galilee, Dan answered, and he continued his story. The new prophet had persuaded many of the fishers to lay down their nets. Simon Peter, thou rememberest him? Well, he's the prophet's right-hand man, and now casts a net but seldom. And thou hast not forgotten James and John, sons of Zebedee? They come next in the prophet's favour, and there are plenty of others walking about the village, neglecting their work and telling of the judgment and the great share of the world that'll come to them when the prophet returns from heaven in a chariot. Among them is Matthew, a publican, the one amongst them that can read or write. Hast forgotten him? Now I come to think on it, he was appointed soon after thy journey to Jerusalem. Soon after I went to Jerusalem? Joseph asked; was the prophet preaching then? No. It all began soon after thy departure for Jerusalem about a year ago; a more ignorant lot of fellows thou'd be puzzled to find, if the world were travelled over in search

of them. The prophet himself comes from the most ignorant village in Galilee — Nazareth. But why look like that, Joseph? What ails thee? Go on, Father, with thy telling of the prophet from Nazareth. He started in Nazareth, Dan answered, but none paid any heed to him but made a mock of him, for he'd have us believe that he is the Messiah that the Jews have been expecting for many a year. But it was predicted that the Messiah will be born in Bethlehem; and everybody knows that Jesus was born in Nazareth. There's some talk, too, that he comes from the line of David, but everybody knows that Jesus is the son of Joseph the Carpenter. His mother and his brothers tried all they could do to dissuade him from preaching about the judgment, which he knows no more about than the next one, but he wouldn't listen to them. A good quiet woman, his mother; I know her well and am sorry for her; but she has better sons in James and Jude. Joseph her husband, I knew him in days gone by — a God-fearing honest man, whom one could always entrust with a day's work. He doted on his eldest son, though he never could teach him to handle a saw with any skill, for his thoughts were always wandering, and when an Essene came up to Galilee in search of neophytes, Jesus took his fancy and they went away together. But what ails thee? As soon as Joseph could get control of his voice he asked his father if the twain were gone away together to the cenoby on the eastern bank of Jordan, and Dan answered that he thought he had heard of the great Essenes' encampment by the Dead Sea. A fellow fair-spoken enough, Dan continued, that has bewitched the poor folk about the lakeside. But, Joseph, thy cheek is like ashes, and thou'rt all of a tremble: drink a little sherbet, my boy. No, Father, no. Tell me, is the Galilean as tall or as heavy as I am, or of slight build, with a forehead broad and high? And does he walk as if he were away and in communion with his Father in heaven? But what ails thee, my son? What ails thee? He came from the cenoby on the eastern shores of the Jordan? Joseph continued; and has been here nearly two years? He received baptism from John in the Jordan? Isn't that so, Father? I know naught of his baptism, Dan answered, but he'll fall into trouble. I was with Banu, Joseph said, when the hermit saw him in a vision receiving baptism from John; but though I ran, I was too late, and ever since have sought Jesus, in
98

Egypt and afterwards among the hills of Judea. I can't tell thee more at present, but I would go out into the garden or perhaps wander by myself under the cliffs by the lake. And thou'lt forgive me leaving thee, Father? Dan put down his glass of sherbet and looked after his son. He had been so happy for a little while, and now unhappiness was by again.

CHAPTER XI.

THE dogs barked as he unlocked the gate, but a few words quieted them (they still remembered his voice) and he crept upstairs to his room, weary in body and sore of foot, for he had come a long way, having accompanied Jesus, whom he had met under the cliffs abutting on the lake, to the little pathway cut in the shoulder of the hill that leads to Capernaum. He had not recognised him as he passed, which was not strange, so unseemly was the ragged shirt and, of all, the cloak of camel's or goat's hair he wore over it, patched along and across, with one long trailing tatter that caught in his feet as he walked. He picked it up, went on again, and Joseph remembered that he had looked upon the passenger as a mendicant wonder-worker on his round from village to village. But Jesus had not gone very far when Joseph was stopped by a memory of a face seen long ago: a pale bony olive face, lit with brilliant eyes. It is he! he cried; and starting in pursuit and quickly overtaking Jesus, he called his name. Jesus turned, and there was no doubt when the men stood face to face that the shepherd Joseph had seen in the cenoby in converse with the president, and the wandering beggar by the lake shore, were one and the same person. Jesus asked him which way he was walking, and he answered that all directions were the same to him, for he was only come out for a breath of fresh air before bedtime. But thinking he had expressed himself vulgarly, he added other words and waited for Jesus to speak of the beauty of God's handiwork. Jesus merely mentioned in answer that he was going to Capernaum, where he lodged with Simon Peter. But he had not forgotten the brotherhood by the Dead Sea, and invited Joseph to accompany him and tell him of those whom he had left behind. We are of the same brotherhood, he said; and then, as if noticing Joseph's embarrassment: or thou'rt a proselyte, maybe,

100

who at the end of the first year retired from the order? Many do so. Joseph did not know how to answer this question, for he had not obtained permission from the president to seek Jesus in Egypt, and it seemed to him that the most truthful account he could give of himself at the cenoby was to say that he was not there long enough to consider himself even a proselyte. He lived in the cenoby as a visitor, rather than as one attached to the order; but how far he might consider himself an Essene did not matter to anybody. Besides he wished to hear Jesus talk rather than to talk about himself, so he compared his residence with the Essenes to a clue out of which a long thread had unravelled — A thread, he said, that led me into the desert in search of thee. Hast knowledge of Banu? Jesus had known Banu, in the desert, and listened attentively while Joseph told him how Banu was interrupted while speaking of the resurrection by a vision of John baptizing Jesus, and had bidden him go to Jordan and get baptism from John. But it was not John's baptism I sought, but thee, and I arrived breathless, to hear that thou hadst gone away with him, John not being able to bear the cold of the water any longer. Afterwards I sought thee along and across Palestine, till hearing of thee in Egypt I went thither and sought thee from synagogue to synagogue.

A man travels the world over in search of what he needs and returns home to find it, Jesus answered gently, and in a tenderer voice than his scrannel peacock throat would have led one to expect. And as if foreseeing an ardent disciple he began to speak to Joseph of God, his speech moving on with a gentle motion like that of clouds wreathing and unwreathing, finding new shapes for every period, and always beautiful shapes. He often stopped speaking and his eyes became fixed, as if he saw beyond the things we all see; and after an interval he would begin to speak again; and Joseph heard that he had met John among the hills and listened to him, and that if he accepted baptism from him it was because he wished to follow John: but John sought to establish the kingdom of God within the law, and so a dancing-girl asked for his head. It seemed as if Jesus were on the point of some tremendous avowal, but if so it passed away like a cloud, and he put his hand on Joseph's shoulder affectionately and asked him to tell him about Egypt, a country which he said he had never heard of before. Whereupon Joseph

101

raised his eyes and saw in Jesus a travelling wonder-worker come down from a northern village — a peasant, without knowledge of the world and of the great Roman Empire. At every step Jesus's ignorance of the world surprised Joseph more and more. He seemed to believe that all the nations were at war, and from further discourse Joseph learnt that Jesus could not speak Greek, and he marvelled at his ignorance, for Jesus knew only such Hebrew as is picked up in the synagogues. He did not seek to conceal his ignorance of this world from Joseph, and almost made parade of it, as if he was aware that one must discard a great deal to gain a little, as if he would impress this truth upon Joseph, almost as if he would reprove him for having spent so much time on learning Greek, for instance, and Greek philosophy. He treated these things as negligible when Joseph spoke of them, and evinced more interest in Joseph himself, who admitted he had returned from philosophy to the love of God.

And now sitting on his bed, kept awake by his memories, Joseph relived in thought the hours he had spent with Jesus. He seemed to understand the significance of every word much better now than when he was with Jesus, and regretting his obtuseness he recast all the answers given to Jesus, recalling with sorrow how he tried to explain the teaching of the Alexandrian philosophers regarding the Scriptures, and though he saw that he was paining Jesus he had continued for the sake of the answer he knew would come at last.

It did come : and what a wonderful answer it was : that philosophies change in different men, but the love of God is the same in all men. A great truth, Joseph said to himself, for every school is in opposition to another school. But how did Jesus come to know this, being without philosophy ? He had been tempted to ask how he was able to get at the truth of things without the Greek language and without education, but refrained lest a question should break the harmony of the evening. The past was not yet past, and sitting on his bed in the moonlight Joseph could re-see the plain covered with beautiful grasses and flowers, with low flowering bushes waving over dusky headlands, for it was dark as they crossed the plain ; and they had heard rather than seen the rushing stream, bubbling out of the earth, making music in the still night. He knew the stream from early childhood, but he had never really known it

102

until he stood with Jesus under the stars by the narrow path cut
in the shoulder of the hill, the way leading to Capernaum, for it
was there that Jesus took his hands and said the words : Our Father
which is in Heaven. At these words their eyes were raised to the
skies, and Jesus said : Whosoever admires the stars and the flowers
finds God in his heart and sees him in his neighbour's face. And
as Joseph sat, his hands on his knees, he recalled the moment that
Jesus turned from him abruptly and passed into the shadow of the
hillside that fell across the flowering mead. He heard his footsteps
and had listened, repressing the passionate desire to follow him
and to say : Having found thee, I can leave thee never again. It
was fear of Jesus that prevented him from following Jesus, and he
returned slowly the way he came, his eyes fixed on the stars, for
the day was now well behind the hills and the night all over the
valley, calm and still. The stars in their allotted places, he said :
as they have always been and always will be. He stood watching
them. Behind the stars that twinkled were stars that blazed;
behind the stars that blazed were smaller stars, and behind them
a sort of luminous dust. And all this immensity is God's dwelling-
place, he said. The stars are God's eyes; we live under his eyes
and he has given us a beautiful garden to live in. Are we worthy
of it? he asked; and Jew though he was he forgot God for a
moment in the sweetness of the breathing of earth, for there is
no more lovely plain in the spring of the year than the Plain of
Gennesaret.

Every breath of air brought a new and exquisite scent to him,
and through the myrtle bushes he could hear the streams singing
their way down to the lake; and when he came to the lake's edge
he heard the warble that came into his ear when he was a little
child, which it retained always. He heard it in Egypt, under the
Pyramids, and the cataracts of the Nile were not able to silence it
in his ears. But suddenly from among the myrtle bushes a song
arose. It began with a little phrase of three notes, which the bird
repeated, as if to impress the listener and prepare him for the runs
and trills and joyous little cadenzas that were to follow. A sudden
shower of jewels it seemed like, and when the last drops had fallen
the bird began another song, a continuation of the first, but more
voluptuous and intense; and then, as if he felt that he had set the

103

theme sufficiently, he started away into new trills and shakes and runs, piling cadenza upon cadenza till the theme seemed lost, but the bird held it in memory while all his musical extravagances were flowing, and when the inevitable moment came he repeated the first three notes. Again Joseph heard the warbling water, and it seemed to him that he could hear the stars throbbing. It was one of those moments when the soul of man seems to break, to yearn for that original unity out of which some sad fate has cast it — a moment when the world seems to be one thing and not several things: the stars and the stream, the odours afloat upon the stream, the bird's song and the words of Jesus: Whosoever admires the stars and flowers finds God in his heart, seemed to become all blended into one extraordinary harmony; and unable to resist the emotion of the moment any longer, Joseph threw himself upon the ground and prayed that the moment he was living in might not be taken from him, but that it might endure for ever. But while he prayed the moment was passing, and becoming suddenly aware that it had gone, he rose from his knees and returned home mentally weary and sad at heart; but sitting on his bedside the remembrance that he was to meet Jesus in the morning at Capernaum called up the ghost of a departed ecstasy, and his head drowsing upon his pillow he fell asleep, hushed by remembrances.

CHAPTER XII.

A FEW hours later he was speeding along the lake's edge in the bright morning, happy as the bird singing in the skies, when the thought like a dagger-thrust crossed his mind that being the son of a rich man Jesus could not receive him as a disciple, only the poor were welcome into the brotherhood of the poor. His father had told him as much, and the beggar whom he had met under the cliffs, smelling of rags and raw garlic, expressed the riches of simplicity. Happy, happy evening, for ever gone by! Happy ignorance already turned into knowledge! For in Peter's house Jesus would hear that the man whom he had met under the cliffs was the son of the fish-salter of Magdala, and perhaps they knew enough of his story to add, who has been making money in Jerusalem himself and has no doubt come to Galilee to engage his father in some new trade that will extort more money from the poor. He is not for thy company. A great aversion seized him for Capernaum, and he walked, overcome with grief, to the lake's edge and stooped to pick up a smooth stone, thinking to send it skimming over the water, as he used to when a boy; but there was neither the will nor the strength in him for the innocent sport, and he lay down, exhausted in mind and body, to lament this new triumph of the demon that from the beginning of his life thwarted him and interrupted all his designs — this time intervening at the last moment as if with a purpose of great cruelty. This demon seemed to him to descend out of the blue air and sometimes to step out of the blue water, and Joseph was betimes moved to rush into the lake, for there seemed to him no other way of escaping from him. Then he would turn back from the foam and the reeds, and pray to the demon to leave him for some little while in peace: Let me be with Jesus for a little while, and then I'll do thy bidding. Tie the tongues of those that would tell him I'm the son of a rich man — Simon Peter, James and John, sons of Zebedee. James would say a word in his favour, but Jesus would answer: Why did he not tell these things to me overnight? And if he loves me, why does he not rid himself of the wealth that separates him from me?

Well, young Master, cried somebody behind him, now what be thy thoughts on this fine morning? Of the fish that our nets will bring to thy father's barrels? My father's barrels be accursed! Joseph exclaimed, springing to his feet. And why dost thou call me master? I'm not master, nor art thou servant. And then, his eyes opening fully to the external world, he recognised the nearly hunchback Philip of Capernaum — a high-necked, thick-set fellow, in whom a hooked nose and prominent eyes were the distinguishing features. A sail-maker, that spoke with a sharp voice, and Joseph remembered him as combining the oddest innocence of mind regarding spiritual things with a certain shrewdness in the conduct of his business. Thy voice startled me out of a dream, Joseph said, and I knew not what I said. Beg pardon, Master — but the word Sir thou likest no better, and it would sound unseemly to call thee Joseph and no more. As we are not born the same height nor strength nor wits, such little differences as Sir and Master get into our speech. All those that love God are the same, and there is neither class nor wealth, only love, Joseph answered passionately. That is the teaching of the new prophet Jesus, Philip replied, his yapping voice assuming an inveigling tone or something like one. I was in Magdala yester evening, and spent the night in my debtor's house, and as we were figuring out the principal and interest a neighbour came in, and among his several news was that thou wast seen with Jesus by the lake. We were glad that without warning from us thou shouldst have discovered on the night of thy arrival home the great prophet that is Simon Peter's lodger. But I must be hastening away, for a meeting is at Simon Peter's house. I have promised Jesus to be there, Joseph answered. So we may step the way out together, Philip answered, looking up into Joseph's face, and — as if he read there encouragement to speak out the whole of his mind — he continued: I was saying that it was a great step up for him when Simon Peter took him to lodge in his house, for beforetimes he had, as the saying is, no place to lay his
106

head : an outcast from Cana, whither he went first to his mother's house, and it is said he turned water into wine on one occasion at a marriage feast; which cannot be true, for if it were, there is no reason that I can see why he should stay his hand and not turn all water into wine. Joseph replied that that would be a misfortune, for the greater part of men would be drunk as Noah was when he planted a vineyard, and we know how Lot's daughters turned their father's drunkennesss to account. Moreover, Philip, if Jesus had turned all the water into wine there would be no miracle, for a miracle is a special act performed by somebody whom God has chosen. Thou beest right, Master, for certain, though the ways of God are known to no man, not Jesus himself. For my troth, there's no saying what is true and what is false in this world, for what one man says another man denies, and it is not even sure that all men see and hear alike. But, Philip, thou must know that though men neither hear nor see alike, yet the love of God is the same in every man. But is it? Philip asked. For can it be denied that some men love God in the hope that God may do something for them, while others love God lest he may punish them? But methinks that such love as that is more fear than love; and then there are others that can love God — for in their minds God is by them as I'm by thee whilst we walk to Capernaum. Jesus is such an one. But there be not many like him, and that was why his teaching found no favour either in Cana or in Nazareth. In them parts they knew that he was the carpenter's son, and his mother and his brothers and sisters were a hindrance to him, for thinking him a bit queer, they came ofttimes to the synagogues to ask him to come home with them, for they are shrewd enough to see that such talk as his will bring him no good in the end, for priests are strong everywhere and have the law of the land on their side; governors would make but poor shift to govern without them. But why then, Philip, shouldst thou, that art a cautious man, be going to Peter's house to meet him? Well, that's the question I've been asking myself all the morning till I came upon thee, Master, sitting by the lake, not unlikely asking thyself the same question. He casts a spell upon me and 'tis oft I am afraid to go near him, but I must, whether I would or no, and it may have been the same with thee the night that brought thee back to us. But wilt tell me, Philip, how long he has been in

107

these parts? Well, I should say it must be two years or thereabouts that he came up from Jericho, staying but a little while in Jerusalem and going on to his mother at Cana, and afterwards trying his luck, as I have said, in Nazareth. But his mother hasn't seen him for many a year? He has been away since childhood, living with a certain sect of Jews called the Essenes, and it was John —— Yes, John was then baptizing in Jordan, Joseph interrupted; he baptized Jesus. And after that he went into the desert, said Philip hurriedly, for he did not like being interrupted in his story. He came up to Nazareth, I was saying, about two years ago, but was thrown out of that city and came here; he was more fortunate here, picking up bits of food from the people now and then, who, thinking him harmless, let him sleep in an odd hole or corner; but he must have often been like dying of hunger by the wayside, for he was always travelling, going his rounds from village to village. But luck was on his side, and when he was near dying a traveller would come by and raise him and give him a little wine. He is one of them that can do with little, and after the first few months he had the luck to cast out one or two devils, and finding he could cast out devils, he turned to the healing of the sick; and many is the withered limb that he has put right, and many a lame man he has set walking with as good a stride as we are taking now, and many a blind man's eyes he has opened, and the scrofulous he cured by looking at them — so it is said. And so his fame grew from day to day; the people love him, for he asks no money from them, which is a sure way into men's affections; but they whose children he has cured cannot see him go away hungry, and they put a loaf into his shirt, for he takes anything that he can get except money, which he will not look upon. There has been no holier man in these parts, Sir, these many years. The oldest in the country cannot remember one like him — my father is nearer ninety than eighty, and he says that Jesus is a greater man than he ever heard his father tell of, and he was well into the eighties before he died. Now, Sir, as we are near to Peter's house, thou'lt not mind my telling thee that there is no Sir or Master at Peter's house. But, Philip, has it not already been said that thou mayst drop such titles as Sir and Master in addressing me? And wert thou not at one with me that we should be more courteous and friendly one
108

between the other without them? Well, yes, Master, I do recollect some such talk between us, but now that we be coming into Capernaum it would be well that I should call thee Joseph, but Joseph would be difficult to me at first, and we are all brothers amongst us, only Jesus is Master over all of us, and God over him. But it now comes to my mind that I have not told thee how Jesus and Peter became acquainted. One day as Jesus was passing on his rounds a man ran out of his house and besought him to help him to stop some boys who were playing drums and fifes and psalteries, saying to him: I know not who thou art, but my wife's mother is dying of fever, and the boys jeer at me and show no mercy. Let us take stones and cast them at them. But Jesus answered: No stone is required; and turning to the boys he said: Boys, all this woman asks of you is to be allowed to die in quiet, and you may ask the same thing some day, and that day may not be long delayed. Whereupon the boys were ashamed, and Jesus followed Peter into his house and took his wife's mother's hand and lifted her up a little and placed her head upon the pillow and bade her sleep, which she did, and seeing that he had such power Peter asked him to remain in the house till his mother-in-law opened her eyes, and he has been there ever since. Now here we are at the pathway through which Jesus comes and goes every day on his mission of healing and preaching the love of God. Thy father, Sir, is much against Jesus, who he says has persuaded Peter away from his fishing, and James and John and many others, but no doubt thy father told thee this last night.

CHAPTER XIII.

YONDER is Capernaum, Sir, or it would have been more in our speech had I said: Why, Brother, yonder is Capernaum. But habit's like a fly, Brother, it won't leave us alone; it comes back however often and angrily we may drive it away.

Joseph made no reply, hoping by silence to quiet Philip's tongue which returned to the attack, he was fain to admit, not altogether unlike a fly. He tried not to hear him, for the sight of the town at the head of the lake awakened recollections of himself and his nurse walking valiantly, their strength holding out till they reached Capernaum, but after eating at the inn they were too weary to return to Magdala on foot and Peter had had to take them back in his boat. Peter's boat was his adventure in those days, and strangely distinct the day rose up in his mind that he and Peter had gone forth firm in the resolution that they would ascend the Jordan as far as the waters of Merom. They succeeded in dragging the boat over the shallows, but there was much wind on the distant lake. Peter thought it would not be well to venture out upon it, and Andrew thought so too. He was now going to see those two brothers again after a long absence and was not certain whether he was glad or sorry. It seemed to him that the lake, its towns and villages, were too inseparably part of himself for him to wish to see them with the bodily eyes, and that it would be wiser to keep this part of Galilee, the upper reaches of the lake at least, for his meditations; yet he did not think he would like to return to Magdala without seeing Capernaum. Perhaps because Jesus was there. That Jesus should have pitched upon Capernaum as a centre revived his interest in it, and there was a sadness in the memory of a question he had once put to his father. He asked him if Capernaum was the greatest city in the world, and for years
110

after he was teased till Capernaum became hateful to him; but Capernaum within the last few minutes had regained its place in his affections. And as the town became hallowed in recollection he cried out to Philip that he could not go farther with him. Not go any farther with me! Philip answered; now why is that, Brother? for Peter is waiting to see thee and will take on mightily when I tell him that thou didst come to the head of the lake with me and turned back. But it is Peter whom I fear to meet, Joseph muttered, and then at the sight of the long lean street slanting down the hillside towards the lake, breaking up into irregular hamlets, some situated at the water's edge close to the wharf where Peter's boats lay gently rocking, he repeated: It is Peter that I fear. But unwilling to take Philip into his confidence he turned as if to go back to Magdala without further words, but Philip restrained him, and at last Joseph confessed his grief — that being the son of a rich man he could not be chosen into the company of the poor. Thou'lt ask me, he said, to give up my money to the poor, a thing I would willingly do for the sake of Jesus, whom I believe to be God's prophet; but how can I give that which does not belong to me — my father's money? That was my grief when thou didst come upon me sitting on the stone by the lake's edge. Whereupon Philip stood looking at Joseph as one suspended, for the first time understanding rightly that the rich have their troubles as well as the poor. At last words coming to him he said: Money has been our trouble since Jesus drew us together, for we would live without money and yet we know not how this is to be done. Like thee, Sir, I'm asking if I'm to sell my sails, those already out and those in the unrolled cloth, and if I do sell and give the money to the poor how am I to live but by begging of those that have not given their all? But why should I worry thee with our troubles? But your troubles are mine, Joseph answered; and Philip went away to fetch Peter, who, he said, would be able to tell him if Jesus could accept a rich man as a disciple. If a man that has a little be permitted to remain, who is to say how much means rejection? Joseph asked himself as he kept watch for Peter to appear at the corner of the street. And does he know the Master's mind enough to answer the question of my admission or —— The sentence did not finish in his mind, for Peter was coming up the street at that moment, a great broad

111

face shaping into its features and expression. The same high-shouldered fisher as of yore, Joseph said to himself, and he sought to read in Peter's face the story of Peter's transference from one master to another. It wasn't the approach of the Great Day, for Peter never could see beyond his sails and the fins of a fish; and if Jesus had been able to lift his thoughts beyond them he had accomplished a no less miracle than turning water into wine.

Well, young Master, we're glad to have thee back among us again. There be no place like home for us Galileans. Isn't that so? And no fishing like that on these coasts? But, Peter, Joseph interrupted, my father tells me that thou hast laid aside thy nets —— But that isn't what I'm here to talk to thee about, he interjected suddenly, but about Jesus himself, whom I've been seeking for nearly two years, very nearly since I parted from you all, well-nigh two years ago, isn't it? I've sought him in the hills of Judea, in Moab, in the Arabian desert and all the way to Egypt and back again. Its about two years since thy travels began, Master Joseph, and a fine story there'll be for us to listen to when our nets are down, Peter said. I'd ask thee to begin it now, Master Joseph, if the Master wasn't waiting for us over yonder in my house. But is it true, Master, that thou hast a mind about joining our community? Thou hast seen no doubt a good deal of the Temple at Jerusalem and knowest everything about the goings on there, and art with us in this — that the Lord don't want no more fat rams and goats and bullocks, and incense is hateful in his nostrils. So I've heard. They be Isaiah's words, bean't they, young Master? But there's no master here, only Jesus: he is Master, and if I call thee Master it is from habit of beforetimes. But no offence intended. Thou wilt always be master for me, and I'll be servant always in a sense, which won't prevent us from being brothers. The Master yonder will understand and will explain it all to thee better than I. . . . And Peter nodded his great head covered with frizzly hair. But, Peter, I am a rich man, and my father is too, and none but the poor is admitted into the Community of Jesus. That's what affrights him, Peter — his money, Philip interjected, and I have been trying to make him understand, that Jesus won't ask him for his father's money, he not having it to give away. I'm not so sure of that, Peter said. The Master told us a story yesterday of a steward
112

who took his master's money and gave it to the poor, he being frightened lest the poor, whom he hadn't been over-good to in his lifetime, might not let him into heaven when he died. And the Master seemed to think that he did well, for he said : It is well to bank with the poor. Them were his very words. So it seems to thee, Peter, that I should take my father's money? Joseph asked. Take thy father's money! Peter answered. We wouldn't wrong thy father out of the price of two perch, and never have done, neither myself nor John and James. Now I won't say as much for —— We love thy father, and never do we forget that when our nets were washed away it was he that gave us new ones. I am sure thou wouldst not wrong my father, Joseph answered, and he refrained from asking Peter to explain the relevancy of the story he had just told lest he should entangle him. It is better, he said to himself, to keep to facts, and he told Peter that even his own money was not altogether his own money, for he had a partner in Jericho and it would be hard to take his money out of the business and give it all to the poor. Giving it to the poor in Galilee, he said, would deprive my camel-drivers of their living. Which, Peter observed, would be a cruel thing to do, for a man must be allowed to get his living, whether he be from Jericho or Galilee, fisher or camel-driver or sail-maker. Which reminds me, Philip, that thou be'st a long time over the sail I was to have had at the end of last month. And the twain began to wrangle so that Joseph thought they would never end, so prolix was Philip in his explanations. He had had to leave the sail unsewn, was all he had to say, but he embroidered on this simple fact so largely that Joseph lost patience and began to tell them he had come to Galilee, Pilate wishing him to add the portage of wheat from Moab to the trade already started in figs and dates. So Pilate is in the business! Peter ejaculated, for Peter did not think that a Jew should have any dealings with Gentiles, and this opinion, abruptly expressed, threw the discourse again into disarray. But Pilate is in Jerusalem, Joseph began. And has he brought the Roman eagles with him? Peter interrupted. And seeing that these eagles would lead them far from the point which he was anxious to have settled — whether the trade he was doing between Jerusalem and Jericho prevented him from being a disciple — Joseph began by assuring Peter that the eagles had been

113

sent back to Cæsarea. Cæsarea, Peter muttered; our Master has been there, and says it be as full as it can hold of graven images. Well, Peter, what I have come to say is, that were I to disappoint Pilate he might allow the robbers to infest the hills again, and all my money would be lost, and my partner's money, and the camel-drivers would be killed; and if my convoys did not arrive in Jerusalem there might be bread riots. How wouldst like that, Peter? The young Master speaks well, don't he? And what answer hast thou for him, Peter? and Philip looked into Peter's great broad face. Only this, Peter answered, that money will shipwreck our Community sooner or later — we're never free from it. Like a fly, Philip suggested, the more we chase it away the more it returns. The fly cannot resist a sweating forehead, Philip, Peter said. Thine own is more sweaty than mine, Philip retorted, and a big blue fly is drinking his belly full though thou feelest him not, being as callous as a camel. The Master's teaching is, Peter continued, having driven off the fly, that no man should own anything, that everyone should have the same rights, which seems true enough till we begin to put it into practice, for if I were to let whosoever wished take my boats and nets to go out fishing, my boats and nets would be all at the bottom of the lake before the sun went down as like as not, for all men don't understand fishing. As we must have fish to live I haven't parted with my boats; but every time we take that turning down yonder to the lake's edge and I see my boats rocking I offer up a little prayer that the Master may be looking the other way or thinking of something else. James and John, sons of Zebedee, are of the same mind as myself — that we shouldn't trouble the Master too closely with the working out of his teaching. The teaching is the thing. Why, they be coming towards us, as sure as my name's Simon Peter, sent perhaps by the Master to fetch us, so long have we been away talking.

Joseph turned to greet the two young men, whom he had known always; as far back as he could remember he had talked to them over the oars, and seen them let down the nets and draw up the nets, and they had hoisted the sail for his pleasure, abandoning the fishing for the day, knowing well that Joseph's father would pay them for the time they lost in pleasuring his son. And now they were young men like himself, only they knew no Greek; rough

114

young men, of simple minds and simple life, who were drawn to Jesus — James a lean man, whose small sullen eyes, dilatory speech and vacant little laugh used to annoy Joseph. James always asked him to repeat his words though he had heard perfectly. Joseph liked John better, for his mind was sturdy and his voice grew sullen at any word of reproof and his eyes flamed, and Joseph wondered what might be the authority that Jesus held over him, a rough turbulent fellow, whom Joseph had always feared a little; even now in their greeting there was a certain dread in Joseph, which soon vanished, for John's words were outspoken and hearty. We're glad to have thee back again amongst us, Master, I've been saying since I left Capernaum this morning. But Master is a word, John, that I've heard isn't used among you. Truly it is not used among the brotherhood, John answered. And I came to ask admission, Joseph said. Well, that be good news, Master — Brother I should say, for our Master will be glad to meet thee. But that, Philip began, is just what we were scratching our heads over before we saw thee coming towards us. For there is a twist in it. He is as earnest as any of us, but our rule is what thou knowest it to be. Despite John's knowledge of the rule Philip began the story, and again he was so prolix in it that Joseph, wishing John to decide on the strict matter of it, and not to be lost in details, some of which were true and some of which were false and all confused in Philip's telling, interrupted the narrator, saying that he would give all the money that was strictly his, but his father's he couldn't give nor his partner's. We've many camels, he said, in common, and how are these to be divided? Nor is it right, it seems to me, that my partner should be left with the burden of all the trade we have created together; yet it is hard that I who have sought Jesus in the deserts of Judea as far as Egypt, and found him in Galilee, at home, should be forced to range myself apart from him, with whom my heart is. Would that the Master were here to hear him speak, Philip interjected. He was with the Master last night, and the Master was well pleased with him. It all depends on what mood the Master is in, John answered, and they all fell to asking each other what the Master's mood was that morning. But it would seem that all read him differently, and it was with joy at the prospect of a new opinion that they viewed Judas coming towards them.

115

And taking Judas into the discussion Peter said : Now I've two
boats, and John and James have four, so we bean't without money,
though our riches are small compared with the young Master's.
Are we to sell our boats and give the money to the poor, and if
we do who then will look after the Master's wants? They are small,
it is true — a bit of fish and bread every day, and a roof over his
head; but who will give him a roof if mine be taken from me?
Is not this so? All seemed in agreement, and Peter continued :
I am thinking, John, that our new brother might help us to buy the
Master a new cloak, for his is falling to pieces and my wife's mother
is weary with patching it. He cured her of the fever, but she thinks
that a great cost is put upon me and would ask the Master something for his keep. Whereupon John spoke out that the story of
his mother-in-law was for ever the same; and seeing that he was
offending Peter with the words he addressed against his wife's
mother, though indeed Peter liked her not too much himself,
Joseph put his hand in his pocket and said : Here are some shekels;
go and buy Jesus a cloak, but say not to him whence the money
came. Say not to him! Judas interjected. No need to tell him that
can read the thoughts in the mind. It would be better for the young
Master to give him one of his old cloaks. Jesus would question the
new cloak and say it savours of money. He sees into the heart.
We have tried to keep things from him before, Judas continued,
turning to Joseph. . . . It is our duty to save him as much as we
can. Peter has done much and I've shared the expense with Peter,
though I am a poor man; we pick the stones from his path, for he
walks with his eyes fixed upon the Kingdom of God always. Yes,
he sees into our hearts, Philip interrupted, and reads through all
we are thinking even before the thoughts come into our minds.
It is as Philip says, Judas muttered : our hearts are open to him
always. But James, who had not spoken till now, put forward the
opinion, and no one seemed inclined to gainsay it, that if Jesus
knew men's thoughts before they came into men's minds he must
be warned of them by the angels. He goes into the solitude of the
mountains to converse with the angels, James said — for what
else? Moses went into the clefts of Mount Sinai, Joseph added, and
he asked Peter to tell him if Jesus believed that the soul existed
apart from the body, at which question Peter was fairly embar-
116

rassed : For the soul must be somewhere, he said, and if there be
no body to contain it —— You must ask the Master about these
things, we have not considered them. All the same we're glad that
thou'rt with us and ready to follow him into danger, for if the Sadducees and Pharisees are against him we are with him. Is that not
so, sons of Zebedee ?

At the challenge the two lads came forward again and all began
to talk of the Kingdom of Heaven, and the enthusiasm of the disciples catching upon Joseph he, too, was soon talking of the Kingdom that was to come, and whether they should all go down to
Jerusalem together to meet the Kingdom and share it, or wait for
it to appear in Galilee. Share and share alike, Joseph said. Ay,
ay, sure we shall, and enjoy it, Peter rolled out at his elbow. But we
must set our hearts in patience, for there be a rare lot to be converted yet. Every man must have his chance, and seeing Jesus
coming towards him Peter waited till Jesus was by him. Haven't I
thy promise, Master, he asked, laying his hand on Jesus's shoulder,
that my chair in the Kingdom will be next to thine ? Before Jesus
could answer John and James asked him if their chairs would not be
on his left and right. But not next to the Master's, Peter answered.
I'm on the right hand of the Master, and my brother Andrew on
the left. Look into his face and read in it that I have said well.
But the disciples were not minded to read the Master's face as
Peter bade them read it, and might have come to gripping each
other's throats if Jesus had not asked them if they would have the
fat in the narrow chairs and the thin in the wide, as often happens
in this world. The spectacle of Peter trying to sit on James's chair
set them laughing, and as if to make an end of an unseemly disputation John asked the Master whither they were going to cure the
sick that day ? To which question Jesus made no answer, for he
felt no power on him that day to cure the sick or to cast out demons.
Thou'lt see him do these things on another occasion, Peter whispered in Joseph's ear; to-day he be deep in one of his meditations,
and we dare not ask him whither he be going, but must just follow
him. As likely as not he'll lead us up into the hills for —— But
I see Salome coming this way. Thou knowest her sons, John and
James. The woman bears me an ill will and would have my chair
set far down, belike as not between Nathaniel and Philip, who as

117

thou hast noticed do not hold their heads very high in our company. But let us hasten a little to hear what she has to say. Listen, 'tis as I said, Master, Peter continued; didst hear her ask him that her sons should sit on either side of him? Now mark his answer, if he answers her; I doubt if he will, so dark is his mood.

But dark though it was he answered her with a seeming cheerfulness that in the coming world there is weariness neither of spirit nor of body, and therefore chairs are not set in heaven. A fine answer that! and Peter chuckled; too wise for thee. Go home and ponder on it. We shall lie on couches when we are not flying, he added, and being in doubt he asked Joseph if the heavenly host was always on the wing. A question that seemed somewhat silly to Joseph, though he could not have given his reason for thinking it silly. Peter called on Jesus to hasten, for the disciples were half-way up the principal street at a turning where their way led through the town by olive garths and orchards, and finding a path through these they came upon green corn sown in patches just beginning to show above ground, and the fringe of the wood higher up the hillside — some grey bushes with young oaks starting through them, still bare of leaves, ferns beginning to mark green lanes into the heart of the woods, and certain dark wet places where the insects had already begun to hum. But when the wood opened out the birds were talking to one another, blackbird to blackbird, thrush to thrush, robin to robin, kin understanding kin, and every bird uttering vain jargon to them that did not wear the same beak and feathers — Just like ourselves, Joseph said to himself, and he stood stark before a hollow into which he remembered having once been forbidden to stray lest a wolf should pounce upon him suddenly. Now he was a man, he was among men, and all had staves in their hands, and the thoughts of wolves departed at the sight of a wild fruit tree before which Jesus stopped, and calling John and James to him, as if he had forgotten Peter, he said : You see that tree covered with beautiful blossoms, but the harsh wind which is now blowing along the hillside will bear many of the blossoms away before the fruit begins to gather. And the birds will come and destroy many a berry before the plucker comes to pick the few that remain for the table. How many of you that are gathered about me now —— He stopped suddenly, and his eyes falling on John he addressed his question directly to
118

THE PARABLE OF THE FRUIT TREE

him as if he doubted that Peter would apprehend the significance of the parable. But Joseph, whom it touched to the quick, was moved to cry out : Master, I understand; restraining himself, however, or his natural diffidence restraining him, he could only ask Peter to ask Jesus for another parable. Peter reproved Joseph, saying that it were not well to ask anything from the Master at present, but that his mood might improve during the course of the afternoon. Thomas, who did not know the Master as well as Peter, could not keep back the question that rose to his lips. Our trade, he said, is in apricots, but is it the same with men as with the apricots, or shall we live to see the fruit that thou hast promised us come to table? Whereupon James and John began to ask which were the blossoms among them that would be eaten by the birds and insects and which would wither in the branches. Shall I feed the insects, Master? Matthew asked, or shall I be eaten by the birds? A question that seemed to everyone so stupid that none was surprised that Jesus did not answer it, but turning to Philip he asked him : Canst thou not, Philip, divine my meaning? But Philip, though pleased to come under the Master's notice, was frightened, and could think of no better answer than that the apricots they would eat in Paradise would be better. For there are no harsh winds in Paradise, isn't that so, Master? Thy question is no better than Salome's, Jesus answered, who sees Paradise ranged with chairs. Then all were troubled : if there were no chairs nor apricots in Paradise, it would be no Paradise for them; and they were dissatisfied with the answer that Jesus gave to them, that the soul is satisfied in the love of God as the flower in the sun. But with this answer they had to content themselves, for so dark was his face that none dared to ask another question till Matthew said : Master, we would understand thee fairly. If there be no chairs nor apricots in Paradise there cannot be a temple wherein to worship God. To which Jesus answered : God hath no need of temples in Paradise, nor has he need of any temple except the human heart wherein he dwells. It is not with incense nor the blood of sheep and rams that God is worshipped, but in the heart and with silent prayers unknown to all but God himself who knows all things. And the day is coming, I say unto you, when the Son of Man shall return with his Father to remake this world afresh, but before that

119

time comes ye would do well to learn to love God in your hearts, else all my teaching is vainer than any of the things in this world that ye are accustomed to look upon as vain. Upon this he took them to a mountain-side where the rock was crumbling, and he said : You see this crumbling rock? Once it held together, now it is falling into sand, but it shall be built up into rock again, and again it shall crumble into sand. At which they drew together silent with wonder, each fearing to ask the other if the Master were mad, for though they could see that the rock might drift into sand, they could not see how sand might be built up again into rock.

Master, how shall we know thee when thou returnest to us? Wilt thou be changed as the rock changes? Wilt thou be sand or rock? It was Andrew that had spoken; and Philip answered him that the Master would return in a chariot of fire, for he was angry that a fellow of Andrew's stupidity should put questions to Jesus whether they were wise or foolish; but could they be aught else than foolish coming from him? Andrew, persisting, replied : But we may not be within sight of the Master when he steps out of his chariot of fire, and we are only asking for a token whereby we may know him from his Father. My Father and thy Father, Andrew, Jesus answered, the Father of all that has lived, that lives, and that shall live in the world; and the law over the rock that crumbles into sand and the sand that is built up into rock again, was in that rock before Abraham was, and will abide in it and in the flower that grows under the rock till time everlasting. But, Master, wilt thou tell us if the rock we are looking upon was sand or rock in the time of Abraham? Philip asked, and Jesus answered him : My words are not then plain, that before that rock was and before the sand out of which the rock was built, was God's love — that which binds and unbinds, enduring always though the rock pass into sand and the sand into rock a thousand times. And it was then that a disciple poked himself up to Jesus to ask him if they were not to believe the Scriptures. He answered him that the Scriptures were no more than the love of God. This answer did not quell the dissidents; it caused them to murmur more loudly against him; but Jesus, though he must have seen that he was about to lose some disciples, would retract nothing. The Scriptures are, he repeated, but the love of God. Judas said : And the Gentiles that haven't the

Scriptures? Jesus answered that all men that have the love of God in their hearts are beloved by God. Is it then of no value to come of the stock of Abraham? the man asked, and Jesus replied: None, but a loss if ye do not love God, for God asks more from those whose minds he has opened than from those whose minds he has suffered to remain shut. At which Peter cried: Though there be not a pint of wine in all heaven we will follow thee, and though there be no fish in heaven but the scaleless that the Gentiles eat —— He stopped suddenly and looked at Jesus, saying: There are no Gentiles in heaven. Heaven is open to all men that love God, Jesus said, and after these words he continued to look at Peter, but like one that sees things that are not before him; and the residue followed him over the hills, saying to themselves: He is thinking about this journey to Jerusalem, and then a little later one said to the others: He is in commune with the spirits that lead him, asking them to spare him this journey, for he knows that the Pharisees will rise up against him, and will stone him if he preach against the Temple. What else should he preach against? asked another disciple; and they continued to watch Jesus, trying to gather from his face what his thoughts might be, thinking that his distant eyes might be seeking a sign of the coming kingdom in the sky. We might ask him if he sees the kingdom coming this way, an apostle whispered in the ear of another, and was forthwith silenced, for it was deemed important that the Master should never be disturbed in his meditations, whatever they might be.

His apostles and his disciples watched from a little distance, whilst he stood at gaze, recalling the day his dog Coran refused to follow him and, seeing that the dog had something on his mind, he had left his flock in charge of the other dogs and followed Coran to the hills above the Brook Kerith, down a little crumbling path to Elijah's cave, where he found the Baptist, and recognising in him Elijah's inheritor — at that moment a flutter of wings in the branches awoke him from his reverie, and assembling his disciples about him, he asked them whose inheritor he was. Some said Elijah, some said Jeremiah, some said Moses. As if dissatisfied with these answers, he looked into their faces, as if he would read their souls, and asked them to look up through the tree tops and tell him what they could see in a certain space of sky. In fear of his

121

mood, and lest he might call them feeble of sight or purblind, his disciples, or many among them, fell to disputing among themselves as to what might be discerned by human eyes in the cloud; till John, thinking to raise himself in the Master's sight, so it seemed to Joseph (who dared not raise his eyes to the sky, but bent them on the earth), said that he could see a chariot drawn by seven beasts, each having on its forehead seven horns; the jaws of these beasts, he averred, were like those of monkeys, and in their paws, he said, were fourteen golden candlesticks. Andrew, being misled by the colour of the cloud which was yellow, said that the seven beasts were like leopards; whereas Philip deemed that the beasts were not leopards, for him they were bears; and they began to dispute one with the other, some discerning the Father Almighty in a chariot, describing him to be a man garmented in white — His hair is like wool, they said. And seated beside him Matthew saw the Son of Man with an open book on his knees. But these visions, to their great trouble, did not seem to interest Jesus; or not sufficiently for their intention; and to the mortification of Peter and Andrew, James and John, he turned to Thaddeus and Aristion and asked them what they saw in the clouds, and partly because they were loth to say they could see naught, and also thinking to please him, they began to see a vision, and their vision was an angel whom they could hear crying: At thy bidding, O Lord; on which he emptied his vial into the Euphrates, and forthwith the river was turned to blood. A second angel crying likewise: At thy bidding, O Lord, emptied his vial; and when a third angel had emptied his, three animals of the shape of frogs crawled out of the river; and then from over the mountains came a great serpent to devour the frog-shapen beasts, and after devouring them he vomited forth a great flood, and the woman that had been seated on it was borne away. It was Thaddeus that spoke the last words, and he would have continued if Jesus's eyes had not warned him that the Master was thinking of other things, perhaps seeing and hearing other things. It is known to you all, he said, that Jeremiah kneels at the steps of my Father's throne praying for the salvation of Israel? Tell me then what is your understanding of the words: Praying for the salvation of Israel? Was the prophet praying that Israel might be redeemed from the taxes the Romans had imposed upon them?

122

Being without precise knowledge of how much remission Jeremiah might obtain for them, it seemed to them that it would be well to say that Jeremiah was praying to God to delay no longer, but send the Messiah he had promised. At which Jesus smiled, and asked them if the Messiah would remit the taxes; and the disciples answered craftily that the Messiah would set up the Kingdom of God on earth. In which kingdom no taxes are levied, Jesus replied. Come, he said, let us sit upon these rocks and talk of the great prophecies, for I would hear from you how you think the promised kingdom will come to pass. And the disciples answered, one here, one there, and then in twos and threes. But, Master, thou knowest all these things, since it is to thee our Father has given the task of establishing his Kingdom upon earth; tell us, plague us no longer with dark questions. We are not alone, Thaddeus cried, a rich man's son is amongst us. If he have come amongst us God has sent him, Jesus said, and we should have no fear of riches, since we desire them not. This kindness heartened Joseph, who dared to ask Jesus how he might disburden himself of the wealth that would come to him at his father's death.

As no such dilemma as Joseph's had arisen before, all waited to hear Jesus, but his thoughts having seemingly wandered far, they all fell to argument and advised Joseph in so many different ways that he did not know to whom he should hearken, so contradictory were all their notions of fairness; and the babble becoming louder it waked Jesus out of his mood, and catching Joseph's eyes, he asked him if he whom our Father sent to establish his Kingdom on earth would not have to give his life to men for doing it. A question that Joseph could not answer; and while he sought for the Master's meaning the disciples began again aloud to babble and to put questions to the Master, hurriedly asking him why he thought he must die before going up to heaven. Did not Elijah, they asked, ascend into heaven alive in his corporeal body? — and the cloak he left with Elisha, Aristion said, might be held to be a symbol of the fleshly body. This view was scorned, for the truth of the Scriptures could not be that the disciples inherited not the spiritual power of the prophet, but his fleshly show. Then the fate of Judas the Gaulonite rising up in Peter's mind, he said: But, Master, we shall not allow thee to be slain on a cross and given as food to the birds.

123

The disciples raised their staves, crying: We're with thee, Master, and the forest gave back their oaths in echoes that seemed to reach the ends of the earth; and when the echoes ceased a silence came up from the forest that shut their lips, and, panic-stricken, all would have run away if Peter had not drawn the sword which he had brought with him in case of an attack by wolves, and swore he would strike down the man that raised his hand against the Master. To which Jesus replied that every man is born to pursue a destiny, and that he had long known that his led to Jerusalem; whereupon Peter cried out: We'll defend thee from thyself; for which words Jesus reproved him, saying that to try to save a man from himself were like trying to save him from the decree that he brings into the world with his blood. And what is mine, Master? It may be, Jesus answered, to return to thy fishing. Whereupon Peter wept, saying: Master, if we lose thee we be as sheep that have lost their shepherd, a huddled, senseless flock on the hillside, for we have laid down our nets to follow thee, believing that the Kingdom of God would come down here in Galilee rather than in Jerusalem; pray that it may descend here, for thou'lt be safer here, Master; we have swords and staves to defend thee — so let us kneel in prayer and ask the Lord that he choose Galilee rather than Judea for the setting up of his kingdom. To which Jesus answered nothing, and his face was as if he had not heard Peter; and then Peter's fears for Jesus's life, should he go to Jerusalem, seemed to pass on from one to the other, till all were possessed by the same fear, and Peter said: Let us lift up our hearts to our Father in Heaven and pray that Jesus be not taken from us. Let us kneel, he said, and they all knelt and prayed, but to their supplication Jesus seemed indifferent. And seeing they were unable to dissuade him from Jerusalem, Peter turned to Joseph. Here is one, he said, who knows the perils of Jerusalem and will bear witness, that if thou preach that God has no need of a Temple or a sacrifice, thou'lt surely be done to death by the priests.

Peter's sudden appeal to his knowledge of the priests of Jerusalem awoke Joseph, who was wholly absorbed in his love of Jesus, and thought only of rushing forward and worshipping; but he was held back and strained forward at the same time, and seeing he was over-come, Peter did not press him for an answer, and Joseph fell back

124

among the crowd, ashamed, thinking that if Peter came to him
again he would speak forthright. He had words that would bring
him into the sympathy of Jesus, but instead of speaking them he
stood, held at gaze by the beauty of the bright forehead, large and
arched; and so exalted were the eyes that Joseph could not but
think that Jesus was looking upon things that his disciples did not
see. It seemed to Joseph that Jesus was meditating whether he
should confide all he saw and heard to his disciples. He waited,
tremulous with expectation, watching the thin throat out of which
rose a voice to which the ear became attuned quickly and was
gratified as by a welcome dissonance. It rose up among the silences
of the pines, and the delight of listening to it, Joseph thought, was
so near to intoxication that he would have pressed forward if he
had not remembered again that he was a new-comer into the community; one who might at any moment be driven out of it for
possessing riches of which he could not unburden himself. So he
kept his seat in the background among the casual followers, by
two men whose accents told him they were Samaritans, and these
now seemed within the last few minutes to have become opposed to
Jesus, and Joseph wondered at the change that had come over them
and lent an ear to their discourse so that he might discover a reason
for it. And it was not long before he discovered that their objection
related to the Book of Daniel, for they were of the sort that receive
no Scriptures after the five Books of the Law. Joseph knew the book
less perhaps than any other book of the Scriptures; he had looked
into it with Azariah, but for a reason which he could not now discover he had read it with little attention; and since his schooldays
he had not looked into it again. Peter and Andrew and John and
James were listening intently to the story of Nebuchadnezzar's
dream for the sake of the story related and without thought of what
might be Jesus's purpose in relating it. But to Joseph Jesus's purpose was the chief interest of the relation; and the purpose became
apparent when he began to tell how the great statue seen by Nebuchadnezzar in his dream, whose head was gold, whose arms and
breast were silver, whose belly was brass, and whose legs and feet
were iron and clay intermingled, was overthrown by a stone that
hand had not cut out of the mountain. This stone became forthwith as big as a mountain and filled the whole earth, and Joseph fell
125

to pondering whether this stone were the fifth kingdom which the Messiah would set up when the Roman kingdom had fallen to dust, or whether the stone were the Messiah himself. And while Joseph sat thinking he heard suddenly that when Nebuchadnezzar looked into the furnace, and saw the three men whom he had ordered to be thrown into it walking through the flames safely, he said : And there is a fourth, and the form of the fourth is like the son of God. At these words the hearts of the disciples were exalted, and they asked Jesus to tell them the further adventures of Daniel; and as if wishing to humour them he began to relate that a hand had appeared writing on the wall during the great feast at Babylon, a story to which Joseph could give but little heed, for his imagination was controlled by the words : Whose form is like the son of God — an inspiration on the part of the Babylonian king. If ever since then a man had seemed to another like the son of God, Jesus was that man ; and Joseph asked himself how it was that these words had passed over the ears of the disciples — over the ears of those who knew Jesus's mind, if any could be said to know Jesus's mind. Jesus, though he lived near them and loved them, lived in the world of his own thoughts, which, so it seemed to Joseph, he could not share with anybody. Not one of the men he had gathered about him, neither Peter, nor John, nor James, had seized the notable words : And the form of the fourth is like the son of God. It was for these words, Joseph felt sure, that Jesus had related the story of Daniel in the furnace. But his disciples had not apprehended the significance ; and like one whose confidence was unmoved by the slowness or the quickness of his listeners, almost as if he knew that the real drift of his speech was beyond his hearers, Jesus began to tell that Darius's counsellors had combined in a plot against Daniel and succeeded in it so well that Daniel was cast into a den of lions. But there being nothing in the story that pointed to the setting up of the Kingdom of God upon earth, Joseph was puzzled to understand why Jesus was at pains to relate it at such length. Was it to amuse his disciples? he asked himself, but no sooner had he put the question to himself than the purpose of the telling passed into his mind. Jesus had told the marvellous stories of Daniel's escapes from death so that his disciples might have no fear that the priests of Jerusalem would have power to destroy him : Whomso-

126

ever God sends into the world to do his work, Jesus would have us understand they are under God's protection for ever and ever; and Joseph rejoiced greatly at having discovered Jesus's intent, and for a long time the glen, the silent forest and the men sitting listening to the Master were all forgotten by him. He even forgot the Master's presence, so filled was he by the abundant hope that his divination of the Master's intent marked him out as one to be associated with the Master's work — more than any one of those now listening to him, more than Peter himself.

And so sweet was his reverie to him that he regretted its passing as a misfortune, but finding he was in spirit as well as in body among realities, he gave his ear to the story of the four winds that had striven upon the great sea and driven up four great beasts. These beasts Joseph readily understood to be but another figuration of the four great empires; the Babylonian, the Persian, and the the Grecian had been blown away like dust, and as soon as the the fourth, the Roman Empire, was broken into pieces the kingdom of the whole world would be given to the people of the saints of the Most High. It was Philip the nearly hunchback that asked Jesus for an explanation of this vision — saying, and obtaining the approval of several for the question, would he, Jesus, acquiesce in this sharing of the earth among the angels who had not seen him, nor heard him, nor served him upon earth. If the earth is to be shared among the angels we follow thee in vain, he muttered; and Joseph felt that he could never speak freely again with Philip for having dared to interrupt the Master and weary him with questions that a child could answer. To whom Philip said: But thou, young Master, that have received good instruction in Hebrew and Greek from the scribe Azariah, and have travelled far, do thou answer my question. If the earth is to be shared among angels —— He was not allowed to repeat more of his question, for a clamour of explanation began among the disciples that the earth would not be shared among the angels of God — God would find his people repentant when he arrived with his son. At last the assembly settled themselves to listen to the story of the vision in which a ram pushed westward and northward and southward, till a he-goat came from the west — one with a notable horn between the eyes — and butted the ram till he had broken his two horns. Joseph had

127

forgotten these visions, and he learnt for the first time, so it seemed to him, that the goat meant the Syrian king, Antiochus, who had conquered Jerusalem, polluted the sanctuary and set up heathen gods. But how are all these visions concerned with the setting up of the Kingdom of God on earth? and Jesus's purpose did not appear to him till Daniel heard a voice between the banks of the Ula crying: Make this man understand. Joseph understood forthwith that Jesus's purpose was still the same, to make it plain to the disciples that Daniel was protected and guided by God, and, that being so, Jesus could go to Jerusalem fearing nothing, he being greater than Daniel. So he sat immersed in belief, hearing but faintly the many marvellous things that Daniel heard and saw, nor did he awake from his reverie till Jesus announced that Gabriel flew about Daniel at the hour of the evening oblation, telling him that seventy weeks was the measure of time allowed by God to make reconciliation for iniquity and bring everlasting righteousness, and build Jerusalem unto the Messiah; and that after threescore and two weeks the Messiah should be cut off but not for himself.

The words: Cut off but not for himself, troubled Joseph, and he pondered them, while the disciples marvelled at hearing Jesus speak of these things (he seemed to know the Scriptures by rote), and his voice went upward into the silence of the firs, and they heard as if in a dream that the king of the south should come into his kingdom and return to his own land. But his sons shall be stirred up and shall revolt against him, Jesus said, and the disciples marvelled greatly, for Jesus made clear the meaning that lay under these dark sayings, and they heard and understood how the robbers of the people should exalt themselves and establish a vision: But these shall fall and the king of the north shall come and cast up mounds and take the fortified cities. And they heard of destructions and leagues and armies and sanctuaries that were polluted, and of peoples who did not know their God, but who nevertheless became strong; and they heard of Edom and Moab and the children of Ammon, but at the end of all these troubles the Tabernacle was placed between the seas of the glorious holy mountain. And that day the fishers from the lake of Galilee and others heard that Michael had told the people of Israel that those that were dead should rise out of the earth and come into everlasting life. But can the dead be raised up and come to life in their corruptible

bodies? asked the Samaritans that sat by Joseph, and their mutterings grew louder, and they denied that the prophet Daniel had
spoken truth in this and many other things, and as he had not
spoken truth he was a false prophet; whereupon so great a clamour
arose that the wild beasts in the ravine began to growl, being
awaked in their lairs. And the disciples, foreseeing that it would
soon be dark night in the forest, fell to seeking the way back to
Capernaum, the Galileans in one group with Jesus among them,
the Samaritans speeding away together and stopping at times for
fresh discussion with the Galileans, asked among many other things
how the corruptible body might be raised up to heaven and live
indulging in the many imperfections inherent in our bodies. It was
vain to ask them what justice there would be if the men that had
died before the coming of the Kingdom of God were not raised up
into heaven. If this were true the dead had led virtuous lives in
vain; they might for all it had profited them have lived like the
heathen. It was at Capernaum that the truth became manifest
that not only was Daniel rejected, but Isaiah, Jeremiah, Ezekiel,
all the prophets since Moses, at which the disciples were greatly
incensed and raised their staves against the Samaritans, but Jesus
dissuaded his followers, and the dissidents were suffered to depart
unhurt. Let them go, Jesus said, for they are in the hands of God,
like ourselves, and he bade them all good-night, and there seemed
to Joseph to be a great sadness in Jesus's voice, as if he felt that in
this world there was little else but leave-taking.

Joseph, too, resented this parting, though it was for but a few
hours; he would unite himself to Jesus, become one, as the mother
and the unborn babe are one — he would be of the same mind and
flesh; all division seemed to him loss, till, frightened at his own
great love of Jesus, he stopped in the Plain of Gennesaret, star-
gazing. But the stars told him nothing, and he walked on again.
Nor was it till about a half-hour's walk from Magdala that he
overtook the Samaritans, and these sought to draw him into argument. But he was in no humour for further discussion, and dismissed them, saying: What matter if all the prophets were false
since the promised Messiah is among us? He has come, he has
come! he repeated all the way home: and at every flight of the
high stairs he tried to collect his thoughts. But his brain was
whirling, and he could only repeat: He has come, he has come!

129

CHAPTER XIV.

IT seemed to Joseph as he hurried along the Plain of Gennesaret that the sun shone gayer than his wont, but as he approached Capernaum he began to think that the sun had risen a little earlier than usual. Nobody was about! He listened in vain for some sound of life, till at last his ear caught a sound as of somebody moving along the wharves, and, going thither, he came upon Peter storing his oars in the boathouse. Making ready, Joseph said, for fishing? Thou seest not, Master, that I'm putting my oars away, but I'd as lief take them out again and fish till evening. Here was a mysterious answer from the least mysterious of men, and Peter continued in his work, throwing the oars into a corner like one that cared little if he broke them, and kicking his nets aside as if he were never going to let them down again into the lake, Joseph looking on, wondering at the great change wrought in Peter, one that he had not foreseen in the good-humoured, simple fellow. Had he been bidden to leave the community or sell his boats? If that were so, his (Joseph's) chance of entering the community was a poor one indeed; and he begged Peter to relate his trouble to him — for trouble there had been last night, he was sure of it. Trouble there always is in this world, Peter answered, so long as I've known it, and will be till God sets up his kingdom. The sooner he does it the better, so say I. I know naught about the saints we heard of yesterday, or what business they have in it. The Master's mood is stranger than I can remember it, he said, standing up straight and looking Joseph in the eyes. It was thyself that said it yesterday, Peter, Joseph rejoined. I'm thinking it may have been the Samaritans that vexed him. Peter lifted his heavy shoulders and muttered: The Samaritans? We give no heed to them: and he began to speak, at first with diffidence; Joseph had to woo him into speak-

130

ing, which he did; but after the first few minutes Peter was glib enough, telling Joseph that last night there had been stirs and quarrels among the disciples regarding his boats. And John's and James's boats too, he said; and by the jealous and envious, he muttered, who would like to come between us and the Master. Joseph asked who had raised the vexatious question, but Peter avoided it, and went about the wharf grunting that none could answer it: was it to Matthew, the publican, he was to give his boats? One, he said, who never was on the water in his life till I took him out for a sail a week come Tuesday. A fine use they'd be to him but to drown himself. A puff of wind, and not knowing how to take in a reef, the boat would be over and the nets lost. Now who would be the better for the loss of my nets? answer me that. And I'd like to be told when my boats and nets were at the bottom of the lake to whom would the Son of Man turn for a corner in which to lay his head, or for a bite or a sup of wine. John and James would give their boats to Judas belike, and he'd bring home about as much fish as would —— But I'm thinking of thy father. What will he be saying to all this, and his business dwindling all the while, and we beggars? — the words my wife roused me with this morning. Of course, says she, if the stone that never was cut out of the mountain with hands is going to be slung and send the Romans toppling, I've naught to say against sharing, but the Kingdom had better come quickly, Simon Peter, if thou'rt to fish no more; and the woman is right, say I, though I hold with every word that falls from the Master's lips, only this way it is, he looks to my fishing for his supper, and Miriam is quick to remind me of that. A good woman, one that has been always yielding to my will and never had a word against our lodger, but sets the best before him out of thankfulness for his saving of her mother's life, though one more mouth in a house is always a cost, though the Master is as easily fed as a sparrow. But restive she is now about the delay: as I was saying just now she wakes me up with a loud question in my ear: Now, Simon Peter, answer me, art thou going into Syria to bid the blind to see, the lame to walk, and the palsied to shake no more, or art thou going to thy trade? for in this house there be four little children, myself, their mother, and thy mother-in-law. I say nothing against the journey if it bring thee good money, or if it bring

131

the Kingdom, but if it bring naught but miracles there'll be little enough in the house to eat by the time of thy return. And, says she, the feeding of his children is a nobler work for a married man (she speaks like that sometimes) than bidding those to see who would belike be better without their eyes than with them. None would guess it, but 'tis as I say : she talks up to me like that, and ofttimes I've to go to the Master and ask him to quiet her, which he rarely fails to do, for she loves him for what he has done for her mother, and is willing to wait. But last night when the busybodies brought her news that the Master had been preaching in the forest, of the sharing of the world out among the holy saints, she gave way to her temper and was violent, saying, by what right are the saints of the Most High coming here to ask for a share of this world, as if they hadn't a heaven to live in. Thou seest, good Master, there's right on her side, that's what makes it so hard to answer her, and I'm with her in this, for by what right do the holy saints down here ask for a share in the world ? that's what keeps drumming in my head ; and, as I told thee a while ago, I'd as lief put out upon the lake and fish as go to Syria for nothing, say the word —— And leave the Master to go alone ? Joseph interposed. Well, I suppose we can't do that, Peter answered, and then it seemed to Joseph wiser not to talk any more, but to allow things to fashion their own course, which they did very amiably, the little band going forth in about an hour's time, with Joseph walking by Peter's side, hoping he would not have to wait long before seeing a miracle. Their first stop was at Chorazin, about five miles distant, and the sick began to rise quickly from their beds, and Jesus had only to impose his hands for the palsied to cease quivering. The laws of nature seemed suspended and Joseph forgot his father at Magdala and likewise Pilate's business which had brought him to Galilee. It will have to wait, he said, talking with himself, and now certain that he had come upon him whom he had always been seeking, he deemed it as lost time to look at anything but Jesus, or to hear any words but his, or to admire aught but the manifestations of his power ; and every time a sick man rose from his bed Joseph thanked God for having allowed him to live in the days of the Messiah. He saw sight restored to the blind, hearing to the deaf, swiftness of foot to cripples, issues of blood that had endured ten years
132

stanched; the cleansing of the leper had become too common a miracle; he looked forward to seeing demons taking flight from the bodies of men and women, and accepted Peter's telling that the day could not be delayed much longer when he would see some dead man rise up in his cere-clothes from the tomb; and having a mind only for the miraculous, one of the vexations of his spirit was that Jesus forbade his disciples (among whom Joseph now counted himself) to tell anybody that he was the Messiah.

In every town they were welcomed by the Gentiles as well as by the Jews, which was surprising, and set Joseph's wits to work; and these being well trained, he soon began to apprehend that the Jews accepted the miracles as testimony that Jesus was really the Messiah and that his teaching was true; whereas the Gentiles admired the miracles for their own sake, failing, however, and completely, to see that because he cured the blind, the palsied, the scrofulous and the halt, they should no longer visit their temples and sacred groves, and admire no more Pan's huge sexuality and hang garlands upon it, nor carve images of Diana and Apollo. Such abstinence they could not comprehend, and deemed it enough that they were ready to proclaim him a god on the occasion of every great miracle, a readiness that gave great scandal and caused many Jews to turn away from Jesus. It was not enough that he should repudiate this godhead; and the hardness of heart and narrowness of soul that he encountered among his own people afflicted Jesus as much as did the incontinency of the Gentiles, whom he sometimes met, bearing images in procession, going towards some shrine — the very same who had listened to his teaching yester evening. Joseph once dared throw himself in front of one of these processions, and he begged the processionists to Pan to throw aside the garlands and wreaths they had woven. This they would not do, but out of respect to the distinguished strangers that had come to their town they listened for some minutes to his relation that on the last day the dead would be roused by the trumpets of angels to attend the judgment and that the man Jesus before them — the Messiah announced hundreds of years ago in many a prophetic book — would return to earth in a chariot of fire by his Father's side, the Judgment Book in his hands. May we now proceed on our way? they asked, but Joseph besought them to listen to him for another few minutes, and thinking he had perhaps explained the resurrection badly, and forthwith calling to mind the philosophy of Egypt and Mathias, he asked them to apprehend that it would not be the corruptible body that would rise from the dead but the spiritual body, whereby he only succeeded in perplexing still further the minds of the good pagans of Cæsarea Philippi, and provoking stirs and quarrels among his own people. And the processionists, taking advantage of this diversion of opinion among the Jews, passed on and disposed of their wreaths and votive offerings as it pleased them to do. All the same, on their way back they begged Jesus to perform some more miracles, but he answered them not, and to their great amazement he left them for the Tyrians and Sidonians. But the same difficulties occurred in Tyre and Sidon, the Gentiles accepting the miracles with delight but paying little heed to the doctrine. They begged him to remain with them and offered gifts for his services as healer, but he refused these and returned to Galilee, having performed miracles of all sorts, without, however, having bidden a dead man rise from the grave, to the great disappointment of Joseph, who would have liked to witness this miracle (the greatest of all); seemingly it was not his lot to do so. But Peter bade him hope! — the great miracle might happen in Galilee, and as such a miracle would establish the truth of Jesus's Messiahship even to Dan, Joseph remained in Capernaum, going out in the boats with Jesus and his disciples, sailing along the shores till the people gathered in numbers enough for an exhortation. As there were always many Pharisees and Sadducees among the crowds assembled to hear the Master, he did not land, but preached standing up in the bow, Peter vigilant with an oar, for priests are everywhere enemies of reformation and stir up attacks upon reformers, and those made on Jesus were often so violent that Peter had to strike out to the right and to the left, but he always managed to get free, and they sailed for less hostile coasts or back to the wharf at Capernaum.

It once occurred to them to try their luck with the Gadarenes, and it was in returning from their coasts one evening that Peter's boat was caught in a great storm and that Joseph was met by one of his father's servants as he jumped ashore. The man had come to tell him that if he wished to see his father alive he must hasten

134

to Magdala, and Joseph glared at him dumbfounded, for he had suspected all along that he had little or no right at all to leave his father for Jesus. I did not know I was like this, he blurted out to himself. And as much to silence his accusing conscience as anything else he questioned the stupid messenger, asking him if his father had seen a physician, and if the physician had held out any hopes of a recovery. But the thin and halting account which was all the messenger could give only increased Joseph's alarm, and it was with much difficulty that he learnt from him that the master had brought some walnuts to the parrots, and just after giving a nut to the green parrot had cried out to Tobias that a great pain had come into his head. Joseph dug his heels into his ass's side and cried to the messenger: And then? The messenger answered that the pain in the back of his father's head had become so great that he began to reel about, overthrowing one of the parrots on its perch. The parrot flew at Master, thinking he had done it —— Never mind the parrot, Joseph replied angrily, confusing the messenger, who told him that the master entered the house on Tobias's arm, and sat down to supper, but ate nothing to speak of. None of us dared to go to bed that night, the messenger continued. We sat up, expecting every moment somebody to come down from the room overhead to tell us that the master was dead. The next part of the messenger's story was like a tangled skein, and Joseph half heard and half understood that the great physician that came from Tiberias said that he must awaken the master out of the swoon and at any cost. And he kept bawling at him, the messenger said. Bawling at him, Joseph repeated after the messenger, and the messenger repeated the words: Bawling at him, saying that the physician had said that the master's swoon was like a wall and that he must get him to hear him somehow. He said the effort would cost thy father, Sir, a great deal, but he must get him to hear him. The story as the servant related it seemed incredible, but he reflected that servants' stories are always incredible, and Joseph learned with increasing wonder that Dan had heard the physician and sat up in bed and spoken reasonably, but had fallen back again unconscious, and that the physician on leaving him said that they must get his mouth open somehow and pour a spoonful of milk into his mouth, and call upon him as loudly as they could to swal-

135

low. What physician have they sent for? Joseph asked the messenger, but he could not remember the name. It was Ecanus sitting by Dan's bedside when he arrived, and Joseph learnt by careful nursing and feeding him every ten minutes there was just a chance of saving Dan's life.

For seven days Dan's life receded, and it was not till the eighth day the wheel of life paused on the edge of the abyss. Dan, with his eyes turned up under the eyelids, only the white showing, lay motionless; and it was not till the morning of the ninth day that the wheel began to revolve back again; but so slow were its revolutions that Joseph was in doubt for two or three days. But on the fifth day he was sure that Dan was mending, and in about three days more the pupils of Dan's eyes looked at his son's from under the eyelids. He spoke a few words and took his milk more easily, without being asked to swallow. The pains in his head returned with consciousness; he often moaned; the physician was obliged to give him opiates, but he continued to mend and in three weeks was speaking of going out to walk in the garden. To gain his end he often showed a certain childish cunning, urging Joseph on one occasion to go to the verandah to see if somebody was coming up the garden, and as soon as Joseph's back was turned he slipped out of bed with the intention of getting to his clothes. He fell, without, however, hurting himself, and was put back to bed and kept there for three more weeks before he was allowed a short walk. Even then the concession seemed to be given too soon; for he could not distinguish the different trees, nor could he see the parrots, though he could hear them, and he remained in purblindness for some two or three weeks; but his sight returned, and he said to Joseph: That is a palm-tree and that is a pepper-tree. Joseph answered that he said truly and hastened across the garden to meet Ecanus, for he desired to ask him privily if his father were out of all danger; and the answer to his question was that Dan's life would pass away in a swoon like the one he had just come out of, but he might swoon many times — two or three times, perhaps oftener — before he swooned for the last time. More than that Ecanus could not say. A silence fell suddenly between them, and wondering what term of life his father had still to traverse before he passed into eternity, Joseph followed the physician through the wilting alleys, seeking the shadiest parts, for the summer was well-nigh upon them now. At the end of one of these, out of the sun's rays, the old man lay propped up among cushions, dreaming, or perhaps only conscious of the refreshing breeze that came and went away again. But he awoke at the sound of their steps on the sanded paths, and raised his stick as a sign to them to come to him, and, seeing that he wished to speak, Joseph leaned over his chair, putting his ear close to his father's face, for Dan's speech was still thick and often inarticulate. So, Joseph, thou hast returned to me! Didst thou not expect me, Father? I hoped that the Lord might save thee from the storm for my sake, Dan answered, and Joseph was astonished and could not believe that he had heard rightly, for what could a man lying in deep swoon, beyond the reach of words, know of the storm fallen upon the lake in which Peter's boat had barely escaped shipwreck? So he put questions to his father and heard from him that a voice had told of a boat in a great storm and Joseph about to be engulfed. Miracle upon miracle! Joseph cried, and he related how when coming in Peter's boat from the opposite shore the wind had raised the lake into great waves against them. But unmindful of the turmoil Jesus had continued to teach them, even after the splitting of a plank. Master, if the boat be not bailed we perish, Peter said, for which Jesus rebuked Peter and called them to come forward and kneel about him. Kneel, he said, your faces towards me; forget the sundered plank and repent your sins. We could not do else but as we were bidden, and we all knelt about him, our thoughts fixed as well as we were able to fix them on our sins, but the water was coming into the boat all the while, and in the midst of our prayers we said: In another moment we perish if he stay not the wind and waves. We thought that he would stand up in the bow and command, but he remained seated, and continued to teach us, but the wind lulled all the same, and when we looked round the boat was staunch again, and we made the wharf at Capernaum easily.

Ecanus, who was a man of little faith, asked Joseph if he had seen anybody put his hand to the plank and restore it to its place, and Joseph answered that all were grouped round the Master praying, and that none had fallen away from the group. But there were some in the boat that saw a little angel speeding over the

waves. Philip saw both wings and the angel's feet, but I had only a glimpse. If thou wouldst let me bring him to thee —— But, reading his father's face, Joseph continued : If thou have not faith, Father, he couldn't do anything for thee. Father, let me bring him. This signifies no distrust in your learning, he interjected suddenly, turning to Ecanus. Each man has powers given to him : some are physical and some spiritual; some are powerful in one element and some in another. But no magician that I have met has power over fire and water. Only those into whom God has descended can command both fire and water alike. And he related that when they passed through Chorazin and a woman ran out of her house crying that her little boy had fallen into the fire, Jesus had asked her if she had applied any remedy, and on her saying she had not, he had said : Then I will cure him. With his breath he restored him, and five minutes after the child was playing with his little comrades in the street. If, however, she had poured oil on the wounds he couldn't have cured them, Joseph explained, for his affinity with fire would have been interrupted. In the village of Opeira a child while carrying a kettle of boiling water from the fire tipped it over, burning a good deal of the flesh of one foot, which, however, healed under Jesus's breath almost as soon as he had breathed upon it. And yet another child was healed of the croup, but this time it was John who imposed his hands : Jesus had transmitted some of his power over the ills of the flesh to the disciples. On Dan asking if Joseph had seen Jesus cast out devils, Joseph replied that he had, but it would take some time to tell the manner of the exorcism. Whereupon Ecanus remembered that other patients waited for his attendance and took his leave, warning Joseph before leaving against the danger of tiring his father, a thing that Joseph promised not to do; but as soon as the door closed after the physician Dan began to beg so earnestly for stories that Joseph could not do else than tell him of the miracle he had witnessed. Better to submit, he thought, than to agitate his father by refusal; and he began this narrative : the morning of the storm, which they would not have succeeded in weathering had it not been for the intervention of the angel, Jesus and some of the disciples, including Joseph, had set their sail for the Gadarene coasts; and finding a landing-place by a shore seeming desolate, they proceeded into the country; and
138

while seeking a sufficient number to exhort and to teach, their search led them past some broken ruins, shards of an old castle, apparently tenantless. They were about to pass it without examination when a wailing voice from one of the turrets brought them to a standstill. They were not at first certain whether the wailing sound was the voice of the wind or a human voice, but they had hearkened and with difficulty had separated the doleful sound into : Woe! woe! woe! unto thee, Jerusalem, woe! woe! It sounds to me, Peter said, like one that is making a mock of thee, Master. Having heard that thou foretellest woe to Chorazin —— But Judas, seeing a cloud gathering on Jesus's face, nudged Peter, and the twain went up together and some minutes after returned with a half-naked creature, an outcast whom they had found crouching like a jackal in a hole among the stones, one clearly possessed by many devils. Now as all were in wonder what his history might be, a swineherd passing by at the time told them how the poor, naked creature would take with the same gentle grace a beating or a gift of food for his singing. The words had hardly passed the swineherd's lips than the possessed began to sing :

> Woe! woe! woe! the winds are wailing.
> The four great sisters, the winds of the world,
> Call one to the other, and it is thy doom
> They are calling, Jerusalem.
> Woe! woe! woe!
> The North brings ruin, the South brings sorrow,
> The East wind grief, and the West wind tears
> For Jerusalem.
> Woe! woe! woe!

And he sung this little song several times, till the hearts of the disciples hardened against the outcast and they were minded to beat him if he did not cease; but the swineherd warned them that a surer way to silence him was by giving him some food; and while he stood by eating, the swineherd confided the story of the fool, or as much of it as he knew, to Jesus. The fool, he said, came from Jerusalem some two years ago. He had been driven out of the Temple, which he frequented daily, crying about the courts the song with which he wearied you just now, till the most patient were unable to bear it any longer; and every time he met a priest he

139

looked into his face and sang: Woe! woe! woe! unto Jerusalem, and whenever he met a scribe he would cry: Woe! woe! woe! unto Jerusalem, hindering them in their work about the Temple. Some stones were thrown, but enough life was left in him to crawl away, and as soon as he recovered from his wounds he was about again, singing his melancholy ditty (he knows but one). He was told if he did not cease he would be beaten with rods, but he could not cease, and started it again as soon as he could bear a shirt on his back; and then he must have travelled up here afoot, picking up a bit here and a bit there, getting a lift in an ox-cart. He is without memory of anything, who he is, whence he came, or who taught him his song. He does not know why he chose that broken tower for a dwelling, nor do we, but fortunately it stands in a waste. We hear him singing as we go by to our work and fling him scraps of food from time to time. We hear him as we return in the evening to our homes making his ruined dwelling sadder with his song. A harmless, poor fool, save for the annoyance of his song, which he cannot stay any more than the wind in the broken turrets. A harmless fool who will follow whosoever asks him to follow, unafraid, and taking a blow or a hunch of bread in the same humour, and distinguishing no man from the next one. As the swineherd said these words the fool said: Jesus, thou hast come to my help, but woe to thee, Son of God, thou wilt suffer thy death in Jerusalem; and looking up into Jesus's face more intensely: Oh, Son of Man, what aileth thee or me? And knowest thou aught of the cloud of woe that hangs over Jerusalem? To which Jesus made no answer, but called upon the devils to say how many there were, and they answered: Three. Then depart ye three, Jesus replied, and was about to impose his hands when the three devils asked whither they should go, to which Jesus answered: Ye must seek another refuge, for here ye cannot remain. Seek among the wolves and foxes. But these will flee from us, the devils answered; allow us to enter the hogs rooting the ground before thee. But at this the swineherd cried out: Forbid the devils to enter into my hogs, else they will run over the cliffs and drown themselves in the sea. Though ye are Jews, and do not look favourably on hogs, they are as God made them. To which Jesus answered, turning to his disciples: The man speaks well, for if unclean they be, it was the
140

will of God that made them so. And taking pity on the hogs that were rooting quietly, unaware of the devils eager to enter into them, he said : There are statues of gods and goddesses in Tiberias, enter into those. And immediately the devils took flight, giving thanks to Jesus as they departed thither.

Joseph waited a moment and tried to read his father's face. But Dan's face remained fixed, and as if purposely, which vexed Joseph, who cried : Now, Father, thou mayest believe or disbelieve my story, but thou knowest that two days after the great storm on the lake a statue of the goddess Venus fell from her pedestal in the streets of Tiberias and was broken. But, Joseph, when the statue fell I was sick and had no knowledge of the fall. But if a statue of the goddess Venus did fall from her pedestal, I'd ask why the devils should choose to destroy false gods? Were it not more reasonable for them to uphold the false gods safe and secure on their pedestals? The gods were overthrown for a sign that the devils had left the fool's body, Joseph answered. But why, Dan replied, didn't three statues fall? — a statue for each devil — and whither did the devils go? That one statue should fall was enough for a sign, Joseph said, but no more would he say, for his father's incredulity irritated him, and seeing that he had angered his son, Dan stretched his hand to him and said : Perhaps we are more eager to believe when we are young than when we are old. And he asked Joseph to tell him of some other miracle that he might have seen Jesus perform. Joseph had seen Jesus perform many other miracles, but he was loth to relate them, for none, he felt sure, would bring his father to the belief that Jesus was the Messiah that was promised to the Jews. All the same the miracle of the woods rose in his mind, and so plainly that he could not keep the story back, and almost before he was aware of it he began the story, telling how Jesus, James, John, Andrew, and himself were at table, mingling jest with earnest (Peter was not with them, being kept at home, for his wife was in childbirth at the time), when the women of the village were heard running up the street crying together to the men to take part in the chase of the wild man of the woods, who had come down amongst them once more questing the flesh of women. But this time we'll put a stop to his leaping, they cried. A goatherd coming from the hills has seen him make into a cave and as soon as he has

141

folded his goats he will lead us to it. But the villagers were in no mood for waiting; the goats could be folded by another; and the goatherd was bidden to leave his goats and lead the way, Jesus and his disciples following with the others through the forest till we came to a ravine. And the goatherd said : Look between yon great rocks, for it was between them he passed out of my sight. And let one of you creep in after him, but I must return to my goats, having no certainty that they were properly folded for the night. The goatherd would have run away if he hadn't been held fast, and there were questions as to who would enter. The first said no, the second the same, giving as reason that they were not young or strong enough, whereas the goatherd was both, and none better endowed for the struggle; and the people became of one mind that they would beat the goatherd with the crows if he did not go down into the cave, but Jesus, arriving in time, said : It is not lawful to break into any man's dwelling with crows, nor to kill him because his sins affront you; let us rather give him means to cut himself free from sins. At which words the people were nigh to jeering, for it seemed to them that Jesus knew little of the man they were pursuing, and they knew not what to understand when he asked if any among them had a long, sharp knife, and there was a movement as if they were about to leave him; but one man said : Thou shalt have mine, Master, and, taking it out of his girdle, he gave it to Jesus, who tested it with his thumb, and, satisfied with it, laid it on the rock beside the cave. But the people began to mutter : He will use the knife against us, Master. Not against you, Jesus answered, but against himself, thereby defending himself against himself. There were mutterings among the people, and some said that his words were too hard to understand, but all were silent as soon as Jesus raised his hands and stepped towards the cave, and began to breathe his spirit against the lust that possessed the man's flesh. We must return hither, he said, with oil and linen cloths. At which all wondered, not knowing what meaning to put upon his words, but they believed Jesus, and came at daybreak to meet him at the edge of the forest and followed the path as before till they came to the hillside. The man was no longer hidden in his cave, but sat outside by the rock on which Jesus had laid the knife, and Jesus said : Happy is he born into the world without sting,
142

and happy is he out of whom men have taken the sting before he knew it, but happier than these is the man that cuts out the part that offends him, setting the spirit free as this man has done.

Joseph ceased speaking suddenly and stood waiting for his father to admire the miracle he had related, but Dan's tongue struggled with words; and Joseph, being taken as it were with another flux of words, and like one apprehensive of the argument that none shall undo God's handiwork, set out on the telling that the cause of man's lust of women was that God and the devil had a bet together — the devil saying that if God let him sting a man in a certain part of his flesh he would get him in the end despite all that God might do to save him from hell. To which God, being in the humour, consented, and the sting was put into nearly all men. A few the devil overlooked, and these have much spared to them, and those out of whom the sting is taken in childhood are fortunate, but those who, like the wild man of the wood, cut the sting out of their own free will are worthy of all praise; and he cited the authority of Jesus that man should mutilate his body till it conform perforce to his piety. But the story of man's fall is told differently in the Book of Genesis, my son. The admonition that he was laying violent hands on a sacred book startled Joseph out of his meditations, and in some confusion of words and mind he began to prevaricate, saying that he thought he had made himself clear: the release of pious souls from the bondage of the flesh was more important than the continuance of the impious. Moreover in the days of Moses, Israel was not steeped in as many iniquities as she is now, and the Day of Judgment was not so close at hand. More men meant more sins, and sin has become so common that God can endure the torture no longer. . . . Again Joseph ceased speaking suddenly and, almost agape, stood gazing into his father's face, reading therein a great perplexity, for Dan was asking himself for what good reason had God given him so strange a son. He would have been content to let the story pass into another, but Joseph was waiting for him to speak, and speaking presently he said he had heard that in the Temple of Astoreth the Phœnician youths often castrated themselves with shards of shells or pottery and threw their testicles in the lap of the goddess crying out: Art thou satisfied now, Astoreth? But he did not know of any text in their

143

Scriptures that counselled such a practice; and the introduction of it seemed to savour of borrowing from the heathen. Whereupon Joseph averred that whereas the wont of the Phœnician youths is without reason, the same could not be said of Jesus's device to save a soul. To which Dan rejoined that the leaving of the knife for the man to mutilate himself with seemed to him to be contrary to all the rumours of Jesus that had come to his ears. I have heard that he would set the law aside and the traditions of our race, declaring the uncircumcised to be acceptable to God as the Jew; that he sits down to food with the uncircumcised and lays no store on burnt offerings. Nor did Isaiah, Joseph interrupted, and circumcision is itself a mutilation. I would not dispute its value with thee; but if thou deniest that Jesus was right to leave a knife whereby the sinner might free himself from sin thou must also deny circumcision. Circumcision is the sign of our race, Dan answered. A physical sign, an outward sign, Joseph cried, and he asked his father to say if the Jews would ever forget priests and ritual; and he reminded his father that the once sinner, now a holy anchorite, did not bring an appetency into the world that could be overcome by prayer, and so had to resort to the knife that he might live in the spirit. It seems to me, Joseph, that we should live as God made us, for better or worse. But, Father, once you admit circumcision —— A man should not be over-nice, Joseph, and though it be far from my thought to wish to see thee a fornicator or adulterer it would rejoice me exceedingly to see grandchildren about me. There is a maiden —— Another reason, Father, of which I have not yet spoken makes the marriage of the flesh seem a vanity to me, and that is —— I know it well, Joseph, that the great day is coming when the world will be remoulded afresh. But, Father, dost thou believe in nothing but observances? Tell me, Joseph, did thy prophet ever raise anybody from the dead? Yes, and hoping to convince his father by another miracle he fell to telling eagerly how a young girl who was being carried to the grave was called back to life. She was, he said, coming from her wedding feast.

And he told how there were in the village two young girls, one as fair as the other, rivals in love as well as in beauty, both having the same young man in their hearts, and for a long time it seemed
144

uncertain which would get him; for he seemed to favour them alternately, till at length Ruth, unable to bear her jealousy any longer, went to the young man, saying that she was close on a resolve to see him no more. Thy lover? he answered, his cheek blanching, for he dearly loved her. I haven't gotten a lover, she said; only a share in a lover. Thy words, Ruth, relieve me of much trouble, he replied, and took her in his arms and said: It was a good thought that brought thee hither, for if thou hadst not come I might never have been able to decide between you, but thy coming hath given me strength, and now I know which I desire. And then it was the girl's cheek that grew pale, for he hadn't answered at once which he would have. Which? she asked, and he replied: Thee, not Rachel. If that be so, she answered, I am divided between joy and sorrow; gladness for myself, sorrow for my friend; and it behoves me to go to her and tell her of her loss. I am the chosen one, she said to Rachel, who turned away, saying: Had I gone to him and asked him to choose between us he would have chosen me. He couldn't do else. Whereupon she began to brood and to speak of a spell laid upon the young man, and her visits to a sorceress came to be spoken about so openly that it was against the bridegroom's wish that Rachel was asked to the wedding feast; but Ruth pleaded, saying that it would be no feast for her if Rachel did not present herself at the table. The twain sat opposite each other at table, Rachel seemingly the happier, eating, drinking, laughing, foretelling that Mondis would fill Ruth's life with happiness from end to end. Thou wilt never see the face of an evil hour, she said, and Ruth in her great joy answered: Rachel, I know not why he didn't choose thee; thou'rt so beautiful; and the young Mondis wooed her at the table, to Ruth's pleasure, for she knew of his thankfulness to Rachel for allowing the wedding to pass in concord, without a jarring note. She seemed to listen to him as a sister might to a beloved brother, and as the wedding feast drew to a close she said: Ruth shall drink wine with me, and the cups were passed across the table, and laughter and jest flowed on for a while. But soon after drinking from Rachel's cup Ruth turned pale and, leaning back into the arms of her bridegroom, she said: I know not what ails me. . . . And then a little later on she was heard to say: I am going, and with a little sigh she went out of her life, lying

145

on her bridegroom's arm white and still like a cut flower. The word
poison swelled up louder and louder, and all eyes were directed
against Rachel, who to prove her innocence drank the wine that
was left in Ruth's cup; but it was said afterwards that she had
not drunk out of the same that she had handed to Ruth. Be this
as it may, a house of joy was turned into a house of tears. Bridegroom, parents and friends fell into procession, and we who were
coming down the street met the bier, and after hearing the story of
the girl's death Jesus said: Let me speak to her, and, leaning over
her, he whispered in her ear, and soon after we thought it was the
wind that stirred the folds of her garments, but her limbs were astir
in them; the colour came back to her cheeks; she raised herself
on her bier, and with his bride in his arms the bridegroom worshipped Jesus as a god; but Jesus reproved him, saying: It was
by the power of God working through me that she was raised from
the dead: give thanks to him who alone merits our thanks. But
Rachel, who had been following the bier in great grief, hanging on
the bridegroom's arm, could not contain herself at the sight of
Ruth raised from the dead, and it wrenching her reason out of her
control compelled her to call upon the people to cast out the Nazarene, who worked cures with the help of the demons with whom he
was in league, which proved to everybody that her friendly words
to Ruth at the feast were make-believe, and that she had been
plotting all the while how she might ruin her.

At the sight of Ruth beautiful and living naught mattered to
Rachel but revenge, and she crossed the street as if with the intention of striking her with a dagger, but as she approached Jesus the
flame of fury died out of her face, and like one overwhelmed with a
great love she cast herself at his feet, and could not be removed.
Why do you turn the woman from me? he asked. Whatever her
sins may have been they are forgiven, for she loveth me. But she
loved the other man five seconds before, Dan submitted, and
Joseph replying to him said: She only knew that passion of the
flesh which we share with the beasts of the fields, the fowls of the
air and the fish in the sea. But now she loves Jesus as we love him
— with the spirit. And next day she brought all her wealth to him;
the golden comb she was wont to wear in her hair she would place
in his; and the silks and linen in which she was wont to clothe her-
146

self she laid at his service; but he told her to sell all these things and give the money to the poor. Give to the poor! That is what I hear always, cried Dan; but if we gave all to the poor we would be as poor as the very poorest; and where, then, would the money come from with which we now help the poor? Give to the poor that thou mayest become worthy of a place in the world to come; this world is but a shadow — an illusion, Joseph answered defiantly. Thou hast that answer for everything, Joseph; and another day when I'm stronger I'll argue that out with thee. I have tired thee, Father; but if I've told thee many stories it was because —— Because, Dan retorted, thou wouldst have Jesus cast his spells over me. But I've no use for them; thou art enough. And while Joseph debated how he might convince his father that the girl was really dead, Dan asked for news of Rachel, and Joseph answered that she was with them every day, that their company had been increased by several devoted women. Thou hast talked enough, Father, and more than enough; if Ecanus were to return he would accuse me of planning to talk thee to death.

CHAPTER XV.

LIKE every other old Jew, Dan liked the marvellous, and listened to his son's stories, not knowing whether he believed or disbelieved, nor seeking to inquire; content to enjoy the stories as they went by, he listened, suffering such a little disappointment when his son's voice ceased as he might at the death of a melodious wind among the branches, the same little sadness. Moreover, while Joseph talked he had his attention, and it irritated him to see Joseph's thoughts wander from him in search of parrots and monkeys; and he begged his son to tell him another miracle, for he was sure that Joseph had not told him the last one. Joseph pleaded that there was no use relating miracles to one who believed only in ancient miracles, a statement that Dan combated, saying that one could like a story for its own sake. Like a Gentile, Joseph interposed gaily, bringing all the same a cloud into his father's face, which he would have liked to disperse with the relation of another miracle, but he continued to plead that he had told all his stories. There was, however, a certain faint-heartedness in his pleading, and Dan became more certain than ever that his son was holding back a miracle, and becoming suddenly curious, he declared that Joseph had no right to hold back a story from him, for to do that provoked argument, and argument fatigued him.

Joseph thought the device to extort a story from him which he did not wish to tell, a shabby one, but, fearing to vex his father in his present state of health, he began to think it would be better to tell him the miracle he had heard of that morning at Capernaum; but, still loth, he tried instead to divert his father's attention from Jesus, reminding him of the numerous matters that would have to be settled up between them, especially Dan's responsibility in the new adventure, the transport of grain from Moab to Jerusalem.

148

Dan's curiosity was not to be diverted, and seeing him give way to his rage like a petulant child, Joseph decided that he must tell him, and he began with a disparagement of his story, the truth of which he did not vouch for. At Capernaum they were all telling how some two or three weeks ago Jesus heard God speaking within him, and, naming those he wished to accompany him, led them through the woods, up the slow ascending hills in silence, no word being exchanged between him and them. Every one of the disciples was aware that the Master was in communion with his Father in heaven, and that his communion would be shared by them as long as a word was not spoken. A word would break it; and so they journeyed with their eyes set upon the stars or upon the ground, never daring to look for Jesus, who remained amongst them for an hour or more and then seemed to them to pass into shadow, only his voice remaining with them bidding them to journey on, which they did, each man in his faith, until they reached a lonely hill on the top of which stood a blighted tree. Why didst thou lead us hither, Master? they asked, and receiving no answer, they looked round for Jesus, but he was missing, and, thinking they had walked too fast and had left him on the road behind them, they returned to the place where he had last spoken to them; and, not finding him there, they returned to the hill-top, and, seeing him among the white branches waiting for them, they knelt and prayed till the stars began to grow dim. When the night was over and the dawn at hand, a voice was heard crying: Behold he is with you, he who brings salvation to all men, Jew and Gentile; and ye twelve are bidden to carry the joyful tidings to the ends of the earth. At these words the disciples rose from their knees, and they looked round astonished, for though four only had gone with Jesus up the hillside, twelve were kneeling at the foot of the tree; and the four that had come with Jesus knew not how the eight were gathered with them, nor could the eight tell how they reached the hill-top, nor what spirit guided them thither. The day is breaking, someone said; and looking towards the east they saw innumerable angels and all of them singing hosanna; hosannas fell from the skies and blossoms from the tree; for the tree was no longer a blighted but a quickened tree. Jesus was amongst them, talking to them, telling those who were standing around him that they were chosen by his

149

Father in heaven first of all, and then by him, to carry the joyful tidings to the ends of the earth, and they all answered : We heard the words that thou hast spoken, Master. And he answered : Ye have heard truly, and I am here to carry out my Father's will; ye shall go forth and bring salvation to all, Jew and Gentile alike.

Father, of what art thou thinking — that the twelve slept and dreamed? But before Dan could find an answer to his son's question Joseph sank away into regrets that he had acceded to his father's request and told him this last miracle, and that he had not been able to disguise the fact, in the telling, that Jesus had chosen as his apostles those who accompanied him into the mountains. He intended to omit all mention of this election, but it slipped from him unawares in the excitement of the telling, and now to divert his father's thoughts from the unfortunate admission Joseph called to one of the parrots and spoke cheerfully to the bird, and to the monkey that came hopping across the sward and jumped into his arms; but Dan knew his son's face too well to be deceived by the poor show Joseph could paint upon it, and guessing that his father divined the truth, words deserted him altogether. He sat striving against regret and hoping that his father did not think he loved him less than he loved Jesus. At last something had to be said, and Dan could find nothing better to say than : Joseph, there is gloom in thy face; but be not afraid to tell me if thou art disappointed that thou wert not with Jesus when his Father spoke to him out of heaven, and thereby missed being among the apostles. For this suspicion Joseph rebuked his father, but as it was his dearest wish to be numbered amongst the apostles his rebukes were faint, and feeling he was making bad worse, he put as bold a face upon it as he could, saying to his father that he would have liked to have been numbered among the twelve, but since it did not befall he was content; and to himself that he was younger than any that were elected, and if one of them were to die he would be called to fill his place. So much admission was forced upon him, for it was important that his father should accept his absence from the mountain that day as a sufficient reason for his not having been elected an apostle, the real reason being, not his absence from the mountain, but the fact that he chose to turn aside from Jesus and leave him to attend his father's sick-bed. That was the sin he was guilty
150

of, and judged himself reprobate and for ever unworthy to follow
Jesus, whose teaching was that to love God a man must learn to
hate his father, his mother, his wife, his children. A cruel law! his
heart cried. But who am I that dares to question God's law? The
reproof that had come unwittingly into his mind was cast out, but
the thought that preceded the words had been too quick for him;
he had sinned, and foresaw himself estranged from Jesus always, as
many other disciples were by the hardship of the doctrine. It would
have been better to have withheld the miracle, he said to himself,
and then he lost himself thinking how the election of the apostles
had dropped from him, for it had nothing to do with the miracle,
and then awakening a little from his reverie he prayed that God
would withhold Jesus's new teaching from his father. Dan would
never understand Jesus. But if some accident should bring the
knowledge to his father? It wasn't likely that this could happen,
for who knew it? Hardly was it known among those whom he had
met that morning as he crossed the Plain of Gennesaret. He had
seen the disciples with Jesus, Jesus walking ahead with Peter and
with James and John, to whom he addressed not a word, the others
following him shamefacedly at a little distance. One of his black
moods is upon him, Joseph said to himself, and gliding in among
the crowd he questioned the nearest to him, who happened to be
Judas, who told him that Jesus didn't know for certain if he were
called to go to Jerusalem for the Feast of the Tabernacles. The
Master foresees his death in Jerusalem, but he is not sure if it be
ordained for this year or the next. Peter would dissuade him, he
added, and in the midst of his wonderment Joseph heard from
Judas that Jesus had elected his apostles, and now Joseph remembered how, speaking out of his heart, he uttered a little cry and
said: It was because I am a rich man that he had no thought for
me. But Judas answered that there might be another reason, to
which he replied: There can be no other reason except the simple
one — not being there, I was forgotten. Not forgotten, Judas
answered, but reprobate. Jesus never allows a disciple to withdraw
from him; no matter the reason, he may not return. 'Tis the law
of the Essenes. But my father's illness! Wait in patience, Judas
had said, till the Master has fallen out of his mood, for he is in his
blackest now; we dare not speak to him. But it was hard to believe

151

that Jesus would not hear my supplication, Joseph said to himself, and he put the monkey away from him somewhat harshly, and fell to thinking how he ran to Jesus, his story on his lips. But it all seemed to drift away from him the moment he looked upon Jesus, so changed was he from the Jesus he had seen in the cenoby, a young man of somewhat stern countenance and cold and thin, with the neck erect, walking with a measured gait, whose eyes were cold and distant, though they could descend from their starry heights and rest for a moment almost affectionately on the face of a mortal. That was two years ago. And the Jesus whom he met in rags by the lake-side one evening and journeyed with as far as Cæsarea Philippi, to Tyre and Sidon, was no doubt very different from the severe young man he had seen in the monastery. He had grown older, more careworn, but the first Jesus still lingered in the second, whereas the Jesus he was looking at now was a new Jesus, one whom he had never seen before; the cheeks were fallen in and the eyes that he remembered soft and luminous were now concentrated; a sort of malignant hate glowered in them: he seemed to hate all he looked upon; and his features seemed to have enlarged, the nose and chin were more prominent, and the body was shrunken. A sword that is wearing out its scabbard was the thought that passed through Joseph's frightened mind; and frightened at the change in Jesus's appearance, and still more by the words that were hurled out at him, intimidated and trembling, he babbled out: My father lay between life and death for eight days and came out of his swoon slowly. He could say no more, the rest of his story was swallowed up in a violent interruption, Jesus telling him that there was no place among his followers for those who could not free themselves from such ghosts as father, mother and children and wife.

Jesus had flung his father's wealth and his own in his face, and his own pitiful understanding that had not been able to see that this world and the world to come were not one thing but twain. And whosoever chooses this world must remain satisfied with its fleshly indulgences and its cares and its laws and responsibilities, and whosoever chooses the Kingdom of Heaven must cast this world far from him, must pluck it, as it were, out of his heart and throw it away, bidding it depart; for it is but a ghost. All these,

152

he said, pointing to his apostles, have cast their ghosts into the lake.
The apostles stood with eyes fixed, for they did not understand how
they had despoiled themselves of their ghosts, and only Peter
ventured into words: All my family is in the lake, Master; and
at his simplicity Jesus smiled, then as if to compensate him for his
faith he said: I shall come in a chariot sitting on the right hand of
our Father, the Judgment Book upon my lap. As the rocks of this
world are shaken and riven by earthquakes, my words shall sunder
father from son, brother from brother, daughter from mother;
the ties that have been held sacred shall be broken and all the things
looked upon as eternal shall pass away even as the Temple of Jerusalem shall pass away. My words shall sunder it beam by beam,
pillar by pillar, and every stone of it shall be scattered. For I say
unto you that God is weary of the fat of rams and goats, and incense
delights not his nostrils; it is not our flocks and herds that our
Father desires nor the sweet-smelling herbs of this world, but a
temple in which there shall be nothing but the love of God. It is
for the building of this temple that I have been called hither; and
not with hands during laborious years will it be built, but at once,
for the temple that I speak to you of, is in the heart of every man;
and woe, woe, woe, I say unto you who delay to build this temple,
for the fulfilment of the prophecies is at hand, and when the last
day of this world begins to dawn and the dead rise up seeking their
cere-clothes it will be too late. Woe! woe! woe! unto you, Chorazin, Bethsaida and Magdala, for ye have not repented yet, but still
choose the ghosts that haunt the sepulchres out of which ye shall
be called soon; too soon for many; for I say unto you that it is
not the dead that sleep but the living. At these words there were
murmurings among the disciples, and they said, turning from one
to the other: He says we sleep, Brother, but this is not true. He
mocks at us. But Jesus, as if he did not hear these rebukers, and
moved as if by a sudden sympathy for Joseph, said: Here is one
that left me to attend his father's sick-bed, but I would have you
understand me in this, that if we would love God we must abandon
father, mother, wife and children, for there is not room in our hearts
for two loves. Ye say that I lay heavy burdens on your backs, but
I say unto you that I lay no burdens on your backs that I did not
first weigh upon my own shoulders; for have I not denied myself

153

brothers and sisters, and did I not say to my mother, who came to dissuade me: God chose thee as a vehicle to give to man a redeemer to lead him out of this kingdom of clay. Thou hast done it and so there is no further need of thee. Out of this corruptible body I shall rise in Jerusalem, my mission accomplished, into the incorruptible spirit. His passion rising again and into flood, he seemed like one bereft of reason, for he said that all men must drink of his blood if they would live for ever. He who licked up one drop would have everlasting life. Joseph recalled the murmurings that followed these words, but Jesus would not desist. These murmurings seemed to sting him to declare his doctrine to the full, and he added that his flesh, too, was like bread, and that any crumb would give to him who ate it a place before the throne of the Almighty. Whereupon many withdrew, murmuring more loudly than before, saying among themselves: Who is this man that asks us to assuage our thirst with his blood and our hunger with his flesh? Moses and Elijah did not ask such things. Who is he that says he will scatter the Temple to build up another?

Many other animadversions Joseph remembered among the multitude, and he recalled them one by one, pondering over each till one of the monkeys sprang into his arms and snatched some flowers out of his hand and hobbled away shrieking, awaking Dan, who had been dozing, and who, seeing whence the shrieking came, closed his eyes again. While his father slept Joseph remembered that Peter, John and James stood by the Master throughout the dissidence. But what answer will they give, Joseph asked himself, when they are questioned as to what the Master meant when he said that they must drink his blood and eat his flesh? What answer will they make when the people question them in the different countries? — for they are to go to every part of the world, carrying the joyful tidings. It seemed to Joseph that the apostles would be able to make plain these hard sayings even less well than he, and he could not make plain to anybody what the Master had meant, and still less would he be able to convince others that the Master had said well that a man must leave his father though he were dying. He said that he should leave his father unburied, the dead not needing our care, for they are the living ones, and the hyenas and crows would find to eat only that which had always been
154

dead. Of course if the old world were going out and the new coming in, it mattered very little what happened within the next twenty-four hours. But was the new world as near as that? He wondered! It might be nearer still without his being able to leave his father to die among strangers, and a feeling rose up within him that he knew he would never be able to subdue though he were to gain an eternity of happiness by subduing it; and following this thread of thought, it led him into thinking that he was mayhap but a weakling, without great heart for this world or the next; were this so, Jesus was right to discard him, for, as he knew himself, he would be an insufficient apostle, as he was an insufficient son. But his father did not think him a bad son. He raised his eyes, and, finding his father's eyes upon him, he remembered that he had left him because he wished to see the world, to go to Jerusalem, to live with the Essenes, to go to Egypt; and that he had remained away for nearly two years, and had returned to settle a business matter between himself and his father. Therefore it was not love of his father but a business matter that brought him back from Egypt; and now he was going to leave his father again, though he knew that his father wished him to marry some lusty girl, who would bear healthy children. If he were a good son he would take a maid to bed. But that he couldn't do!

I am afraid, he said, speaking seemingly out of long thinking, I am not the son God should have given thee, Father; I am not the son according to thy heart. Thou shouldst not say that, Joseph, for we have loved each other dearly. It is true that I hoped to see little children about me, and it may be that hope will never be fulfilled, which is sad to think on. I've never seen thee over-busy with one of our serving girls, nor caught thee near her bed, and the family will end with thee, and the counting-house will end with me, and these things will happen through no fault of mine or thine, Joseph. Our lives are not planned by ourselves, and when life comes sweetly to a man a bitter death awaits him, for death is bitter to those that have lived in ease and health as I have done. I am still obdurate, for I can sit down to a meal with pleasure, but a time will come when I shall not be able to do this, and then the sentence that the Lord pronounced over all flesh will seem easy to bear, and the grandchildren I have not gotten will be desired no

155

longer; only the peace of the grave, where there is no questioning nor dainties. But, Father, this world is but the shadow of a reality beyond the grave, and I beseech thee to believe in thine eternity and in mine. In the eternity of my body or of my soul — which, Joseph? Thou knowest not, but of this we are sure, that there is little time left for me to love thee in this comfortable land of Galilee. And, this being so, I will ask thee to promise me that thou wilt not leave Judea in my lifetime. Thou'lt have to go to Jerusalem, for business awaits thee there, and to Jericho, perhaps, which is a long way from Galilee, but I'd not have thee leave Judea to preach a strange creed to the Gentiles. I know no reason now, Father, for me to leave Judea, since I am not among the chosen. If thou hadst been, Joseph, thou wouldst not have left me in these last years of my life? Jesus is dear to thee, but he isn't thy father, and every father would like his son to be by him when the Lord chooses to call him. I would have thee within a day's journey or two; death comes quicker than that sometimes, but we must risk something. I'd have thee remain in Judea so that thou mayest come, if thou art called, to receive my last blessing. I'd have thee close my eyes, Joseph. The children I'll forgive thee, if thou wilt promise me this. I promise it, Father, and will hold to my promise if I live beyond thee. If thou livest beyond me, Joseph? Of course thou wilt live many years after me. But, Joseph, I would have thee shun dangerous company. And guessing that his father had Jesus in his mind, Joseph asked him if it were so, and he answered that it was so, saying that Jesus was no new thing in Judea, and that the priests and the prophets had ever been in strife. That is my meaning, he said. The exactions of the priests weigh heavily, and Jesus is right in this much, that priests always have been, and perhaps always will be, oppressors of the poor; they are strong, and have many hirelings about them. Thou hast heard of the Zealots, Son, who walk in the streets of Jerusalem, their hands on their knives, following those who speak against the law and the traditions, and who, when they meet them, put their knives into their ribs, and when the murdered man falls back into their arms call aloud for help? So do the priests free themselves from their opponents, and, my good son, Joseph, think what my grief would be if I were to receive tidings that thou hadst been slain in the streets. Dost think that the news would not slay me as quickly as any knife? I ask little of
156

thee, Joseph, the children I'll forgo, but do thou separate thyself from these sectaries during my lifetime. Think of me receiving the news of thy death; an old man living alone among all his riches without hope of any inheritance of his name. But, Joseph, I can't put away altogether the hope that the day will come when thou'lt look more favourably on a maid than now. Thy thoughts be all for Jesus, his teaching, and his return to this world, sitting by the side of his Father in a fiery chariot, but maybe the day will come when these hopes will fade away and thine eyes will rest upon a maid. It is strange that thou shouldst be so unlike me. I was warmer-blooded at thy age, and when I saw thy mother —— Father, the promise is given to thee already, and my hand upon it. I'll not see Jesus during thy life. If the sudden news of my death were to kill thee, I should be thy murderer. Jesus will forgive thee these few years, Dan said. The expression on Joseph's face changed, and Dan wondered if Jesus were so cruel, so hard, and so self-centred that he would not grant his son a few years, if he were to ask it, so that he might stay by his father's bedside and close his eyes and bury him. It seemed from Joseph's face that Jesus asked every-thing from his disciples, and if they did not give everything it was as if they gave nothing. And while Dan was thus conferring with his own thoughts he heard Joseph saying that if he were to keep the promise he had just given, not to see Jesus again, he must not remain in his neighbourhood. Yes, that is so, Joseph; go to Jeru-salem. And the old man began to babble of the transport of figs from Jericho, till Joseph could not but ponder on the grip of habit on a man's heart, and ask himself if the news of his death would affect his father's health more than the news that there was no further demand in Damascus for his salt fish. He repented the thought as soon as it had passed through his mind, and he under-stood that, however much it would cost him, he must go away to Jerusalem. He dared not risk the accusation that would for ever echo in his heart: My father has no peace by day, nor rest at night, he is thinking always that a Zealot's knife is in my back. But after my father's death —— His thoughts brought him back again to a sudden shame of himself. I am like that, he said, and shall always be as I am. And, not daring to think of himself any more, he jumped to his feet: I must tell my servant that I shall start soon after daybreak.

157

CHAPTER XVI.

AND on his arrival in Jerusalem Joseph stood for a moment before his camel thanking the beast for his great, rocking stride : Which has given me, he said, respite from thinking for two whole days and part of two nights. But I cannot be always on the back of a camel, he continued, and must now rely on my business to help me to forget; and he strove to apply his mind to every count that came before him, but in the middle of every one his thoughts would fly away to Galilee; and the two merchants, one waiting to receive the provisions he had come to fetch, and the other to pay a debt, wondered of what the young man was thinking, and the cause of the melancholy in his face. And they left him still less master of his thoughts when he sat alone, his ledger before him; unable to add up the figures, he abandoned himself without restraint to the grey, formless void of grief, so deep that when his clerk opened the door it took Joseph some moments to remember that he was in his counting-house; and when the clerk spoke of the camel-drivers that were waiting in the yard behind the counting-house for orders, it was only by an effort of will that he collected his thoughts sufficiently to realise that the yard was still there, and that a caravan was waiting for orders to return to Jericho. The orders were forgotten on the way to the yard, and the clerk had to remind him, saying : Master, with thy permission I will settle this business for thee. Joseph was glad of his clerk's help, and he returned to the ledger, and, staring at figures which he did not see, he sat thinking of Jesus, of the night they walked by the lake's edge, of the day spent in the woods above Capernaum, and the various towns of Syria that they visited. It seemed to him that the good days had gone over for ever, and it was but a sad pleasure to remember the pagans that liked Jesus's miracles without being able to aban-
158

don their own gods. Only Peter could bring a smile into his face; a smile wandered round his lips, for it was impossible to think of Peter and not to smile. But the smile faded quickly and the old pain gripped his heart, to abide in it, so he thought, for ever. I have lost Jesus for ever, he said, and at that moment a sudden rap at his door awoke him from his reveries.

He was angry with his clerk, but he tried to disguise his anger, for he was conscious that he must present a very ridiculous appearance, unless, indeed, which was quite likely, his clerk was indifferent to anything but the business of the counting-house. Be this as it may, he was an old and trusted servant who made no comments and asked no questions. Joseph was grateful to him for his assumed ignorance and an hour later bade him good-night. I shall see thee in the morning, to which Samuel answered : Yes, sir; and Joseph was left alone in the crowded street of Jerusalem, staring at the passengers as they went, wondering if they were realities, everyone compelled by a business or a desire, or merely shadows, figments of his imagination and himself no more than a shadow, a something that moved and that must move across the valley of Jehoshaphat and up the Mount of Olives. Why that way more than any other way? he asked himself : because it is the shortest way. As if that mattered, he added, and as soon as he reached the top of the Mount of Olives he looked over the desert and was surprised by the smallness of the hills; like the people who lived among them, they seemed to him to have dwindled. The world is much smaller than I thought, he said. That is it, the world seems to have dwindled into a sort of ash-heap; life has become as tasteless as ashes. It can only end, he said to himself, by my discovering something that interests me, but nothing tempts me but Jesus. Lack of desire, he said, is my burden, for, desiring one thing too much, I have lost desire for all else, and life has begun to seem no more than an ash-heap. My father divides me from Jesus. And he bethought himself of another journey to Egypt, whither he would ride for fifteen days through the desert, the rocking stride of the camel keeping him from thinking and bringing him eager, perchance, to listen to the philosophers again. But the temptations that Egypt presented faded almost as soon as they had arisen, and he deemed that it might be better for him to choose a city oversea. A sea-

159

voyage will cheer me more than a long journey across the desert, and Joppa is but a day's journey from Jerusalem, he thought. But the shipping is more frequent from Cæsarea, and it is not as far; and for a moment it seemed to him that he would like to be on board a ship watching the wind making the sail beautiful. But what port should I be making for? he asked. Why not to Greece? — for there are philosophers as great or greater than those of Alexandria. But philosophers are out of my humour, he added, and, putting Athens aside, he bethought himself of Corinth, and the variegated world he would meet there. From every port ships come to Corinth, bringing different habits, customs, languages, religions; and for the better part of the evening Corinth seemed to be his destination. But Corinth was famous for its courtesans; the most celebrated were there; and he asked himself why God held him alien from them, so alien that it may have been these women that kept him from the journey; and his thoughts turning from vice to marriage a bitterness rose up in his mind against his father for the persistency with which Dan reminded him in and out of season that every man's duty is to bring children into the world.

It had seemed to him that in asking him to take a wife to his discomfort, his father was asking him too much, and he had put the question aside; but he was now without will to resist any memory that might come to him, and for the first time he allowed his thoughts to dwell on his father's implied regret that he had never caught his son near a servant girl's bed. His unwillingness to doubt his father's notions kept him heretofore from pondering on his words, but feeling his life to be now broken and cast away, there seemed to arise some reasons for an examination of his father's words. They could not mean anything else than that a young man was following the natural instincts if he lingered about a young girl's room; and that to be without this instinct was almost a worse misfortune than to be possessed by it to the practical exclusion of other interests. His father, it is true, may have argued the matter out with himself somewhat in this fashion: that love of women in a man may be controlled; and looking back into his own life he may have found this view confirmed. Joseph remembered that his grandmother often spoke to him of Dan's great love of his wife, and it might be that he had never loved another woman;
160

few men, however, were as fortunate as his father, and Joseph could not help thinking that it were better to put women out of his mind altogether than to become inflamed by the sight of every woman. He believed that was why he had always kept all thoughts of women out of his mind; but it seemed to him now that a wife would break the monotony that he saw in front of him, and were he to meet a woman such as his father seems to have met he might take her to live with him. He thought of himself as her husband, though he was by no means sure that married life was a possible makeshift for the life he sought and was obliged to forgo, but as life seemed an obligation from which he could not reasonably escape he thought he would like to share it with some woman who would give him children. His father desired grandchildren, and since he had partly sacrificed his life for his father's sake, he might, it seemed to him, sacrifice himself wholly. But could he? That did not depend altogether on himself, and with the view to discovering the turn of his sex instinct he called to mind all the women he had seen, asking himself as each rose up before him if he could marry her. There were some that seemed nearer to his desire than others, and it was with the view to honourable marriage that he called upon his friends, and his father's friends, and passed his eyes over all their daughters; but the girl whose image had lingered more pleasantly than any other in his memory had married lately, and all the others inspired only a physical aversion which he felt none would succeed in overcoming. He had seen some Greek women, and been attracted in a way, for they were not too like their sex; but these Jewish women — the women of his race — seemed to him as gross in their minds as in their bodies, and it surprised him to find that though many men seemed to think as he did about these women, they were not repelled as he was, but accepted them willingly, even greedily, as instruments of pleasure and afterwards as mothers of children. But I am not as these men are, he said; my father must bear his sorrow like another; and in meditation it seemed to him that it would not be reasonable that his father should get everything he desired and his son nothing. His father had gotten more out of life than ever he should get; he would have his son till he died (so far as he could he would secure him that satisfaction), and after death this world and its shows

161

concern us not. But it may well be that we die out of one life to be born into another life, that everything that passes is replaced by an equivalent, he said, repeating the words of a Greek philosopher to whom he had been much addicted in happy days gone by, and that reality is but an eternal shaping and reshaping of things. All that is beyond doubt, he continued, is that things pass too quickly for us to have any certain knowledge of them, our only standard being our own flitting impressions; and as all men bring a different sensitiveness into the world, knowledge is a word without meaning, for there can be no knowledge. Every race is possessed of a different sensitiveness, he said, as he passed up the Mount of Olives on his way home. We ask for miracles, but the Greeks are satisfied with reason. Am I Greek or Jew? he asked, for he was looking forward to some silent hours with a book of Greek philosophy and hoped to forget himself in the manuscript. But he could not always keep his thoughts on the manuscript, and, forgetful of Heraclitus, he often sat thinking of Jesus's promise — that one morning men would awake to find that God had come to judge the world and divide it among those that repented their sins. He remembered he had forfeited his share in the Kingdom for his father's sake, or had he been driven out of the community for that his belief in the coming of the Kingdom was not enough? It is true that his belief had wavered, but he had always believed. Even his natural humility, of which he was conscious, did not allow him to doubt that his belief in Jesus was as fervid as that of Peter, James, John and the residue. The conviction was always quick in him that he felt more deeply than these publicans and fishers, yet Jesus retained them and sent him away.

The manuscript glided from his hand to the floor, and his thoughts wandered back to Alexandria, and he sat thinking that death must be rather the beginning than the end of things, for it were impossible to believe that life was an end in itself. Heraclitus was right : his present life could be nothing else but the death of another life. And as if to enforce this doctrine a recollection of his grandmother intruded upon his meditation. She was seventy-eight when she died, and her intellect must have faded some months before, but with her passing one of the servants told him that a curious expression came into her face — a sort of mocking expres-

162

sion, as if she had learnt the truth at last and was laughing at the dupes she left behind. She lay in a grave in Galilee, under some pleasant trees, and while thinking of her grave it occurred to him that he would not like to be put into the earth; his fancy favoured a tomb cut out of the rocks in Mount Scropas, for there, he said to himself, I shall be far from the Scribes and Pharisees, and going out on the terrace he stood under the cedars and watched for an hour the outlines of the humped hills that God had driven in endless disorder, like herds of cattle, all the way to Jericho, thinking all the while that it would be pleasant to lie out of hearing of all the silly hurly-burly that we call life. But the hurly-burly would not be silly if Jesus were by him, and he asked himself if Jesus was an illusion like all the rest, and as soon as the pain the question provoked had died away, his desire of a tomb took possession of him again, and it left him no peace, but led him out of the house every evening, up a zigzagging path along the hillside till he came to some rocks over against the desert. I shall lie in quiet here till he calls me, on a couch embedded in the wall and surmounted by an arch — but if he should prefer me to rise out of an humble grave? That I may not know, only that the poorest is not as unhappy as I, so I may as well have a tomb to my liking. It was a long time since he had come to a resolve, and having come to one at last, he was happier. And in more cheerful mood he decided that now that the site was settled it would be well to seek information as to which were the best craftsmen to employ on the building of his tomb.

But for him whose thoughts run on death nothing is harder to settle than where his bones shall lie; and next time he visited the hillside Joseph came upon rocks facing eastward, and it seemed to him that the rays of the rising sun should fall on his sepulchre; but a few days later, coming out of his house in great disquiet, it seemed to him he would lie happy if his tomb were visited every evening by the peaceful rays of the setting sun, and he asked himself how many years of life he would have to drag through before God released him from his prison. If he wished to die he could, for our lives are in our own hands. But he did not know that he cared to die and, overpowered with grief, he abandoned himself to metaphysical speculation, asking himself again if it were not true that to be born into this world meant to pass out of one life into another;

163

therefore, if so, to die in this world only meant to pass into another, a life unknown to us, for all is unknown — nothing being fixed or permanent. We cannot bathe twice in the same river, so Heraclitus said, but we cannot bathe even once in the same river, he added; and to carry the master's thought a stage farther was a pleasure, if any moment of his present life could be called pleasurable. He heard these sayings first in Alexandria, and, looking towards Jerusalem, he tried to recall the exact words of the sage regarding the futility of sacrifice. Our priests try, said Heraclitus, to purify themselves with blood and we admire them, but if a filthy man were to roll himself in the mud in the hope of cleaning himself we should think he was mad. In some such wise Heraclitus spoke, but it seemed to Joseph he had lost something of the spirit of the saying in too profuse wording of it. As he sought for the original epitome he heard his name called, and awaking from his recollections of Alexandria he looked up and saw before him a young man whom he remembered having seen at the Sanhedrin. Nicodemus was his name; and he remembered how the fellow had kept his eyes on him for one whole evening, trying at various times to engage him in talk; an insistent fellow who, despite rebuffs, had followed him into the street after the meeting, and, refusing to be shaken off, had led the way so skilfully that Joseph found himself at last on Nicodemus's doorstep and with no option but to accept Nicodemus's invitation to enter. He did not like the fellow, but not on account of his insistence; it was not his insistence that had prejudiced him against him as much as the young man's elaboration of raiment, his hairdressing above all; he wore curls on either side that must have taken his barber a long while to prepare, and he exhaled scents. He wore bracelets, and from his appearance Joseph had not been able to refrain from imagining lascivious pictures on the walls of his house and statues in the corners of the rooms — in a word, he thought he had been persuaded to enter an ultra-Greek house. In this he was, however, mistaken, and in the hour they spent together his host's thoughts were much less occupied than Joseph expected them to be with the jewels on his neck and his wrists, and the rich tassels on his sash. He talked of many things, but his real thoughts were upon arms; and he showed Joseph scimitars and daggers. Despite a long discussion on the steel of Damascus, Joseph could not bring himself to believe that Nicodemus's interests in heroic warfare were more than intellectual caprice: and he regarded as entirely superficial Nicodemus's attacks on the present-day Jews, whose sloth and indolence he reproved, saying that they had left the heroic spirit brought out of Arabia with their language, on the banks of the Euphrates. One hero, he admitted, they had produced in modern times (Judas Maccabeus), and Joseph heard for the first time that this great man always had addressed his soldiers in Hebrew. All the same he did not believe that Nicodemus was serious in his passionate demands for the Hebrew language, which had not been spoken since the Jews emerged from the pastoral stage. We should do well, Nicodemus said, to engage others to look to our flocks and herds, so that we may have leisure to ponder the texts of the Talmud, nor do I hesitate to condemn my own class, the Sadducees, as the least worthy of all; for we look upon the Temple as a means of wealth, despising the poor people, who pay their half-shekel and bring their rams and their goats and bullocks hither.

He could talk for a long time in this way, his eyes abstracted from Joseph, fixed on the darkness of the room. And whilst listening to him Joseph had often asked himself if there were a real inspiration behind that lean face, carven like a marble, with prominent nose and fading chin, or if he were a mere buffoon dressed for the part. He had succeeded in provoking a casual curiosity in Joseph, but he had not infected Joseph with any desire of his acquaintance; his visits to the counting-house had not been returned. Yet this meeting on the hillside was not altogether unwelcome, and Joseph, to his surprise, surveyed the young man's ringlets and bracelets with consideration; he admired his many weapons, and listened to him with interest. He talked well, telling that the sword that hung from his thigh was from Damascus and recommending a merchant to Joseph who could be trusted to discover as fine a one for him. It was not wise to go about this lonely hillside unarmed, and Joseph was moved to ask him to draw the sword from its scabbard, which Nicodemus was only too glad to do, calling Joseph's attention to the beautiful engraving on the blade, and to the hilt studded with jewels. He drew a dagger from his jacket, a hardly less costly weapon, and Joseph was too abashed to speak of

165

his buckler on his left arm and the spear that he held in his right hand. But, nothing loth, Nicodemus bubbled into explanation, saying that it was part of his project to remind his fellow-countrymen that they too must arm themselves if they ever wished to throw off the Roman yoke. So long as the Romans substitute a Hebrew word or letter for the head of Tiberius on the coin we pay the tribute willingly, he said, as they followed the crooked path through the rocks up the hillside towards Joseph's house. And in reply to Joseph, who asked him if he believed in the coming end of the world, he answered that he did, but he interpreted the coming end of the world to mean the freeing of the people of Israel from the Roman yoke, astonishing Joseph by the vigour of his reply; for Joseph was not yet sure which was the truer part of this young man, the ringlets and the bracelets or the shield and the spear. He was partial to long silences; and the next of these was so long that Joseph had begun to wonder, but when they reached the crest of the hill he burst into speech unexpectedly, plying Joseph with questions, asking what was happening in Galilee, avouching much interest in Jesus, whom he had heard of, but never seen. Joseph, guessing that it was to obtain news of Jesus that Nicodemus sought him on the hillside, told him that he had not spoken of Jesus for many weeks, and found a sudden relief in relating all he knew about him: how Jesus said that father, mother, brother and sister must be abandoned. Yes, he had said, we must look upon all sacrifice as naught if we would obtain our ancient kingdom and language. But the Essenes have never spoken like that, Nicodemus urged: he is not an Essene, nor Moses, nor Elijah, nor Jeremiah. He is none of these: he is Judas Maccabeus come to life again; and henceforth I shall look upon myself as his disciple.

He spoke so loudly that any passer-by might have caught up his words; and there was danger from Joseph's servants, for they were now standing by his gate. He looked round uneasily, and as Nicodemus showed no signs of taking leave of him, he thought it would be more prudent to ask him into the house, warning him, however, that he had no beautiful things to show him in the way of engraved weapons, swords from Damascus or daggers from Circassia. It was not, however, to see beautiful weapons that Nicodemus inclined; only so far as they related to Jesus was he interested in arms; and

166

he besought Joseph to tell him more of Jesus, whom he seemed to
have already accepted as the leader of a revolt against the Romans.
But Joseph, who had begun to fear the young man, protested that
Jesus's Kingdom was not of this earth, thinking thereby to discredit
Jesus in Nicodemus's eyes. Nicodemus was not to be put off so
easily: The Jews spoke of the Kingdom of Heaven so that they
might gain the kingdom of earth. A method not very remarkable
for its success, Joseph interposed. The Romans do otherwise, never
thinking about the Kingdom of Heaven, but only of riches and
vainglory, whereas Jesus, he said, says it is as hard for the rich man
to enter the Kingdom of Heaven as it would be for a sword to pass
through the eye of a needle. A sword through the eye of a needle,
Nicodemus repeated, walking up and down the floor, stamping his
lance as he went. He is the leader we have been waiting for. But it
is not always thus that he speaks, Joseph interposed, I have heard
him say myself: It is as hard for a rich man to enter heaven as it
would be for a cow to calve in a rook's nest. As he went to and fro
Nicodemus muttered: There is much to be said for this revision of
his words. Jesus wishes to reach the imagination of the poor that
know not swords. And he spoke for a long time of the indolence
of the rich, of their gross pleasures and sensual indulgences. But
we must give them swords, he added under his breath, as if he were
speaking for himself alone and did not wish Joseph to hear, and
then, awaking from his reverie, he turned to his host: Tell me more
of this remarkable man. And Joseph, who was now a little amused
at his guest's extravagances, asked him if he knew the answer he
had given to Antipas, who had invited him to his court in Tiberias
in consequence of the renown of his miracles. Wishing to witness
some exhibition of his skill, Antipas seated himself in imperial
fashion on his highest throne, and, drawing his finest embroideries
about him, asked Jesus if he had seen anybody attired so beautifully before, to which Jesus, who stood between two soldiers, a
beggar in rags, before the king, replied: I have indeed; pheasants
and peacocks, for nature apparelled them. Neither Moses nor
Elijah nor Jeremiah, Nicodemus declared, could have invented a
reply more apt. He asked Joseph if any further doubt lingered in
his mind that Jesus was the prophet promised to the Jews. How
I envy thy intercourse with him, he cried. How I envy thee, for

167

thou art the friend of him that will overthrow the Romans. Jesus is then the Jew elected? Nicodemus answered: Surely; and as soon as his guest had left his house Joseph was brought to a presentiment of the danger he incurred in being seen in the company of Nicodemus; a young man who walked about extravagantly armed would, sooner or later, find himself haled before Pilate. Joseph felt that it would be better to refuse to see him if he called at the counting-house: an excuse could be found easily: his foreman might say: Master is away in Jericho. But when Nicodemus called a few weeks afterwards Joseph was constrained to tell his foreman to tell Nicodemus that he would see him. The truth was, Joseph was glad of an interruption, for his business was boring him more than it did usually, but he liked to pretend to himself that he could not escape from Nicodemus.

A new opinion of Nicodemus began to shape itself in his mind when the young man said: Many and many a year will have to pass before Rome can be overthrown; the Roman rule is so light that the people feel it not. It saves us from quarrels among ourselves, and who have quarrelled as bitterly as we have done? Joseph's heart softened at this appreciation of the Jewish people, and they began to talk in sympathy for the first time, and it was a pleasure to find themselves in this agreement, that before the Jews could conquer the Romans they would have to conquer themselves. He is more cautious than I thought for, Joseph muttered as he returned to his camel-drivers, for his guest had departed suddenly without giving any reason for his visitation. A spy he cannot be, Joseph said to himself. I stand too well with Pilate to be suspected of schemes of mutiny. But he will soon come under the notice of Pilate; and Joseph was not surprised when Pilate asked him if he knew an extravagantly dressed young man, Nicodemus by name. Joseph replied that he did, giving Pilate to understand that Nicodemus was no more than one of the many eccentrics to be found in every city, with a taste for the beauty of engraved swords, and little for the use of these weapons; and Pilate, who seemed to be of the same opinion himself, suddenly asked him if he had ever met in Galilee one named Jesus. Jesus from Nazareth, Pilate said; and Joseph watched the tall, handsome, pompous Roman, one of those intelligently stupid men of which there are so many about. He
168

arrived, Pilate continued, in Jerusalem yesterday with a number of Galileans, all talking of the resurrection, and news has just reached me that he had been preaching in the Temple, creating some disturbance, which will, I hope, not be repeated, for disturbances in the Temple lead to disturbances in the streets. But thou must have news from thy father of this prophet? As Joseph was about to answer one of Pilate's apparitors entered suddenly with papers that demanded the procurator's attention. We will talk over this on another occasion, Pilate said as he bent over the papers, and Joseph went out muttering: So he has come to Jerusalem at last! We shall meet in the street and speak, alas, if I have not strength to lower my eyes and pass him by. I must refrain from Jerusalem and transact my business from my house by means of messengers. But if Pilate sends for me? If that should chance I must go to Jerusalem. His thoughts melted away into remembrances of the lake, and the days went by in alternate remembrances and fears, till one evening his door was flung open and he started to his feet, believing the intruder to be Jesus.

Nicodemus, Sir, is waiting in the hall and would see thee. I told him thou wast deep in business, but he answered that the matter on which he had come was more important than business. And Joseph, who was glad that Nicodemus had come, for he was weary of his loneliness, said: I will see him. He threw some more olive roots on the fire and told the servant to bring in a lamp. This grey dusk is disheartening, he said to his visitor. The weather is cold, so draw thy chair near to the fire. I am glad to see thee. We shall be more comfortable when the curtains are drawn. The lamp, I see, is beginning to burn up. . . . Nicodemus sat grave and hieratic, thin and tall, in the high chair, and the gloom on his face was so immovable that Joseph wasted no words. What has fallen out? he said, and Nicodemus asked him if he knew Phinehas, the great money-changer in the Temple. Joseph nodded, and, holding his hands before the fire, Nicodemus told his story very slowly, exasperating Joseph by his slowness; but he did not dare to bid him to hasten, and, holding himself in patience, he listened to him while he told that Phinehas was perhaps the worst of the extorters, the most noisy and arrogant, a vicious and quarrelsome man, who, yester morning, was engaged with a rich Alexandrian Jew, Sham-

169

huth, who had lately arrived from Alexandria and was buying oxen, rams and yoes in great numbers for sacrifice. We wondered at his munificence, Nicodemus said, not being able to explain it to ourselves, for the Feast of the Tabernacles is over; and our curiosity was still more roused when it became known that he was distributing largess. The man's appearance aroused suspicion, for it is indeed a fearful one. From his single eye to his chin a fearful avariciousness fills his face, and the empty, withered socket speaks of a close, sordid, secret passion, and so clearly that Jesus said : That man has not come to glorify God nor to repent of his sins. He is guilty of a great crime, and he would have it forgiven him. But the crime? Of what crime is he guilty? we asked. Jesus did not answer us, for at that moment some young man had come to listen to him, and the man's crime appeared to him as of little importance compared to his own teaching. Has he come, we asked, to pray that his sight may be restored to him? Jesus motioned to us that that was so; and he also bade us be silent, for stories of miracles have a great hold upon the human mind, and Jesus wished to teach some young men who had come to ask him how they were to live during these last days. But myself, consumed with desire to hear the man's story, mingled with the herdsmen who had brought in the cattle, and inquired how Shamhuth had lost his eye. None could tell me, and I failed to get tidings of him till I came upon an Alexandrian Jew with a strange story about him. Shamhuth's money came from his friend's wife, whom he married after causing him to be killed by hirelings; and when his senses tired of her he persuaded her daughter to come over to him in the night. Shamhuth always walked praying aloud, his eyes cast down lest they should fall upon a woman, and his wife did not suspect him. But one night she was bidden in a dream to seek her husband, and rising from her bed she descended and opened the door very softly, not wishing to disturb him in his sleep. The sight that met her eyes kindled such a great flame of hate in her that she returned to her room for a needle, and placing her hand upon her daughter's mouth she quickly pricked out both her eyes, and then, approaching her husband, she pricked out his right eye, and was about to prick out the other, but he slid from her hands and escaped, blind of an eye, to Jerusalem, bringing with him great sums of money in
170

the hope that he may purchase a miracle, which is a great blasphemy in itself, and shows what the man really is in his heart. And the story I tell to thee, Joseph, is the story as it was told to us by the Alexandrian Jew; and as soon as these abominations became known in the Temple a riot began, and somebody cried: The adulterer must be put away. Whereupon Phinehas, seeing the large profits he had expected vanishing, turned to Jesus and said: It is thou who hast brought this disaster upon me, lying Galilean, who callest thyself the son of David, when all know thee to be the son of Joseph the Carpenter. Son of David! Son of David! How can that be? the people began to ask each other, and in the midst of their questioning a great hilarity broke over them. In great wrath Jesus overturned Phinehas's table, and Phinehas would have overthrown Jesus had not Peter, who had armed himself with a sword, raised it. The people became like mad: tables were broken for staves, some rushed away to escape with a whole skin, and the frightened cattle dashed among them, a black bull goring many. And in all the mob Jesus was the fiercest fighter, lashing the people in the face with the thongs of the whip he had taken from a herdsman, and felling others with the handle. The cages of the doves were broken, the birds took flight, and the priests, at their wits' end, called for the guards to come down from the porticoes, and it was not till much blood had been spilt that order was restored.

Joseph asked how Phinehas came out of all this trouble, and heard that he had escaped without injury. Merely losing a few shekels, not more, though he deserved to lose his life, for he placed his money above the Temple, not caring whether it was polluted by the presence of an adulterer, only thinking of the great profit he could make out of the man's sins, differing in no wise in this from the priests and sacristans. Jesus should never have gone to the Temple nor come to Jerusalem, Joseph said. But in this Nicodemus could not agree with him, for if Jesus were the Messiah his mission was nothing less than to free Jerusalem from the Roman yoke. But he should have brought a larger body of disciples with him — some thousands, instead of a few hundreds — not enough to bring about the abolition of the Temple, which, according to Nicodemus, was the Galilean's project — one more difficult to accomplish than he thinks for. The Romans support the Temple,

171

he cried, because the Temple divides us. I say it myself, Sadducee though I am. It was these last words that proved to Joseph that the ringlets and bracelets did not comprise the whole of this young man's soul, and he was moved forthwith to confide the story of his father's sickness to him, dwelling on all its consequences : he had not been elected an apostle, and Jesus consequently had no one by to tell him that he must not speak of the abolition of the law in Jerusalem. But if he did not come to incite the people against the Temple, for what did he come? Nicodemus asked. Thou hast heard him preach in Galilee, tell me who he is, and in what does his teaching consist? — a direct question that prompted Joseph to relate his associations with the Essenes, Banu, John, the search for Jesus in Egypt and among the Judean hills —— A long story I'm afraid it is, Joseph mentioned apologetically to Nicodemus, who begged him to omit no detail of it. Nicodemus sat with his eyes fixed on Joseph while Joseph told of the discovery of Jesus in Galilee among his father's fishermen ; and as if to excuse the almost immodest curiosity awakened in Nicodemus, Joseph murmured that the story owed nothing to his telling of it ; he was telling it as plainly as it could be told for a purpose ; Nicodemus must judge it fairly. Resuming his narrative, Joseph related the day spent in the forest and Jesus's interpretation of the prophecies. Nicodemus cried : He is the stone cut by no hand out of the mountain ; the idol shall fall, and the stone that felled it shall grow as big as a mountain and fill the whole earth.

CHAPTER XVII.

AS they sat talking the servant brought in a letter which, he said, had just arrived from Galilee. The messenger rode the whole journey in two days, Sir, and thou'lt have to do the same, Sir, and to start at once if thou wouldst see thy father alive. If I would see my father alive! If I would see my father alive! Joseph repeated, and, seizing Nicodemus by the hand, he bade him farewell. Let an escort be called together at once, he cried, and an hour later he was on the back of a speedy dromedary riding through the night, his mind whirling with questions which he did not put to the messenger, knowing he could not answer any of them. And they rode on through that night and next day, stopping but once to rest themselves and their animals — six hours' rest was all he allowed himself or them. Six hours' rest for them, for him not an hour, so full was his mind with questions. He rode on, drinking a little, but eating nothing, thinking how his father's life might be saved, of that and nothing else. Were they feeding him with milk every ten minutes? — he could not trust nurses, nobody but himself. Were they shouting in his ear, keeping him awake, as it were, stimulating his consciousness at wane? Once, and only once, while attending on his father did Joseph remember that if his father died he would be free to follow Jesus : a shameful thought that he shook out of his mind quickly, praying the while upon his knees by the bedside that he might not desire his father's death. As the thought did not come again, he assumed that his prayer was granted, and when he returned to Jerusalem a month later (the new year springing up all about him), immersed in a sort of sad happiness, thanking God, who had restored his father to health (Joseph had left Dan looking as if he would live to a hundred), a strange new thought came into his mind and took possession of it : the promise given

173

his father bound him only during his father's lifetime; at his father's death he would be free to follow Jesus; but the dead hold us more tightly than the living, and he feared that his life would be always in his father's keeping.

He was about his father's business in the counting-house; his father seemed to direct every transaction, and, ashamed of his weakness, he refrained from giving an order till he heard, or thought he heard, his father's voice, speaking through him, and when he returned to his dwelling-house, over against the desert, it often seemed to him that if he were to raise his eyes from the ashes in which some olive roots were burning he would see his father, and as plain as if he were before his eyes in the flesh. But my father isn't dead, so what is the meaning of this dreaming? he cried one evening; and, starting out of his chair, he stood listening to the gusts whirling through the hills with so melancholy a sound that Joseph could not dismiss the thought that the moment was fateful, his father was dying . . . something was befalling, or it might be that Jesus was at the door asking for him. The door opened, and he uttered a cry: What is it? Nicodemus, the servant answered, has come to see thee, Sir. And he waited for his order to bid the visitor to enter or depart. Nicodemus! Joseph repeated, and he stared at the servant, trying to escape from his thoughts and failing to do so, till the servant reminded him that Nicodemus was waiting in the hall; and then, as if yielding to superior force, Joseph answered he was willing to receive the visitor, regretting his decision almost at once, while the servant descended the stairs, and vehemently on seeing Nicodemus, who entered, the lamplight falling upon him, more brilliantly apparelled than Joseph had ever seen him. A crimson mantle hung from his shoulders and a white hand issuing from a purfled sleeve grasped a lance; weapons, jewelled and engraved, appeared among the folds of his raiment, and he strode about the room in silence, as if he thought it necessary to give Joseph a few moments in which to consider his war gear (intended as an elaborate piece of symbolism). In response to the riddle presented, Joseph began to wonder if Nicodemus regarded himself rather as a riddle than as a reality — a riddle that might be propounded again and again, or if he could not do else than devise gauds and trappings to conceal his inner emptiness, a dust-
174

heap of which he himself was grown weary. A great deal of dust-heap there certainly is, Joseph said to himself as his eyes followed the strange figure prowling along and across the room, breaking occasionally into speech. But he could not help thinking that beneath the dustheap there was something of worth, for when Nicodemus spoke, he spoke well, and to speak well means to think well, and to think well, Joseph was prone to conclude, means to act well, if not always, at least sometimes. But could an apt phrase condone the accoutrements? He had added a helmet to the rest of his war gear, and the glint of the lamplight on the brass provoked Joseph to beg of him to unarm and relate his story —— That burdens thee more than thine armour, he said. At these words Nicodemus was raised from the buffoon to a man of sense and shrewdness. I have come here, he said, to speak to thee about Jesus. But the story is a somewhat perilous one, and as it rains no longer I will walk with thee along the hillside and tell it to thee.

He raised his hand to Joseph, forbidding him to speak, and it was not till they reached a lonely track that Nicodemus stopped suddenly. His death has been resolved upon, he said, and the two men stood for a moment looking into each other's eyes without speaking. It was Nicodemus who fell to walking again and the telling of his tale. He had come straight from the Sanhedrin, where he defended Jesus against his enemies and accusers at some personal risk, as he was quickly brought to see by Raguel's retort: And art thou too a Galilean? And walking with his eyes on the ground, as if communing with himself, Nicodemus related that there was now but one opinion in the Sanhedrin: Jesus and Judaism were incompatible; one or the other must go. Better that one man should perish than that a nation should be destroyed, he said, are the words one hears. Stopping again, he said, looking Joseph in the face: It is believed that he hath given sufficient warrant for his death, for he said not many days ago he could destroy the Temple and build it again in three days, which can be interpreted as speech against the law. Joseph asked that a meaning should be put on the words, and Nicodemus answered that Jesus spoke figuratively. To his mind the Temple stood for no more than observances from which all spiritual significance had faded long ago, and Jesus meant that he could and would replace dead formulæ by a religion of

175

heart: the true religion which has no need of priests or sacrifices. We must persuade him to leave Jerusalem and return to Galilee, Joseph cried, his voice trembling. By no means! By no means! Nicodemus exclaimed, raising his voice and stamping his lance. He has been called to the work and must drive the plough to the headland, though death be waiting him there. But he can be saved, I think, Nicodemus continued, his voice assuming a thoughtful tone, for though he has spoken against the law the Jews may not put him to death: his death can be obtained only by application to Pilate. Will Pilate grant it to please the Jews? Joseph asked. The Romans are averse, Nicodemus answered, from religious executions and will not away with putting a man to death for saying he can destroy the Temple and build it again in three days. The story turned into tediousness, Nicodemus repeating again and again that it was the second part of the sentence that would save Jesus, for it was obvious that though a man might destroy the Temple in three days (a great fire would achieve the destruction in a few hours), he could not build it again in three days. This second part of the sentence proved beyond doubt that Jesus was speaking figuratively, and the Romans would refuse to put a man to death because he was a poet and spoke in symbols and allegories. The Romans were hard, but they were just; and he spoke on Roman justice till they came round the hills shouldering over against Bethany, and found themselves in the midst of a small group of men taking shelter from the wind behind a large rock.

Why, Master, it is thou! And Joseph recognising Peter's voice, and afterwards the voices of James and John, who were with him, called to Matthew and Aristion, who were at some little distance, sitting under another rock, and the five apostles crowded round Joseph, bidding him welcome, Peter, James and John demonstratively, and Aristion and Matthew, who knew Joseph but little, giving him a more timid but hardly less friendly welcome. We did not know why thou hadst left us, they said. But it is pleasant to find thee in Jerusalem, for we are lonely here, Matthew said, and the Hierosólymites mock at us for not speaking as they do. But thou'rt with us here, young Master, as thou wert in Galilee? John asked. We knew not why thou didst leave us. But we did, John,

176

Peter interposed, we knew well that Jesus said to him, when he returned from his father's sick-bed, that those who would follow him must leave father and mother, brother and sister, wives and children to live and die by themselves, which is as we have done. Yes, Sir, Peter continued, freeing himself from John and turning to Joseph, we've left this world behind us, or if not this world itself, the things of this world: our boats and nets, our wives and our children. All that Jesus calls our ghostly life we have thrown into the lake. My wife and children and mother-in-law are all there, and John and James have left their mother, Salome. But, said James, the neighbours will not be lacking to give her a bite if she wants something when she is hungry. She'll be getting men to fish for her, for we've left her our boats and nets. They've done this, Peter chimed in, and my wife and children will have to be fishing for themselves; but we hope they'll manage to get somehow a bite and a sup of something till the Kingdom comes, which we hope will not be delayed much longer, for we like not Jerusalem, and being mocked at in the Temple. But sayest thou, Master, that we've done wrong in leaving our wives and children to fish for ourselves? It seemed hard at first, and thou wast weak, Master, and stayed with thy father; but after all he has money and could pay for attendance, whereas our wives and little ones have none; ourselves will be in straits to get our living if the Kingdom be delayed in its coming, for what good are fishermen except along the sea-coast or where there is a lake or a river, and here there isn't enough water for a minnow to swim in. Our wives and our children are better off than we are, for they'll be getting someone to fish for them, and will stand at the doors at Capernaum waiting for the boats to return, praying that the nets weren't let down in vain; but we aren't as sure of the Kingdom as we were of a great take of fishes in Galilee when the wind was favourable to fishing. Not that we'd have thee think our faith be failing us; we be as firm as ever we were, as John and James will be telling thee. And Peter, breaking in again, reminded Joseph that if they lacked faith the promised Kingdom would not come. It was Jesus's faith that upheld us, John said, pushing Peter aside, and the promises he made us that we might hear the trumpets of the cherubims and seraphims announcing the Kingdom at any moment of the day or night. And making himself

177

the spokesman of the five, John told Joseph and Nicodemus that Jesus now looked upon the arrival of the Kingdom as a very secondary matter, and his own death as one of much greater import. He says that he'll have to give his blood to the earth and his flesh to the birds of the air else none will believe his teaching. He says that God demands a victim, and looks upon him as the victim; but if that be so, the world will get his teaching and we shall get nothing, for we know his teaching of old. As Peter has told you, James interrupted, there is no water here, not a spring nor a rivulet in which a fish could live; we be poor fishermen stranded in a desert without knowledge of anything but of boats and nets, and if he give himself as a victim we shall perish here. How get back to Galilee? for he seems to have forgotten us, and everything else but his Father and his Father's will, and we cannot make him understand when we try that we shall want money, that money will be wanting to get us back to Galilee, nor does he hear us when we say: Our nets and our boats may have passed into other hands. We know not what is come over him; he's a changed man; a lamb as long as you're agreeing with him, but at a word of contradiction he's all claws and teeth. The walk is a long one, Matthew interjected, and the taxes will be collected by the time we get back if the Kingdom don't come, and sore of foot I'll be sitting in a desolate house without wife or children or fire in the hearth. But we have faith, they all cried out together, and having followed Jesus so far we'll follow him to the end. But we are glad, Sirs, James said, that you've come, for you'll see Jesus and tell him that we would like to have a word from him as to when we may expect the Kingdom; and a word, too, as to what it will be like; whether there'll be rivers and lakes well stocked with fish in it, and whether our chairs shall be set; Peter on the Master's right hand to be sure, we are all agreed as to that. But thou rememberest, Master, our mother, Salome, how she took Jesus aside and said that myself and John were to be on his left with Andrew one below us? Peter began to raise his voice, and, straightening his shoulders, he declared that his brother Andrew must sit on Jesus's left. Thou rememberest, Master? I remember, Joseph interrupted, that the Master answered you all saying that every chair had been made and caned and cushioned before the world was. Thou canst not have

178

forgotten, Peter, this saying: that everyone would find a chair according to his measure? Yes, Master, he did say something like that. I'm far from saying we'd all sit equally easy in the same chairs, and if the chairs were before the world was, all I can say is that there seems to have been a lack of foresight, for how could God himself know what our backsides would be like years upon years before they came into being?

About that we will speak later; but now point out to us the house of Simon the Leper where Jesus lodges, Joseph said. Ye see yon house, James replied, and they went forward together, meeting on the way thither several apostles and many disciples; and these accompanied Joseph and Nicodemus to the door, telling them the while that Jesus had driven them out of the house. It is a main struggle that is going by in him, Philip said, and so we left him, being afraid of his looks. Isn't that so, Bartholomew? And they all acquiesced, and Bartholomew nodded, saying: Yes, we were afraid of his looks. It was then that Simon the Leper opened the door, and Joseph, remembering his promise to his father, laid his hand on Nicodemus's shoulder: I may not enter, he said. I have come thus far but may not go into the house; but do thou go in and tell him, Nicodemus, that in spirit I am with him. On these words Nicodemus passed into the house, leaving Joseph in the centre of a small crowd of apostles, disciples and sympathisers in several degrees, all eager to talk to him and to hear him say that they had but to follow Jesus to Jerusalem and the Scribes and Pharisees would give way before them at once. Thou that art of the Sanhedrin should know if we are strong enough to cast them out of the Temple. But, my good men, I know nothing of your plot to clear the Temple of its thieves, Joseph answered, and there'll always be thieves in this world, wherever you go. But the Day of Judgment is approaching. When may we expect his second coming? somebody shouted from out of a group of men standing a little way back from the others, and the cry was taken up. He is coming with his Father in a chariot, one said. With our Father, somebody interrupted, and an eddying current of theology spread through the crowd. I've come from Galilee, from my father's sick-bed, and know nothing of your numbers, and have not seen him these many months, Joseph said. He is the true Messiah, and we believe in

him, was an unexpected utterance; but Joseph was not given time to ponder on it, for a woman, thrusting her way up to him, cried out in his face: He can destroy the Temple and build it again in three days. And when Joseph asked her who had said that, she told him that Jesus had said it. He turned to Peter, John and James to ask them the meaning of these words. What did Jesus mean when he said he could destroy the Temple and build it again in three days? He means, said half-a-dozen voices, that the priests and the Scribes are to be cast out, and a new Temple set up, for the pure worship of the true God, who desires not the fat of rams. Joseph understood that the rams destined for sacrifice were to be given to the poor. And then another voice broke loose, asking Joseph why he would not join with Nicodemus to beg Jesus to delay no longer but lead the people straightway to Jerusalem, and Joseph perforce had to answer that Nicodemus wished to talk privily to Jesus, at which they pressed round him, and from every side the question was put to him: Is he going to lead us into Jerusalem? And then Joseph began to understand that these people would find themselves on the morrow, or perhaps the next day, fighting with the Roman legions, and, knowing how the fight would end, he answered them that the Romans would be on the side of the priests and Scribes. Whereupon they tore their garments and cast dust on their heads, and in his attempt to pacify them he asked if it would not be better for Jesus to go up to Galilee and wait till the priests were less prepared to resist him. No, no, to Jerusalem, to Jerusalem, they cried on every side, and voices were again raised, and the Galileans admitted that they had come down from Galilee for this revolution, and had been insulted in the Temple by the Scribes, and laughed at, and called foolish Galileans; but they would show the Scribes what the Galileans could do. Was it true that Jesus was the Messiah promised to the Jewish people by the prophet Daniel? — and while Joseph was seeking an answer to this question a woman cried: Thou'rt not worthy of a Messiah, for knowest thou not that he is the one promised to us in Holy Writ? And do not his miracles prove that he is the Messiah we have been waiting for? None but the true Messiah could have rid my son of the demon that infested him for two years; and with these words gaining the attention of the crowd she related how the
180

ghost of a man long dead had come into her boy when he was but fourteen, bringing him to the verge of death in two years — a pale, exhausted creature, having no will of his own nor strength for anything. But how knowest thou, asked Joseph, that the demon was the ghost of a man that had lived long ago? Because in life he had dearly loved his wife, but had found her to be unfaithful to him and had died of grief twenty years ago, and was captured then by the beauty of my boy; and his grief entered into the boy and abode in him, and would have destroyed him utterly if Jesus had not imposed his hands upon him and put the demon to flight. Whither I know not, but my boy is free. It is as the woman says, a man cried out, for I've seen the boy, and he is free now of the demon. My limb, too, is proof that Jesus is a prophet. And the lion-hunter told how in a fight with a great beast his thigh had been dislocated, and for seven years he had walked with a crutch; but the moment Jesus laid his hands upon him the use of his limb was given back to him. Another came forward and showed his arm, which for many a year had hung lifeless, but as soon as Jesus took it in his hand the sinews reknit themselves, and now it was stronger than the other. And then a woman pressed through the crowd, and she wished everybody to know that a flux of blood that had troubled her for seven years had been healed. But the people were tired of stories of miracles and were now anxious to hear from Joseph if Jesus was going up to Jerusalem for the Feast of the Passover. But, my friends, I have but just returned from Galilee, and have come from there to learn these things. He is watching for a sign from his Father in heaven, a woman cried, shaking her head. A man tried to get some words privily with Joseph: Will he speak against the taxes? he asked, but before he could get any further Nicodemus appeared in the doorway, and the people pressed round him, asking what Jesus had said to him, and if he were coming down to speak to them. But before Nicodemus could answer any of them the lion-hunter cried out that a priest was not so terrible a beast as a lion, and while he was with them Jesus had nothing to fear. At which his enemy in the crowd began to jeer, saying: Asiel wears the lion's skin, we all know, but he has never told anybody who killed the lion for him. And the men might have hit each other if the woman who suffered for seven years had not cried out: Now,

181

what are you fighting for? know ye not that Jesus cannot come down to us, for he is waiting for a sign from his Father? From our Father, John thundered out. Nicodemus said he had spoken truly, and the crowd followed Nicodemus and Joseph a little way. Do not return to the house of Simon the Leper. Leave Jesus in peace to-night to pray, meditate, and rest, for he needs rest. He'll lead you to Jerusalem as soon as he gets a sign from our Father which is in heaven, Nicodemus said.

At these words the people dispersed in great joy, and Joseph and Nicodemus walked on together in silence, till Joseph, feeling that they were safely out of hearing, asked if Jesus spoke of his intention to take Jerusalem by assault. Nicodemus seemed to examine his memory for a moment, and then, as if forgetting Joseph's question, he began to tell that Jesus was standing in the middle of the room when he entered, seemingly unaware that his disciples were assembled about the house. His eyes fixed, as it were, on his thoughts or ideas, he did not hear the door open, and to get his attention Nicodemus had to lay his hand upon his arm. At his touch Jesus awoke from his dream, but it seemed quite a little while before he could shake himself free from his dream, and was again of this world. Joseph asked Nicodemus to repeat his first words. Was he violent or affectionate? Affectionate, gentle, and winning, Nicodemus answered. A few moments of sweetness, and then he seemed suddenly to become old and wild and savage. The two men stopped on the road, and Nicodemus, looking into Joseph's eyes, said: I asked him if he were going up to Jerusalem for the Feast of the Passover, and after speaking a few words on the subject he broke out, coiling himself like a diseased panther meditating on its spring, and as if uncertain if he could accomplish it, he fell back into a chair and into his dream, out of which he spoke a few words clear and reasonable; and then with a concentrated hate he spoke of the Temple as a resort of thieves and of the priests as the despoilers of widows and orphans, saying that the law must be abrogated and the Temple destroyed. Until then there would be no true religion in Judea. It is like that he speaks now; the one-time reformer sees clearly that the Temple must go. And would he, Joseph asked, build another in its place? I'm not sure that he would. I put the question to him and he was uncertain if the old
182

foundations could be used. The old spirits of lust, and blood, and money would haunt the walls, and as fast as we raised up a new Temple the spirits would pull it down and rebuild it as it was before. We are forbidden by the law of Moses to create any graven image of man, of bird or beast. Would that Moses had added: Build no walls, for as soon as there are walls priests will enter in and set themselves upon thrones. The priests have taken the place of God, and I have come, he said, to cast them out of their thrones, and to cut the knot of the bondage of the people of Israel. I come, he said, with a sword to cut that knot, which hands have failed to loosen, and in my other hand there is a torch, and with it I shall set fire to the thrones. All the world as ye know it must be burnt up like stubble, for a new world to rise up in its place. In the beginning I spoke sweet words of peace, and they were of no avail to stay the sins that were committed in every house; so now I speak no more sweet words to anybody, but words that shall divide father from son, and mother from daughter, and wife from husband. There is no other way to cure the evil. What say I, he cried, cure! There is none. The evil must be cut down and thrown upon the fire, and whosoever would be saved from the fire must follow me. The priests hate me and call me arrogant, but if I seem arrogant to them it is because I speak the word of God. And then, seizing me by the shoulder, he said: Look into my eyes and see. They shall tell thee that those who would be saved from the fire must follow me. I am the word, the truth, and the life. Follow me, follow me, or else be for ever accursed and destroyed and burnt up like weeds that the gardener throws into heaps and fires on an autumn evening. Yes, he cried, we are nearing the springtime when life shall begin again in the world. But I say to thee that this springtime shall never come to pass. Never again shall the fig ripen on the wall and the wheat be cut down in the fields. Before these things come to pass in their natural course the Son of Man shall return in a chariot of fire to make an end of things; or if thou wilt thou canst say that he'll come not to make an end but a new beginning, a world in which justice and peace shall reign. And it is for this end I offer myself, a victim to appease our Father in heaven. I am the sacrifice and the communion, for it is no longer the fat of rams that my Father desires, but my blood, only

183

that; only my blood will appease his wrath. As I have said, I am the communion, and thou shalt eat my flesh and drink my blood, else perish utterly, and go into everlasting damnation. But I love thee and —— And after a pause he said: Those that love God are loved by me, and willingly and gladly will I yield myself up as the last sacrifice. Nicodemus stopped, for his memory died suddenly, and, unable to discover anything in the blank, he turned to Joseph and said: He speaks with a strange, bitter energy, like one that has lost control of his words; he is hardly aware of them, nor does he retain any memory of them. They are as the wind, rising we know not why, and going its way unbidden. I have seen him like that in Galilee, Joseph answered. Ah! Nicodemus answered suddenly, I remember, but cannot put words upon it. He said that before the world was, he and his Father were one, and that his great love of man induced him to separate himself ——

At that moment a man came out from the shadow of a rock and approached the wayfarers, who drew back quickly, thinking they were about to be attacked. It is Judas, Joseph whispered, one of the apostles. You have seen Jesus? Judas asked breathlessly, and when Nicodemus told how Jesus had said he would go up to Jerusalem for the Passover he cried out: To lead us against the Temple? He must be saved. From what? Nicodemus asked: from his mission? He must go on to the end with the work he has been called out of heaven to accomplish. I can see that you have been speaking with him. Called out of heaven to accomplish! And then, clasping his hands, Judas looked with imploring eyes upon them: Save him, save him, for if not, I must myself; for every day his pride redoubles and now he believes himself to be the Messiah — the Messiah as sent by God. By whom else could he be sent? Joseph replied. If he be not taken by the priests and put to death he will be driven by the demon into the last blasphemy; one which no Jew has yet committed even in his heart, and if that word be spoken all will be accomplished, and the Lord will choose another nation from among the Gentiles. He will declare himself God, Judas continued. Nicodemus and Joseph raised their hands. He speaks already of the time before the world was, when he and his Father were one; and setting aside the Scriptures in his madness he has begun to imagine that the angels that revolted against God were
184

changed into men, and given the world for abode till their sins so angered the Father (remark you, of whom Jesus was then a part) that he determined to destroy the world; at which Jesus in his great love of men (or of fallen angels, for bytimes he doesn't know what he is saying) said he would put Godhead off and become man, and give his life as atonement for the sins of men. Sirs, I'll ask you how God or man may by his death make atonement for the sins that men have committed? Hear me to the end, for as many minutes as you have listened, I have listened hours. By this sacrifice of his life his teaching will become known to men and he will reign the one and only king till the world itself crumbles and perishes. Then he will become one with his Father, and from that moment there will be but one God. These are the thoughts, noble Sirs, on which he is brooding, and if he go up to yon town it will be to —— Judas could not bring himself to pronounce the words: declare himself God, so blasphemous did they seem to him. And before the wayfarers could ask him, as they were minded to, if he were sure that he had rightly understood Jesus, the apostle had bidden them farewell, and, running up a by-track, disappeared into the darkness, leaving behind him a memory of a large bony nose hanging over a thin black moustache that barely covered his lips.

As they walked towards the city, over which the moon was hanging, filling the valleys and hills with strange, fantastical shadows, they remembered the black, shaggy eyebrows, the luminous eyes, and the bitter, penetrating voice, and they remembered the gait, the long striding legs as they hastened up the steep path; even the pinched back often started up in their memory. And the next three or four days they sought him in the crowds that assembled to make the triumphal entry with Jesus into Jerusalem, but he was not to be seen; and if he had been among the people they could not have failed to discover him. He is not here to welcome Jesus, Joseph muttered under his breath, and added: Can it be that he has deserted to the other side? He is a sort of other Jesus, Nicodemus said. But yonder Jesus comes riding on an ass, on which a crimson cloak has been laid. As Jesus passed Nicodemus and Joseph he waved his hand, and there was a smile on his lips and a light in his eye. He seems to have become suddenly young again, Joseph said. He is exalted, Nicodemus added sadly, by his follow-

185

ing. And they counted about fifty men and women. Does he think that with these he will drive the Pharisees and Sadducees out of the Temple? he added. He is happy again, Joseph answered. See how he lifts up the fringe of the mantle they have laid upon the ass, and admires it. His face is happier than we have seen it for many a day. He likes the people to salute him as the Son of David. Yet he knows, Nicodemus said, that he is the son of Joseph the Carpenter. Ask him to beg the people not to call him the Son of David, Joseph pleaded. And, running after the ass, Nicodemus dared to say: Ask the people not to call thee the Son of David, for it will go against thee in the end. But Jesus's heart at that moment was swollen with pride, and he answered Nicodemus: What thou hearest to-day on earth was spoken in heaven before our Father bade the stars give light. Be not afraid for my sake. Remember that whomsoever my Father sends on earth to do his business, him will he watch over. He has no eyes for me, Joseph said sadly, for I left him to attend my father in sickness. And, taking Nicodemus's arm, he drew him close, that he might more safely whisper that two men seemed to be searching in their garments as if for daggers. Nicodemus knew them to be hirelings in the pay of the priests. Look, he said, how their hands fidget for their daggers; the opportunity seems favourable now to stab him; but no, the crowd closes round his ass again, and the Zealots draw back. God saved Daniel from the flames and the lions, Joseph answered. But will he, Nicodemus returned, be able to save him from the priests?

CHAPTER XVIII.

NICODEMUS invited Joseph to follow Jesus, saying that at a safe distance he would like to see him ride through the gates into the city; but Joseph, sorely troubled in his mind, could not answer him, and an hour later was hastening along the Jericho road, praying all the while that he might be given strength to keep his promise to his father. But no sooner was he in Jericho than he began to feel ashamed of himself, and after resisting the impulse to return to Jesus for two days he yielded to it, and returned obediently the way he had come, uncertain whether shame of his cowardice or love was bringing him back. One or the other it must be, he said, as he came round the bend in the road into Bethany; and it was soon after passing through that village, somewhere about the ninth hour, that he met his masons coming from Mount Scropas. Coming from my tomb, he said to himself, and, reining up his horse and speaking to them, he heard that his tomb was finished. We've chiselled a great stone to be rolled into the doorway, he heard one of the masons say; another uttered vauntingly that the stone closed the tomb perfectly; and Joseph was about to press his horse forward when the men called after him, and, gathering about his stirrup, they related that Jesus of Nazareth had been tried and condemned by Pilate that morning. And is now hanging on a cross, a-top of Golgotha, said one of the masons. And if thou beest going that way, Master, said another, thou wilt espy him between two robbers. One of them was to have been Jesus Bar-Abba, but the people cried out that he was to be released instead of Jesus. As Joseph repeated the words: Bar-Abba instead of Jesus, as if he only half understood them, the masons reminded him that it was the custom to deliver up a prisoner to the people at the time of the Passover. At the time of the Passover, he repeated. . . . At last, realising what had happened, his face

187

became overwrought; his eyes and mouth testified to the grief he was suffering; and he pressed his spurs to his horse's side, and would have been away beyond call if two of his workmen had not seized the bridle and almost forced the horse on his haunches. Loose my bridle, Joseph cried, astonished and beside himself. A moment with thee, Master. Be careful to speak no word in his favour, and make no show of sympathy, else a Zealot's knife will be in thy back before evening, for they be seeking the Galileans everywhere, at the priests' bidding. Before Joseph could break away he heard that the priests stirred up the people against Jesus, giving it forth against him that he had come to Jerusalem to burn down the Temple, and would set up another —— Built without the help of hands, of what materials he did not know, but not of stones nor wood, yet a Temple that will last for ever, the mason shouted after Joseph, who had stuck his spurs again into his horse and was riding full tilt towards a hill about half-a-mile from the city walls. On his way thither he met some of the populace — the remnant returning from the crucifixion — and he rode up the ascent at a gallop in the hope that he might be in time to save Jesus's life.

He knew Pilate would grant him almost any favour he might ask; but within fifty yards of the crosses his heart began to fail him, for, whereas the robbers were straining their heads high in the air above the crossbar, Jesus's head was sunk on to his chest. He died a while ago, the centurion said, and as soon as he was dead the multitude began to disperse, the Sabbath being at hand; and guessing Joseph to be a man of importance, he added: If thou wilt I'll make certain he is dead, and, taking his spear from one of the soldiers, he would have plunged it into Jesus's side, but Joseph, forgetful of the warning he had received, on no account to show sympathy with Jesus, laid his hand on the spear-head, saying: Respect the dead. As thou wilt, the centurion replied, and gave the spear back to the soldier, who returned to his comrades, it being his turn to cast the dice. They have cast dice, the centurion continued, and will divide the clothes of these men amongst them; and, hearing the words, one of the soldiers held up the rags that had come to him, while another spread upon the ground Jesus's fine cloak, the one that Peter had bought for Jesus with money that Joseph gave to him. That he should see the cloak again, and

188

on such an occasion, touched his heart. It was a humble incident in a cruel murder committed by a priest; and the thought crossed Joseph's mind that he might purchase the cloak from the soldier, but, remembering the warning he had received, he did not ask for the cloak, nor did he once lift his eyes to Jesus's face, lest the sight of it should wring his heart, and if they saw him thus overcome and helpless with grief, the priests and their hirelings might begin to suspect him. He strove instead to call reason to his aid : Jesus's life being spent, his duty was to obtain the body and bury it; far worse than the death he endured would be for his sacred body to be thrown into the common ditch with these malefactors. I know not how thou canst abide here, he said to the centurion; their groans make the heart faint. We shall break their bones presently; the Jews asked us to do this, for at six o'clock their Sabbath begins. And in this the thieves are lucky, for were it not for their Sabbath they would last on for three or four days : the first day is the worst day; afterwards the crucified sinks into mortal numbness, and I doubt if he feels at all on the third day; on the fourth day he dies. But, Sir, what may I do for thee? I've come for him hanging between the robbers, for, however erring, he was not a robber, and deserves decent burial. Thou'lt come with me to testify that I've buried him in a rock sepulchre, the stone of which thyself shall roll into the door. To which the centurion answered that he did not dare to deliver up the body of Jesus without an order from Pilate, though he was dead. Dead an hour or more, truly dead, he added. Pilate will not refuse his body to me, Joseph replied. Pilate and I are well acquainted; we are as friends are. Thou hast seen me at the Prætorium before now, coming to talk with the procurator about the transport of wheat from Moab, and other things. Now that I come to see thy face more clearly, I remember having seen thee come up the steps of the Prætorium and descend them friendly with Pilate. Well then, come with me at once to Jerusalem, Joseph said coaxingly, and thou'lt hear Pilate tell thee to deliver the crucified unto me. But the centurion demurred, saying that his orders were not to leave the gibbets. Upon my own word, Pilate will not deliver up the body unless I bring thee with me; I shall require thee to testify of the death. So come with me.

The unwillingness of the centurion was reduced to naught at the mention of a sum of money, and, giving orders to his soldiers that nothing was to be done during his absence, he walked beside Joseph's horse into Jerusalem, telling to Joseph as they went the story of the arrest in the garden, the haling of Jesus before the High Priest, and the sending of him on to Pilate, who, though unwilling to confirm the sentence of death, was afraid of a riot, and had yielded to the people's wish. And the story of the scourging of Jesus in the hall of the palace, and the bribing of the soldiers by the Jews to make a mocking-stock of Jesus, was not finished when Joseph, who had been listening without hearing, said : Here is the door. And till the door was opened the centurion continued to tell his tale : how a purple cloak was thrown upon the shoulders of Jesus, a reed put into his hand, and a crown of thorns —— We have come to see his worship, Joseph said, addressing the doorkeeper, and the doorkeeper answered that Pilate had sent down an order that he would see no one again that day. Pilate will see me, Joseph replied ; and the doorkeeper being amenable to money, like the centurion, took a bribe whilst excusing himself for taking it, saying that he did not break an order for what he could get by breaking it but because he knew that every order is liable to exception, and Joseph being known to him as Pilate's friend, he could not discharge him unannounced. Pilate will see thee, he added, and they waited till word was brought to them that Joseph was to be admitted ; and after begging Pilate to forgive him for intruding upon his privacy so late in the day, he put his request into words, saying straight away : I have come to ask for the body of Jesus, who was condemned to the cross at noon. At these words Pilate's face became overcast, and he said that he regretted that Joseph had come to ask him for something he could not grant. It would be pleasant to leave Jerusalem knowing that I never refused thee anything, Joseph, for thou'rt the one Jew for whom I have any respect, and, I may add, some affection. But why, Pilate, canst thou not give me Jesus's body ? His body, is that what thou askest, Joseph ? It seemed to me that thou hadst come for nothing less than to ask me to undo the sentence that I pronounced to-day at noon. The body ! Is Jesus dead, then ? The centurion answered for Joseph : Yes, Sir ; he died to-day at the ninth hour. I put a
190

lance into him to make sure, and blood and water came from his side. At which statement Joseph trembled, for he was acquiescing in a lie; but he did not dare to contradict the centurion, who was speaking in his favour for the sake of the money he had received, and in the hope of receiving more for the lie that he told. On the cross at noon and dead before the ninth hour! Pilate muttered: he could bear the cross but for three hours! After the scourging we gave him, Sir, the centurion answered, he was so tottering that we had to pass on his cross to the shoulders of a Jew named Simon of Cyrene, who carried it to the top of the mount for him. If he be dead there is no reason for my not giving up the body, Pilate answered. Which I shall bury, Joseph replied, in my own sepulchre. What, Joseph, hast thou already ordered thy sepulchre? To my eyes thou dost not look more than five or six and twenty years, a man that might live for sixty more years at least; but you Jews never lose sight of death, as if it were the only good. Life is but a fragile gift, Joseph answered. We Romans think so too sometimes, but not so frequently as you. And then this tall, grave, handsome man, whose face reflected a friendly but somewhat formal soul, took Joseph by the arm and walked with him up and down the tessellated pavement, talking in his ear, showing himself so well disposed towards him that the centurion congratulated himself that he had accepted Joseph's bribe. If I had known that Jesus was a close friend of thine, Pilate said to Joseph — but if I had known as much it would have made things more difficult for me. A strange exalted man, a Jew. And now, on thinking it over, it must have been that I was well disposed to him for that reason, for there could have been no other; for what concern of mine is it that you Jews quarrel and would tear each other to pieces for your various beliefs in God and his angels? So Jesus was thy friend? Tell me about him; I would know more about him than I could learn from him in the Prætorium, whither I took him and talked to him alone, and would not have delivered him to the Jews had we not been short of soldiers. And Joseph, who was thinking all the while that the Sabbath was approaching, gave to Pilate only a brief account of Jesus in Galilee.

So thou too, Joseph, inclinest a willing ear to the belief that the bodies of men are raised out of the earth into heaven? I would ask

191

if the body is ridded of its worms before it is carried away by the angels. But I see that thou'rt pressed for time; the Sabbath approaches; I must not detain thee, and yet I would not let thee go without telling that it pleases me to give his body for burial. A body deserves burial that was possessed of a lofty soul, for how many years, Joseph, thirty? I would have saved him if it had been possible; but he gave me no chance; his answers were brief and evasive; and he seemed to desire death; seemingly he looked upon his death as necessary for the accomplishment of his mission. Have I divined him right? Joseph answered that Pilate read Jesus's soul truly, which flattered Pilate and persuaded him into further complaint that if he had not saved Jesus it was because Jesus would not answer him. He seemed to me like a man only conscious of his own thoughts, Pilate said; even while speaking he seemed to rouse hardly at all out of his dream, a delirious dream, if I may so speak, of the world redeemed from the powers of evil and given over to the love of God. This, however, he did say: that any power which I might have over him came to me from above, from his Father which is in heaven, else I could do nothing; and there was bitterness in his voice as he spoke these words, which seemed to hint that his thought was that his Father had gone a little too far in allowing the Jews to send him to me to condemn him to death. His Father which is in heaven and himself are one, and yet they differ in this. So he was thy friend, Joseph? If I had known it there would have been another reason for my trying to save him from the hatred of the Jews; for I hate the Jews, and would willingly leave them to-morrow. But they cried out: Thou art not Cæsar's friend; this man would set up a new kingdom and overthrow the Romans; and, as I have already told thee, Joseph, I asked Jesus if he claimed to be King of the Jews, but he answered me: Thou hast said it, adding, however, that his kingdom was not of this world. Evasive answers of that kind are worthless when a mob is surging round the Prætorium. A cruel, rapacious, vindictive crowd they looked to me, with nothing in their minds but hatred. I suspect they hated him for religious reasons. You Jews are — forgive me, Joseph, thou'rt an exception among thy people — a bitter, intolerant race. You would not allow me to bring the Roman eagles to Jerusalem, for you cannot look upon graven things. All the arts you have abol-

192

ished, and your love of God resolves itself into hatred of men; so it seems to me. It would have pleased me very well indeed to have thwarted the Jews in their desire for this man's life, but I was threatened by a revolt, and the soldiers at my command are but auxiliaries, and not in sufficient numbers to quell a substantial riot. I will tell thee more : if the legion that I was promised had arrived from Cæsarea, the lust of the Jews for the blood of those that disagree with them would not have been satisfied. I went so far as to send messengers to inquire for the legion. But the man is dead now, and further talking will not raise him into life again. Thou hast come to ask me for his body, and thou wouldst bury it in thine own tomb. It is like thee, Joseph, to wish to honour thy dead friend. Methinks thou'rt more Roman than Jew. Say not so in the hearing of my countrymen, Joseph replied, or I may meet my death for thy good opinion. The Sabbath is now approaching, and I shall be forgiven if I indulge in no further words of thanks, Pilate. I may not delay, lest the hour should come upon me after which no work can be done. Not that I hold with such strict observances. A good work done upon the Sabbath must be viewed more favourably by God than a bad work done on another day of the week. But I would not have it said that I violated the Sabbath to bury Jesus. As thou wilt, my good Joseph, Pilate answered, and stood looking after Joseph and the centurion, who, as they drew near to the gate of the city, remembered that a sheet would be wanted to wrap the body in. Joseph reminded the centurion that there was no time for delay, but the centurion replied : In yon shop sheets are sold. Moreover, thou'lt want a lantern, Sir, for the lifting of the body from the cross will take some time, and the carrying of it to the tomb will be a slow journey though thou get help, and the day will be gone when thou art beyond the Mount. Thou hadst better buy a lantern, Sir. Joseph did as he was bidden, and they hurried on to Golgotha to bury Jesus.

Nothing has been done in my absence? the centurion asked the soldiers, who answered : Nothing, Sir; and none has been here but these women, whom we did not drive away, but told that thou wert gone with one Joseph of Arimathea to get an order from Pilate for the body. That was well, the centurion answered. And now do you loose the cords that bind the hands, and get the dead man

193

down. Which was easy to accomplish, the feet of the crucified being no more than a few inches from the ground; and while this was being done Joseph told the centurion that the women were the sisters of Lazarus, whom Jesus had raised from the dead; a story that set the Roman soldiers laughing. Can a man be raised from the dead? they asked; and if this man could do such a thing how is it that he did not raise himself out of death into life? To which neither Joseph nor the two women made any answer, but stood, their eyes fixed on their thoughts, asking themselves how they were to carry Jesus to the sepulchre, distant about a mile and a half. And it not seeming to them that they could carry the body, the centurion offered Joseph the help of one of his soldiers, which they would have accepted, but at that moment an ox-cart came into sight toiling home in the dusk, and Joseph, going after the carrier, offered him money if he would bring the body of one of the crucified to the sepulchre in Mount Scropas for him. To which the carrier consented, though he was not certain that the job might not prevent him from getting home before the Sabbath began. But tempted by the money that Joseph proffered, he allowed Jesus to be laid on the ox-cart, and Mary, Martha and Joseph following it reached Mount Scropas, in which was the tomb, before sunset. As I told thee, with half-an-hour for thee to get home before the Sabbath, Joseph said to the carrier, his eyes fixed on the descending sun. Now take this man by the feet and I'll take him by the head. But wilt thou not light the lantern, Sir? the carrier said; for though there be light on the hillside, it will be night in the tomb, and we shall be jostling our heads against the stone and perhaps falling over the dead man. . . . I have steel and tinder. Wherefrom the lantern was lit and given to Martha, who lighted them into the tomb, Joseph and the carrier bearing the body, with Mary following. Jesus was laid on the couch beneath the arch, and when Mary and Martha held the sheet, ready to drop it over his face, Joseph turned to the women, saying: Now do you go hence to Bethany and prepare spices and cloths for the embalmment, and come hither with them in the early morning the day after the Sabbath. The carrier, who was standing by waiting for his wage, received it thankfully. Now, Master, if thou shouldst need another shoulder to help with that sealing stone, I can give it thee.

194

But Joseph, looking at the stone, said it would offer no trouble to him, for he believed in his strength to do it, though the carrier said : It looks as if two men, or more like three, would be needed. But it is as thou wilt, Master. On this he went to his oxen, thinking of the Sabbath, and whether Joseph had forgotten how near it was to them. He hasn't blown out his lantern yet, and now he is going back into the tomb ! the carrier said; for something forgotten, mayhap for a last look at the crucified — one that hung between two robbers, yet grieved for as if he were the Emperor of Rome or King Solomon himself!

The carrier pricked on his oxen, and Joseph entered the tomb in the mood of grief which the carrier had divined. Life had been coming and going like a dream ever since he met the masons; and asking himself if he were truly awake and in his five senses, he returned to bid Jesus a last farewell, though he would not have been astonished if he sought him in vain through the darkness filled with the dust and the smell of freshly cut stones. But Jesus was where they had laid him ; and Joseph sate himself by the dead Master's side, so that he might meditate and come to see better into the meanings of things, for all meaning seemed to have gone out of life for him since he had come from Jericho. The flickering shadows and lights distracted his meditation, and set him thinking of the masons and their pride in their work; he looked round the sepulchre and perceived it to be a small chamber with a couch at the farther end of it. Martha and Mary have gone, he said to himself, and he remembered he had bidden them go thence to prepare spices, and to return after the Sabbath. Which they will do as soon as the Sabbath is over, he repeated to himself, as if to convince himself that he was not dreaming. . . . God did not save him in the end as he expected he would, he continued : he'd have done better to have given Pilate answers whereby Pilate would have been able to save him from the cross. Pilate was anxious to save him, but, as Nicodemus said, Jesus had come to think that it had been decreed in heaven that his blood must be spilt, so that he might rise again, as it were, out of his own blood, to return in a chariot with his Father in three days. . . . But will he return to inhabit again this beautiful mould? Joseph asked, and striving against the doubt that the sight of the dead put into his mind, he left the

195

tomb with the intention of rolling the stone into the door. Better not to see him than to doubt him, he said. But who will, he asked himself, roll away the stone for Martha and Mary when they come with spices and fine linen for the embalming? His mind was divided whether he should close the tomb and go his way, or watch through the Sabbath, and while seeking to come upon a resolve he was overcome by desire to see his dead friend once more, and he entered the tomb, holding high the lantern so that he might better see him. But as he approached the couch on which the body lay he stopped; the colour went out of his face; he trembled all over; the sheet which Martha and Mary had drawn over the face was fallen, and Joseph lifted a long tress of hair so that he might better see Jesus. He must have moved, or angels must have moved him; and, uncertain whether Jesus was alive or dead, Joseph remembered Lazarus, and stood watching, cold and frightened, waiting for some movement. He is not dead! he is not dead! he cried, and his joy died, for on the instant Jesus passed again into the darkness of swoon. And Joseph having no water to bathe his forehead with, nor even a drop to wet his lips, said : There is none nearer than my house. I shall have to carry him thither in my arms. But can a man carry another in his arms? A dead man is heavier than a living child. On my back I may carry him as a man carries a sheep or bullock. But if a wayfarer meet us the news that a man newly risen from the tomb was seen on the hillside on the back of another will soon reach Jerusalem, and the Pharisees will send soldiers to inquire the matter out. The tomb will be opened and the houses in the neighbourhood searched. Why then did he awaken only to be taken again? Hope came to Joseph. For on the eve of the Sabbath, he said, I shall be able to carry him to my house secretly. But to carry a swooning man half-a-mile up a crooked and steep path among rocks will take all my strength. He took cognisance of his thews and sinews, and feeling them to be strong and like iron, he said : I can do it, and fell to thinking of his servants loitering in the passages, talking as they ascended the stairs, stopping half-way and talking again, and getting to bed slowly, more slowly than ever on this night, the night of all others that he wished them sound asleep in their beds. Half-a-mile up a zigzagging path I shall have to carry him; he may die in my arms; and he entertained the
196

thought for a moment that he might go for his servants, who would bring with them oil and wine; but dismissing the thought as unwise, he left the tomb to see if the darkness were thick enough to shelter himself and his burden. But Jesus might pass away in his swoon. If he had some water to give him! But he had none, and he sat by the couch waiting for Jesus to open his eyes. At last he opened them.

The twilight had vanished and the stars were coming out, and Joseph said to himself : There will be no moon, only a soft starlight, and he stood gazing at the desert showing through a great tide of blue shadow, with the shape of the hills emerging, like the hulls of great ships afloat in a shadowy sea. A dark, close, dusty night, he said, and moonless, deserted by every man and woman; a Sabbath eve. On none other would it be possible. But thinking that some hours would have to pass before he dared to enter his gates with Jesus on his shoulder, he seated himself on the great stone. Though Jesus were to die for lack of succour he must wait till his servants were in bed asleep. And then? The stone on which he was sitting must be rolled into the entrance of the tomb before leaving. He had told the carrier that he would have no trouble with it, and to discover that he had not bragged he slid down the rock, and, putting his shoulder to it, found he could move it, for the ground was aslant, and if he were to remove some rubble the stone would itself roll into the entrance of the tomb. But he had not known this when he refused the carrier's help. Then why? . . . And to escape from the reality of the tomb, he began to ask himself if he had refused the carrier's help because of some thought which was not clear to him at the time; he did not dare to encourage the thought that he had been appointed a watcher by God himself, and that his watch was to extend through the night, and through the next day and night, until Mary and Martha came with spices and linen cloths. The round of his thoughts was brought to a close and with a sudden jerk by some memory of his maybe dying friend; and in his grief he found no better solace than to gaze at the stars, now thickly sown in the sky, and to attempt to decipher their conjunctions and oppositions, trying to pick out a prophecy in heaven of what was happening on earth.

His star-gazing was interrupted suddenly by a bark. A jackal,

197

he said. Other jackals answered the first bark; the hillside seemed to be filled with them; but, however numerous, he could scare them away. A wandering hyena scenting a dead body would be more dangerous, for he was weaponless, but it was seldom that one ventured into the environs of the city; and he listened to the jackals, and they kept him awake till something in the air told him the hour had come for him to go into the tomb and carry Jesus out of it . . . if he were not dead. He slid down from the rock again, and no sooner did he reach the ground than he remembered having left Galilee to keep his promise to his father; but, despite his obedience to his father's will, he had not escaped his fate. In vain he had avoided the Temple and refused to enter the house of Simon the Leper. If he were to take Jesus to his house and hide him he would become a party to Jesus's crime, and were Jesus discovered in his house the angry Pharisees would demand their death from Pilate. If he would escape the doom of the cross he must roll the stone up into the entrance of the sepulchre. . . . A dying man perceives no difference between a sepulchre and a dwelling-house. He would be dead before morning; before the Sabbath was done for certain; and Mary and Martha would begin the embalmment on Sunday. He would be dead certainly on Sunday morning, and dead men tell no tales, so they say. But do they say truly? The dead are voiceless, but they speak, and are closer to us than the living; and for ever the spectre of that man would be by him, making frightful every hour of his life. Yet by closing up the sepulchre and leaving Jesus to die in it he would be serving him better than by carrying him to his house and bringing him back to life. To what life was he bringing him? He could not be kept hidden for long; he could not remain in Jerusalem, and whither Jesus went Joseph would follow, and his bond to his father would be broken then in spirit as well as in fact. A cold sweat broke out on his forehead and for a long time his mind seemed like a broken thing and the pieces scattered; and as much exhausted as if he had carried Jesus a mile on his shoulders, he stooped forward and entered the tomb, without certain knowledge whether he was going to kiss Jesus and close the tomb upon him or carry him to his house about a half-hour distant. As he drew the cere-cloths from the body, a vision of his house rose up in his mind — a large two-storeyed house

198

OUT OF THE TOMB

with a domed roof, situated on a large vineyard on the eastern slopes of the Mount of Olives, screened from the highway by carob hedges, olive garths, and cedar-trees. And this house seemed to Joseph as if designed by Providence for the concealment of Jesus. The only way, he muttered, will be to lift him upon my shoulders, getting the weight as far as I can from off my arms. If he could walk a little supported on my arm. He questioned Jesus, but Jesus could not answer him; and there seemed to be no other way but to carry him in his arms out of the tomb, place him on the rock, and from thence hoist him on to his shoulders. A man is a great weight, he said. But Jesus was carried more easily than he imagined, as easily carried as a child for the first hundred yards, nor did he weigh much heavier for the next, but before three hundred yards were over Joseph began to look round for a rock against which he might rest his burden.

One of the hardships of this journey was that howsoever he held Jesus he seemed to cause him great pain, and he guessed by the feel that the body was wounded in many places; but the stars did not show sufficient light for him to see where not to grasp it, and he sat in the pathway, resting Jesus across his knees, thinking of a large rock within sight of his own gates and how he would lean Jesus against it, if he managed to carry him so far. He stopped at sight of something, something seemed to slink through the pale, diffused shadows in and out of the rocks up the hillside, and Joseph thought of a midnight wolf. The wolves did not venture as near the city, but —— Whatever Joseph saw with his eyes, or fancied he saw, did not appear again, and he picked up his load, thinking of the hopeless struggle it would be between him and a grey wolf burdened as he was. He could not do else than leave Jesus to be eaten, and his fear of wolf and hyena so exhausted him that he nearly toppled at the next halt. A fall would be fatal to Jesus, and Joseph asked himself how he would lift Jesus on to his shoulder again. He did not think that he could manage it, but he did, and staggered to the gates; but no sooner had he laid his burden down than he remembered that he could not ascend the stairs without noise. The gardener's cottage is empty; I will carry him thither. The very place, Joseph said, as he paused for breath by the gate-post. I must send away the two men-servants,

199

he continued, one to Galilee and the other to Jericho. The truth cannot be kept from Esora. I need her help: I can depend upon her to cure Jesus of his wounds and keep the young girl in the house, forbidding her the garden while Jesus is in the cottage. The danger of dismissal would be too great, she would carry the story or part of it to Jerusalem, it would spread like oil, and in a few days, in a few weeks certainly, the Pharisees would be sending their agents to search the house. With Jesus hoisted on to his shoulder he followed the path through the trees round the shelving lawn and crossed the terrace at the bottom of the garden. He had then to follow a twisting path through a little wood, and he feared to bump Jesus against the trees. The path led down into a dell, and he could hardly bear up so steep was the ascent; his breath and strength were gone when he came to the cottage door. Fortune seems to be with us, he said, as he carried Jesus through the doorway, but he must have a bed; and fortune is still with us — they haven't removed the bed; and as soon as Jesus was laid upon it Joseph began to remember many things. He must go to the house and get a lamp, and in the house he remembered that he must bring some wine and some water. When he saw that his hand and his sleeve were stained with blood, he said: He must have been badly scourged, and continued his search for bottles; and after mixing wine and water he returned to the gardener's cottage, hoping that casual ministrations would relieve Jesus of some of the pain he was suffering. In the morning Esora would come with her remedies, and wondering what these might be, he put the lamp on a chair on the opposite side of the bed and turned Jesus over and began to pick out of the wounds the splinters of the rods he had been beaten with, and after binding up the back with a linen cloth he drew Jesus's head forward and managed to get him to swallow a little wine and water. I can do no more, he said, and must leave him. . . . It will be better to lock the door; he must bide there till I hear Esora on the stairs coming down from her room. She is always out of bed first, and if luck is still with us she will rise early this morning. He tried to check his thoughts, but they ran on till he remembered that he must fetch the lantern forgotten among the rocks; and that he should follow the twisting path up and down the hillside seemed more than he could accomplish. Strength and will seemed

200

to have departed from him; yet he must go back to fetch the lantern. He had left it lighted, and some curious person might be led by the light . . . the open sepulchre would attract his eye, and he might take up the light and discover the tomb to be empty. It wasn't likely, but some such curious one might be on the prowl. Now was the only safe time to fetch the lantern. He daren't leave it, for at the first light Mary and Martha would be at the sepulchre, and the finding of a lantern by the door of the empty sepulchre would give rise to —— He passed through his gates, locking them after him, too weary to think further what might and might not befall.

CHAPTER XIX.

AND when he returned with the lantern he had forgotten, he threw himself on his bed, hoping to escape in sleep from remembrances of the day. But all the night long his thoughts whirled on, taking him back to the tomb and later to the cottage, and then to the mountain-side with Jesus on his shoulders, the journey magnified, distorted beyond the limits of reality. God saved him from death, he said, or raised him out of death, but he has not yet raised him into heaven. He is in the gardener's cottage in all the pain that our life on this earth may inflict. Joseph closed his eyes, and a moment after he was pleading with Pilate in the Prætorium that he might be nailed on the cross in place of Jesus. By the side of Jesus, said Pilate, and awakened by Pilate's answer or the sound of footsteps, he listened. Pilate's soldiers, come to take him back to Golgotha! he cried out in an extreme of terror . . . or only Esora; and springing from his bed he stood on the landing, asking himself if Esora was at work so early. And then it seemed to him that he could hear somebody in her pantry. . . . To make sure he descended and found her before her table brushing the clothes he had thrown off. Thou must have come to my room and picked up my clothes without my hearing thee, he said; it was not till thou wast on the second flight of stairs that I awoke. Thou'rt the first servant, and the earliest riser; it is still dusk. If I didn't rise early, Master, I know not how the work would get done. But the Sabbath? Joseph rejoined; and incontinently began to discuss the observances of the Sabbath with her. But even on the Sabbath there is work to be done, she answered; thy clothes — a nasty state thou didst bring them home in, and if they were not cleaned for thee, thou couldst not present thyself in the synagogue to-day. But, Esora, Joseph answered faintly, I don't see

202

why thou shouldst be up and at work in the dusk, with that girl, Matred, still asleep. Does she never help thee in thy work? Esora muttered something that Joseph did not hear, and in answer to his question why she did not rouse Matred from her bed she said that the young require more sleep than the old; an answer that surprised Joseph, for he had never been able to rid himself of his first impression of Esora. He remembered when he was a child how he hated her long nose, her long yellow neck and her doleful voice always crying out against somebody, her son, her kitchen-maid, or Joseph himself. She used to turn him out of her kitchen and larder and dairy, saying that his place was upstairs, and once raised her hand to him; later she had complained to his father of his thefts; for he brought his dogs with him and stole the larder key and cut off pieces of meat for them, and very often dipped jars into the pans of milk that were standing for cream. His father reproved him, and from that day he hated Esora, casting names at her, and playing many pranks upon her until the day he tipped a kettle of boiling water over his foot while running to scald the wasps in their nest — one of the apes was stung; it was to avenge the sting he was running, and no one had known how to relieve his suffering; his father had gone away for the doctor, but Esora, as soon as she heard what had happened, came with her balsam, and it subdued the pain almost miraculously. After his scalding Joseph had brought all his troubles to her to be cured, confiding to her care coughs, colds, and cut fingers; and, as she never failed to relieve his pain, whatever it was, he began to look upon her with respect and admiration. All the same something of his original dislike remained. He disliked her while he admired her, and his suspicion was that she loved him more for his father's sake than for his own. . . . It was his father who sent her from Galilee to look after him. There was no fault to find with her management, but he could not rid his mind of the belief that she was a hard taskmistress, and often fell to pitying the servants under her supervision, yet here she was up before day while Matred lay drowsing. This testimony of her kind heart was agreeable to him, for he had need of as much fellow-feeling as he could get that morning — only with her help could Jesus be cured of his wounds and the story of his escape from the cross be kept a secret from the Jews; and for it to be kept he must confide to her the whole story, and unwilling, but confident of her loyalty to him, he told her that he had left his door open because he wished to speak to her privily whilst the others were still a-bed.

Esora, I have a story to tell thee. Thou hast not been in bed, Master, and there is dust on thy garments, and blood on thy hands and sleeves. Yes, Esora, my cloak is full of dust, and the blood on my sleeve is that of a man who lies wounded in the gardener's cottage belike to death. But thou canst cure him and wilt keep the secret of his burial if we have to bury him in the garden. It may be that some day I'll tell thee his story, but think now only how thou mayst relieve his suffering. Another time thou shalt hear everything; but now, Esora, understand nobody must know that a man is in the gardener's cottage. It is a matter of life and death for us. I am here to serve thee, Master, and it matters not to me what his story may be; but tell how he is wounded : are the wounds the clean wounds of the sword or the torn wounds of rods? If he have been scourged —— A cruel scourging it must have been, Joseph answered. Now, before we go, Esora, understand that I shall send the two men away, one to Galilee and one to Jericho. Better both should go to Jericho, she said. I'd trust neither in Jerusalem. Let them go straight from here as soon as the Sabbath is over, the journey is shorter, and they'll be as well out of the way in one country as in the other. Esora is wiser than I, Joseph thought, and together they shall go to Jericho, and with an important message. But to whom? Not to Gaddi, who might come up to Jerusalem to see me. I'll send a letter to Hazael, the Essene, and after having delivered the message they can remain at the caravansary in Jericho. Some excuse that will satisfy Gaddi must be discovered, Esora. I shall find one later. Both the men are now in bed, but if for some reason one of them should come down to the gardener's cottage! It isn't likely, Esora answered. Not likely, Joseph replied; but we must guard against anything. If thou knewest the risk! I'll lock the door of the passage leading to their rooms, and I'll do it at once. Give me the keys. She handed him the keys, and, having locked the men in, he returned, saying : The wounded man, whom thou'lt cure, Esora, may be here for a month or more, and till he leaves us thou must watch the girl and see she doesn't stray through the garden. I can manage her, Esora answered. But now about the
204

poor man suffering in the gardener's cottage. What hast thou done for him, Master, in my absence? I picked from his back the splinters I could see by the light of the lamp, and gave him some wine and water, and laid him on a linen cloth. The old woman muttered that the drawing of the cloth from the wound would be very painful. I dare say it will, Joseph returned, but I knew not what else to do, and it seemed to relieve him. Canst thou help him, Esora? Yes, I can; and she began telling him of her own famous balsam, the secret of which was imparted to her by her mother, who had it from her mother; and her great-grandmother learnt it from an Arabian. But knowledge of the balsam went back to the Queen of Sheba, who brought the plant to King Solomon. Thou must have seen the bush in the garden in Galilee. It throws a white flower, like the acacia, and the juice when drawn passes through many colours, honey colour and then green. The Egyptians use it for many sicknesses, and it heals wounds magically. The sweet liquor pours from cuts in the branches, and care must be taken not to wound them too sorely. This plant fears the sword, for it heals sword wounds, so the cuts in the tree are best made with a sharp flint or shell, these being holier than steel. If thou hast missed the bush in Magdala, Master, thou must have seen it in Jericho, for I brought some seeds from Galilee to Jericho and planted them by the gardener's cottage. Esora, all that thou tellest me about the balsam is marvellous. I could listen to thee for hours, and thou'lt tell me about thy grandmother and the Arabian who taught her how to gather the juice of the plant, but we must be thinking now of my friend's agony. Hast any of thy balsam ready, or must thou go to Jericho for the juice? — or wilt draw it from the tree? No, Master, Esora answered him, I have here in my press a jar of the balsam, and, going to her press, she held the jar to Joseph, who saw a white, milky liquid, and after smelling and liking its sweet smell he said: Let us go at once. But thou mustn't hurry me, Master; I'm collecting bandages of fine linen and getting this kettle of water to boil; for this I learnt from a man who learnt it from the best surgeons in Rome: that freshly boiled water holds no more the humours that make wounds fructify, and if boiled long enough the humours fall to the bottom. I strain them off, and let the water cool. Thou mustn't hurry me: what I do, I do well, and at my own
205

pace; and I'll not touch a wound with unclean things. Now I'll get some oil. Some hold Denbalassa is best mixed with oil, but I pour oil upon the balm after I have laid it on the wound, and by this means it will stick less when it is removed. But is thy friend a patient man? Wounds from scourging heal slowly; the flesh is bruised and many humours must come away; wounds from rods are not like the clean cut of a sword, which will heal under the balm when the edges have been brought together carefully, so that no man can find the place. This balm will cure all kinds of coughs, and will disperse bile, as many a time I have found. Some will wash a wound with wine and water, but I hold it heats the blood about the wound and so increases the making of fresh humours. Now, Master, take up the pot of water, and be sure to hold it steady; the basket with the oil and the balm I will carry myself. It was the Queen of Sheba who first made the balm known, for she gave it to Solomon. But we must keep the flies from him; and while I'm getting these things go to him and take with thee a fine linen cloth; thou'lt find some pieces in that cupboard, and a hammer and some nails. I'm thinking there are few flies in the gardener's cottage, half of it being underground; but hasten and nail up the linen cloth over the window, for the first sun ray will awaken any that are in the cottage, and, if there aren't any, flies will come streaming in from the garden as soon as the light comes, following the scent of blood. No, not there, a little to the right, he heard her crying, and, finding a piece of linen and a hammer and some nails, he went out into the greyness still undisturbed by the chirrup of a half-awakened bird.

On either side of the shelving lawn or interspace the remains of ancient forests covered the hillside, and taking the path of overnight he followed it, marvelling that he was able to keep in it with a naked man on his shoulders, so difficult was it, twisting suddenly between great rocks. Any false step would have cost Jesus his life, he said; God must have upheld me. And remembering as he walked that he had found the gardener's cottage unlocked, he deemed himself fortunate, for had he found it locked he would have had to lay Jesus down whilst he forced the door open, and after so much striving he might not have been able to lift him up again. And his thoughts returning from the past to the present, he asked
206

himself if Jesus were dead, or passing into a swoon, or lying in agony. His steps hastened, but when he came to the cottage he stood outside listening to the moans of the wounded man within, which were good to hear in this much that they were an assurance that he was still alive. At last he pushed the door open and found Jesus moving his head from side to side, trying to rid himself of a fly that crawled about his mouth. Joseph drove it away and gave Jesus some weak wine and water, which seemed to soothe him, and feeling he could do no more he sat down by the bedside to wait for Esora. A few minutes after he heard her steps; she came into the cottage with balsam and bandages in a basket, and divining before any examination Jesus's state, she said : He is in a bad way; thou hast given him wine and water, but he'll need something stronger; and taking a bottle from her basket, she lifted Jesus's head so that he might drink better. It will help him to bear the pain of the dressing. And now, Master, do thou roll him over on to his side, so that I may see his back. The pain, she said, looking up, when we remove this cloth on which thou hast laid him will almost kill him, but we must get it off. The water with which I'll cleanse the wound thou'lt find in that basket, and cool enough to use now. Take him by the wrists and pull him forward, keeping him in a sitting position. Which Joseph did, Esora washing his back the while and removing the splinters that Joseph had missed overnight. And, taking pleasure in her ministrations, she steeped a piece of linen in the balm, and over the medicated linen laid a linen pad, rolling a bandage round the chest; and the skill with which she wound it surprised Joseph and persuaded him that the worst was over and there was no cause for further fear, a confidence Esora did not share. He'll rest easier, she said, and will suffer no pain at the next dressing; for the oil will prevent the balm from sticking. We can roll him on his back now, and without asking any question she dressed his hands and feet, her reticence pleasing Joseph, and when her work was done he nailed up the fine linen cloth before the window, saying : Now he is secure from the flies. But one or two have got in already, Esora answered, and one or two will trouble the sick man as much as a hundred. We can't leave him alone; one of us must watch by his side; for he is still delirious and knows not yet what has befallen him nor where he is. If he were to return

207

to clear reason and find the door locked he might lose his reason for good and all, and if we left the door open he might run out into the garden, to meet Matred or the two men-servants. It isn't safe to leave him. And Joseph, perceiving all she said to be good sense, took counsel with her, and his resolve was that the two men-servants should remain in the house till sunset —— When I shall send them away to Jericho on my own horses, which will surprise them, but that can't be helped. A day of watching lies before us, Esora. We shall have to take it in turns; neither can be away for more than two hours at a time from the house. Matred will be asking questions whether she is to feed the poultry or to kill a chicken, and though it be the Sabbath, she'll find reasons to be about because we would have her indoors. And when I'm watching by the sick man, Esora answered, she'll be asking: Where, Master, is Esora? Thou'lt have to invent excuses. We've forgotten the servants, Esora. Give me the key. I must run with it and unlock the door of the passage, and do thou wait here for me till I return after waking them.

He hoped to find his servants asleep, and his hopes were fulfilled; and after rousing them with vigorous reproof for their laziness, he descended the stairs, thinking of the letter he would devise for them to carry to Jericho. These men, Sarea and Asiel, were his peril. Once they were away on their journey to Jericho he would feel easier. But all these hours I shall suffer, he said. But, Master, they know the cottage to be empty. One never can think, my good Esora, whither idle men will be wandering, and the risk is great. Having gone so far we must have courage, Esora answered. Now give me the key, and I'll lock myself in with him; we'll take it in turns, and the day will not be as long going by as thou thinkest. It is now the first hour, he answered: the day will have to pass before the men start for Jericho. And then the night will be before us, replied Esora. I hadn't thought of the night, Joseph answered, and she reminded him that it might be days before his friend, who had been scourged, could recover sufficiently for him to leave. For he won't always remain here, she added. No! no! Joseph replied, and gave her the key of the cottage, and returned to the house to tell Sarea and Asiel that he hoped they would remain indoors during the Sabbath, for he wished them to start for Jericho as soon as

208

the Sabbath was over. They shall ride my horses, he said to himself, and bear letters that will detain them in Jericho for some weeks, and if Jesus be not well enough to leave me, another letter will delay their return. It can be so arranged, with a little luck on our side! . . . The lantern suddenly flashed into his mind. He had left it on the table in his room and Esora would see it! But why shouldn't she see the lantern? The centurion and the carrier and Martha and Mary all knew that he had brought from Jerusalem a sheet in which to wrap the body of Jesus, and a lantern to light their way into the tomb. It would be in agreement with what he had already said to tell that he brought the lantern back with him, nor would it have mattered if he had not returned to the tomb to fetch the lantern. The lantern would not cast any suspicion upon him. But he had done well to refrain from closing the sepulchre with the stone, for the story of the resurrection would rise out of the empty tomb, and though there were many among the Jews who would not believe the story, few would have the courage to inquire into the truth of a miracle; and with a faint smile on his lips, he began to wonder what the expression would be on the faces of Martha and Mary when they came to him on the morrow with the news that Jesus had risen from the dead.

CHAPTER XX.

HE said to himself that they would start at dawn, and coming to the sepulchre soon thereafter, and finding it empty, would come running to him, and, so that himself might open the gate to them, he ordered his watch (it should have ended by midnight) to continue for four more hours. And, sitting by the sick man's side, he listened expectant for the hush that comes at the end of night. At last it fell upon his ear. The women are on their way to the sepulchre, he said, and in about an hour and a half I'll hear the bell clang. But the bell clanged sooner than he thought for; and so impatient was he to see them that he did not remember to draw his cloak about him as if he were only half dressed (a necessary thing to do if he were to deceive them) till he was in the middle of the garden. But feigning of disordered raiment was vanity, for the women were too troubled to notice that he had not kept them waiting long enough to testify of any sudden rousing from his bed, and began to cry aloud as he approached: He has risen! he has risen from the dead as he promised us! Joseph came towards them yawning, as if his sleep were not yet dispersed enough for him to comprehend them; and he let them through the gate, inviting them into his house; but they cried: He's risen from the dead! The sepulchre is empty! Mary cried, anticipating her sister's words, and we have come to thee for counsel. Are we to tell what we have seen? Seen! said Joseph. Forthwith both began to babble about a young man in a white raiment. His counsel to them was neither to spread the news nor to conceal it. Let the apostles, he began — but Martha interrupted him, saying: They are all in hiding, in great fear of the Pharisees, who have power over Pilate, and he will condemn them all to the cross, so they say, if they do not escape at once into Galilee. But since we can vouch that we found the

210

stone rolled away and a young man in white garments in the sepulchre, we are uncertain that they may not take courage and delay their departure, for they can no longer doubt the second coming of the Lord in his chariot of fire by the side of his Father, the Judgment Book upon his lap. Those that have already gone will return, Mary answered; and our testimony will cause the wicked Pharisees to repent before it be too late. His words were that his blood was the means whereby we might rise into everlasting life. Martha then broke in with much discourse, which Joseph interrupted with a question : Had the young man they saw in the tomb spoken to them? The sisters were taken aback, and stood asking each other what he said, Martha saying one thing and Mary another; and so bewildered were they that Joseph bade them return to Bethany and relate to Lazarus, and any others of their company they might meet, all they had seen and heard : If you've heard anything, he added. Then thou believest Jesus to be risen from the dead, they cried through the bars as he locked the gates. Yes, I believe that Jesus lives. Will he return to us? Martha cried; and Joseph as he crossed the garden heard Mary crying through the dusk : Shall we see him again? A fine story they'll relate, one which will not grow smaller as it passes from mouth to mouth. Sooner or later it will reach Pilate, and Pilate's first thought will be : The centurion told me that Jesus died on the cross after three hours; and I believed him, though it was outside of all reason to suppose the cross could kill a man in three hours. But if the Pharisees should go to Pilate and say to him : The rumour is about that Jesus has risen from the dead. Wilt thou, Pilate, cause a search to be made from house to house? to which Pilate would answer that the law had been fulfilled, and that the testimony of his centurion was enough; for he hated the Pharisees and would refuse any other answer. But Pilate might send for him, Joseph; and Joseph fell to wondering at the answers he would make to Pilate, and at the duplicity of these, for he had never suspected himself of cunning. But circumstances make the man, he said, and before Jesus passes out of my keeping I shall have learnt to speak even as he did in double meanings, as Pilate did — as indeed all men do. He lay down to sleep, and when he rose it was time to go to help Esora to change the bandages, and while they were busy unwinding them (it was towards the end of the afternoon) they were interrupted suddenly in their work by Matred's voice in the garden calling : Esora, where are you ? and, not getting an answer from Esora, she cried : Master ! Master ! A moment after her voice came from a different part of the garden, and Joseph said to Esora : She'll be knocking at the door in another minute; she mustn't come hither. Go and meet her, Esora, and as soon as the girl is safe come back to me. It shall be as thou sayest, Master; but meanwhile hold the man forward; let him not fall back upon the pillow, for he will stick there and my work will be undone. Joseph obeyed her, quaking lest the Pharisees should come in search of Jesus, saying to himself : The Pharisees might be persuaded that Jesus is risen from the dead, but the Sadducees do not believe in the resurrection. What answer shall I give to them ?

At last he heard Esora's voice outside : Fear nothing, Master, for friends have come; one named Cleophas and another are here with a story of a miracle, and, unable to rid myself of them without rudeness, I asked them into the house, saying that we had business together (meaning that we must finish dressing this poor man's wounds), but as soon as our business was finished thou wouldst go to meet them. The very answer thou shouldst have given, Joseph said, and went towards the house certain and sure that they too came to tell Jesus's resurrection; and the moment he entered it and saw his guests, their faces and demeanour told him that he guessed rightly. Leaning towards them over the table familiarly, so as to help them to narrate simply, he heard Cleophas, whom the friend elected as spokesman, say they heard Martha and Mary telling that they had found the stone rolled away, and a young man in white raiment seated where Jesus was overnight, and from him they had learnt that he whom they sought was risen from the dead. So we said to one another : If he sent an angel to tell these women of his resurrection he will not forget us, for we loved him; and in hopes of getting news of him in the country, and that we might better think of him, we agreed to walk together to Emmaus, a village about threescore furlongs from Jerusalem; for when a man is sad he likes to be with another one who may share his sadness, and Khuza and I have always loved the same Jesus of Nazareth. And thither we walked sadly, without speech, indulging in
212

recollections of Jesus, and were half-way on our journey when a wayfarer approached us and asked us the cause of our grief. We asked him in reply if he were the only one in Jerusalem that had not heard speak of Jesus of Nazareth, a great prophet before God and the people. Dost thou not know that our priests and our rulers condemned him who we hoped would deliver Israel and to-day is the third day since all that has befallen? Some women of our company told us this morning that they had been to the sepulchre at daybreak and found nobody, but had seen angels, who told them that he lived; and then others of our company went to the sepulchre and they found that the women spoke truthfully; the tomb was empty of all but the cere-cloths. So did we tell the story to the wayfarer, who then asked us whither our way was, and we told him to Emmaus, and that our hope was our Master might send an angel to us with news of himself. It was with that hope that we left the city. And thy way, honoured Sir? and he answered me: To Emmaus; and perceiving him as we walked thither to be a pious man, and more learned than ourselves in the Scriptures, we begged him to remain with us. He seemed averse, as if he had business farther on, but myself and my friend here, Khuza, persuaded him to stay and sup with us, so that we might tell our memories of him that was gone. But he seemed to know all we related to him of Jesus, interrupting us often with: As was foretold in the Scriptures, giving us chapter and verse; and enlivened by a glass of good wine, he spoke to us of the fruit of the vine which Jesus would drink with us in the Kingdom of his Father; and he broke bread and shared it with us, as it was meet that the head of the house should, and the gesture with which he broke it is one of our memories of Jesus. We fell to dreaming ourselves back in Galilee, and the intonations of Jesus's voice and the faces of the apostles were all remembered by us. We don't know for how long we dreamed, but when our eyes were opened to reality again we saw that our friend, who was anxious to continue his journey, had risen and gone away without bidding us good-bye, belike not wishing to disturb the current of our recollections. Did we not feel something strange while he was with us? my friend asked me, so to my friend here I put the question: Did not our hearts burn while he spoke to us on the road hither? and I cited prophecies that were

213

testimony that the Messiah must suffer before he entered into glory. And Khuza answered: Didst thou not recognise him, Cleophas, by the manner in which he broke bread? Now you speak of it, I replied . . . Our eyes that had not seen saw, and we knew that Jesus had been with us, and hurried to Jerusalem to tell the apostles that we had seen him. But their hearts are hard and narrow and dry, as Jesus himself well knew, and as he said would be shown at the striking of the hour, and when we told Peter that Martha and Mary had been to the sepulchre and found the stone rolled away he answered: I too have visited the sepulchre and saw nothing. It was open, but I saw no young man sitting in white raiment, nor did an angel greet me. John said: Three days have now passed away since he was put on the cross, and in three days he was to have returned in a chariot of fire by the side of his Father and made a great Kingdom of happiness and peace in this country. But he hasn't come; he has deceived us and put our lives in jeopardy, for if the Pharisees find us here they'll bring us before Pilate, who is a man without mercy, and eleven more will hang on crosses. Salome, mother of John and James, too, got in her word and railed against Jesus for having brought them all from Galilee for naught. John and James, he promised me, were to sit on either side of him in the Kingdom that's to come. Whereupon Peter said: Thou liest, woman. I was to sit on his right hand. And while these disciples disputed on Jesus's words Bartholomew praised Judas, who had withdrawn as soon as Jesus began to talk of the angels that would surround the chariot. Thomas reproved Bartholomew, saying that Jesus never said that there would be angels; and they all began to wrangle, asking each other how many angels would be required to match a Roman legion. Nor were they sure that Jesus said he was God's own son, and equal to God; at which many were scandalised and turned away their faces; nor could they say that they had not desired to find a god in him on account of the chairs. I'm not speaking of James and John. And then the ugly twain turned upon us, saying that we — myself and Khuza — were but disciples and could baptize with water, but not with the holy breath, which was reserved for the apostles; nor with fire. At their words the lightning flashed into the room, and John said: We are in the midst of a great miracle — the baptism by fire of the apostles. And when the

214

storm ceased they were all mixed in a dispute about the imposition of hands; of this rite they were the inheritors, so they said, and all were resolved to practise it as soon as they got back to Galilee, from whence they had foolishly strayed, abandoning their boats and nets. On the morrow they would return thither and pray that the Lord, who is the only god of Israel, would forgive them and send them a great draught of fish, which they hoped thy father would buy at a higher price than they could get in the market at Tiberias, to make good their loss in following the Master hither.

Joseph would have asked him if Thomas and Bartholomew denied Jesus, as well as Peter and James and John, and if there was not one among the eleven who had faith that Jesus might return. But prudence restrained him from putting needless questions, for Cleophas was loquacious, and he had only to listen to hear that Peter and James and John were eager that it should be known that they no longer believed Jesus to be the true Messiah the Jews were waiting for. It is said, Khuza interrupted, becoming suddenly talkative in his turn, it is said that they are afraid lest the agents of the Pharisees should discover them. Many left for Galilee on the Friday evening, and in three days the fishers he brought hither will be letting down their nets again and the publican Matthew will start on his round asking for the taxes. All will be —— But, said Joseph, whose thoughts had gone back to the great draught of fish which Peter and John hoped his father would pay for above the usual price, so that they might be recompensed for their journey to Jerusalem, you did not come to me to pray me to write to my father that he may punish the apostles for their lack of faith by refusing to buy their fish? No, it wasn't for that we came hither, Khuza answered quickly, and Cleophas looked at him, wondering if he would have the courage to put into words the cause of their visit. We thought that because Pilate had given the body of Jesus to thee to lay in thy sepulchre, and as thou wert the last to see him, thou might come into Jerusalem with us and declare the miracle to the people. Thou knowest, Sir, that Martha and Mary have testified to the rolling back of the stone, and no more is needed than thy word for all to believe. Joseph looked in their faces for some moments, unable to reply to them; and then, collecting his thoughts as he spoke, he impressed upon Cleophas and Khuza that

215

for him to go down to Jerusalem and proclaim his belief in the resurrection would only anger the Pharisees and give rise to further persecutions. It will be better, he said, to let the truth leak out and convince men naturally, without suspicion that we are attempting to deceive them with testimony which their hearts are already hardened against. This answer, which showed a knowledge of men that Joseph did not know he possessed, satisfied both Cleophas and Khuza, and perceiving that they were detaining Joseph they rose to go. On the way to the gate Joseph's words lighted up in their minds; he said it would not be well for him to go down to Jerusalem and proclaim his belief in the resurrection; therefore he believed in the resurrection, and, unable to restrain his curiosity, Khuza besought him to answer if Jesus ever said that it would be his corruptible body or a spiritual body (a sort of spirit of sense) that would ascend. It could not be the fleshy body which eats and drinks and passes soil and water, for unless there be in heaven corners where one can loosen one's belt the body would be gravely incommoded; and he began to argue, placing his foot so that Joseph could not close the gate, saying that if the corruptible body had not ascended into heaven it must be upon earth. But where—— Joseph's cheek paled, and Cleophas, noticing the pallor and interpreting it to mean Joseph's anger against his friend for his insistence in putting questions which Joseph could not answer — for had he not rolled up the stone of the sepulchre and sealed it and gone his way? — took his friend by the arm and said: We must leave Joseph of Arimathea some time to attend to his business. We are detaining him. Come, Khuza, we are trespassing on his time. Joseph smiled in acquiescence; but Khuza, who was still anxious to learn how many Roman soldiers equalled one angel, hung on until Joseph's patience ran dry. At last Cleophas got him away, and no sooner were their backs turned than Joseph forgot them completely as if they had never been: for Esora had said that she hoped to be able to get Jesus to swallow a little soup, and he hastened his steps, anxious to know if she had succeeded.

I got him to swallow two or three spoonfuls, she said, and they seem to have done him good. Dost think he seems to be resting easier? Yes; but the fever hasn't left him. His brain is still clouded and feeble. This is but the third day, she replied. Truthfully I can

216

say that I've never seen any man scourged like this one. It is more than the customary scourging; the executioners must have gotten an extra fee. As she had seen men crucified in Tiberias and Cæsarea, he asked her if it were common for the crucified to live after being lifted from the cross. Those that haven't been on the cross more than two days are brought back frequently, but the third day ends them, so great are the pains in the head and heart. But I knew one — and she began to relate the almost miraculous recovery of a man who had been on the cross for nearly three days, and had been brought back by strong remedies to live to a good old age. But none die on the first day? Joseph said, and Esora answered that she never heard of anyone that died so quickly; without, however, asking Joseph if the man before them had been lifted from the cross the first, second or third day. She will bring him back, he said to himself, and he expected her to ask him if Cleophas had come to warn him that inquiries were on foot regarding the disappearance of the body of one of the crucified; but she asked no questions, and he knew not whether she refrained from discretion or because her interest in things was dying. Not dying but dead, he said to himself as he scanned the years that her face and figure manifested, and judged them to be eighty. Now, Esora, I'll go and lie down for a little while, and lest I should oversleep myself I'll tell the girl to call me. But how shall I recompense thee for this care, Esora? I am too old, Master, to hope for anything but thy pleasure, she answered, and when he returned she told him that Jesus was fallen into another swoon, and they began talking of the sick man. His mind wanders up and down Galilee, she said. And now I'll leave thee to him. I've that girl on my mind. And while Jesus slept, Joseph pondered on the extraordinary adventure he found himself in, and gave thanks to God for having chosen him as the humble instrument of his will.

CHAPTER XXI.

IT was after she had persuaded him to take a little soup, which he did with some show of relish, that Esora began to think she might save him: If his strength does not die away, she said. But will it? Joseph inquired. Not if he continues to take food, she replied; and two hours later she returned to the bedside to feed him again, and for a few seconds he was roused from his lethargy; but it was not till the seventh day that his eyes seemed to ask: Who art thou, and who am I? And how came I hither? Thou'rt Jesus of Nazareth, and I am Joseph of Arimathea, whom thou knewest in Galilee, and it was I that brought thee hither, but more than that I dare not tell lest too much story should fatigue thy brain. I do not remember coming here. Where am I? Is this a holy place? Was a prophet ever taken away to heaven from here? Afraid to perplex the sick man, Joseph answered that he never heard that anything of the sort had happened lately. But thou canst tell me, Jesus continued, why thou'rt here? Thou'rt the rich man's son. Ah, yes, and my sorrow for some wrong done to thee brought thee hither. His eyelids fell over his eyes, and a few minutes afterwards he opened them, and after looking at Joseph repeated: My sorrow brought thee here; and still in doubt as to what answer he should make, Joseph asked him if he were glad he was by him. Very glad, he said, and strove to take Joseph's hand. But my hand pains me, and the other hand likewise; my feet too; my forehead; my back; I am all pain. Thou must have patience, Esora broke in, and the pain will pass away. Who is that woman? A leper, or one suffering from a flux of blood? Tell her I cannot impose my hands and cast out the wicked demon that afflicts her. He mustn't be allowed to talk, Esora said; he must rest. And on these words he seemed to sink into a lethargy. Has he fallen asleep again? It is sleep or lethargy,

218

she answered, and they went to the door of the cottage, and, leaning against the doorposts, stood balancing the chances of the sick man's recovery. We can do no more, she said, than we are doing, putting our trust in the balsam, giving him food as often as he'll take it from us, watching by him lest he should rise and wander. And thus they did day after day, relieving each other's watches, standing over Jesus's bed conferring together, asking if he cared to live or would liefer that they suffered him to die; and in their charge he lay like a piece of wreckage. Nor was it till the end of seven more days that he seemed to rouse a little out of his lethargy, or his indifference — they knew not which it was. In answer to Esora he said he felt easier, and would be glad if they would wheel his bed nearer to the door. Outside is the garden, he whispered, for I see boughs waving, and can hear the bees. Wilt thou let me go into the garden? As soon as I've removed the dressing thou shalt have a look into the garden, Esora replied, and she called upon Joseph to pull Jesus forward. All this, she said, was raw flesh a week ago, and now the scab is coming away nicely; thou seest the new skin my balsam is bringing up. His feet, too, are healing, Joseph observed, and look as if he will be able to stand upon them in another few days. Wounds do not heal as quickly as that, Master. Thou must have patience. But he'll be wanting a pair of crutches very soon. We might send to Jerusalem for a pair. There is no need to send to Jerusalem, he answered. I think I'd like to make his crutches. Anybody can make crutches, however poor a carpenter he may be; and every evening as soon as his watch was over Joseph repaired to the woodshed. They won't be much to look at, Esora reflected, but that will not matter, if he gets them the right length, and strong. Come and see them, he said to her one evening, and when she had admired his handiwork sufficiently he said: Tell me, Esora, is a man's mind the same after scourging and crucifixion as it was before? Esora shook her head. I suppose not, Joseph continued, for our minds draw their lives from our bodies. He'll be a different man if he comes up from his sickness. But he may live to be as old as I am, or the patriarchs, she returned. With a different mind, he added. So I've lost him in life whom I saved from death. What meaneth he? Esora asked herself, but put no question; and fearing that her master might tell her things he

219

might afterwards rue having said, she remarked that Jesus would be needing the crutches in about another week. And it was indeed in or about that time that not finding Jesus in the cottage, they came down the pathway in great alarm, to be brought to a sudden stop by the sight of him sitting under the cedars. How could he come there? Esora cried, for the crutches were in the woodshed. They were, Esora, but I took them down to the cottage last night, and seeing them, and finding they fitted him, he has hobbled to the terrace. But he mustn't hobble about where he pleases, Esora said. He is a sick man and in our charge, and if he doesn't obey us he may fall back again into sickness. The bones have not properly set —— We do not know that any bones were broken, do we, Esora? We do not; for the nails may have pierced the feet and hands without breaking any. But, Master, look! Didst ever see such imprudence? Go! drive away my cat, else my work will be undone.

Her cat, large, strong and supple as a tiger, had advanced from the opposite wood, and, unmindful of a bitch and her puppies, seated himself in the middle of the terrace. As he sat tidying his coat the puppies conceived the foolish idea of a gambol with him. The cat continued to lick himself, though no doubt fully aware of the puppies' intention, and it was not till they were almost on him that he rose, hackle erect, to meet the onset in which they would have been torn badly if Jesus had not hopped hastily forward and menaced him with his crutches. Even then the puppies, unmindful of the danger, continued to dance round the cat. You little fools, he will have your eyes, Jesus cried, and he caught them up in his arms, but unable to manage them and his crutches together, he dropped the crutches and started to get back to his seat without them. Go to his help, Joseph; give him his crutches. All my work will be undone if he fall. Run, Joseph, and pick up his crutches; but smite not my cat with them lest he return to the woods wild and we be overrun with mice. Give thine arm to Jesus; lead him back to his seat. . . . And now tell him he must leave cats and dogs alone, she said as soon as Joseph returned to her, else we shall have him on our hands all the winter. All the winter! Joseph repeated. It is for thee to say, Master, how long he is to stay here; three weeks, till he is fit to travel, or all the winter; it is for thee to say. Fit to

220

travel, Joseph repeated. Why should he leave when he is fit to travel? he asked. Only, Master, because it will be hard to keep him in hiding much longer. Secrets take a long time to leak out, but they leak out in the end. But I may be wrong, Master, in thinking that there is a secret. Of this man I know only that he was brought back by thee one night. So thou'rt not certain then that there is a secret, Esora? Joseph said. I won't say that, Master, for I can see by his back that he has been scourged, and cruelly, she answered. His hands and feet testify that he has been on the cross. Therefore, Joseph interposed, thou judgest him to be a malefactor of some sort. Master, I would judge no one. He is what thou choosest to tell me he is. Come then, Esora, Joseph replied, and I will tell thee his story and mine, for our stories have been strangely interwoven. But the telling will take some time. Come, let us sit in the shade of the acacia-trees yonder; there is a seat there, and we shall be in view of our sick man, ready to attend upon him should he require our attention.

She sat listening, immovable, like a figure of stone, her hands hanging over her knees. And when he told how Jesus opened his eyes in the tomb, and how he carried him through the rocks, seeking perhaps to astonish her a little by his account of the darkness, and the wild beasts, he said: Now tell me, Esora, if I could have done else but bring him here on my shoulders. True it is that Pilate believed he was giving me not a live but a dead body; but Pilate wouldn't expect me to go to him with the tidings that Jesus was not dead, and that he might have him back to hoist on to a cross again. Pilate did not want to give him up for crucifixion. He found no fault with him. Dost understand, Esora? I understand very well, Master, that Pilate would think thee but a false friend if thou hadst acted differently. He would not have thanked thee if thou hadst brought back this man to him. But, Esora, thy face wears a puzzled look. One thing puzzles me, she answered. I have no imagination of how he came by the belief that he was sent into the world to suffer for others. For are we not all suffering for others? she asked. The winning reasonableness of her question, and the truth that her simple understanding had discovered, took Joseph aback, and he replied: I suppose thou'rt right in a way, Esora. Thou hast no doubt suffered for thy parents; I have

221

suffered for my father, leaving Galilee to keep my promise not to
see Jesus; and when I heard Jesus was going to ride into Jerusalem
in triumph on an ass from Bethany I ran away to Jericho. Could a
man do more to keep his promise? Alas, it was of no avail, for
we may not change in our little lives the fate we were branded with
a thousand years before we were born. Thou'rt of one mind with
me, Esora, that I couldn't have left him to die in the sepulchre?
Thou couldst not have done such a thing and remained thyself,
she answered, and it was God that gave thee those fine broad shoulders for the burden, as I know well, having seen thee as a baby,
and thou hast grown into a fine image like those they've put up to
Cæsar in Tiberias; and then, as if abashed by her familiarity,
she began : Master, I wouldn't wish him to return to Jerusalem,
for they would put him on the cross again, but he had better leave
Judea. Art thou weary, Esora, of attendance on him? Joseph
asked, and the servant answered : Have I ever shown, Master,
that I found attendance on him wearisome? He is so gentle and
patient that it is a pleasure to attend on him, and an awe, for one
feels him to be a great man. The highest I have met among men,
Joseph interposed, and I have searched diligently, wishing always
to worship the best on earth. He is that, and maybe there's no
better in heaven; after God comes Jesus, on earth as he will be in
heaven. It wouldn't be a woman then that thou wouldst choose to
meet in heaven, but a man? Men love women, Joseph said, for
their corruptible bodies, and women love men for theirs; but even
the lecher would choose rather to meet a man in heaven, and the
wanton another woman. If we would discover whom we love most,
we can do so by asking ourselves whom we would choose to meet in
heaven. Heaven without Jesus would not be heaven for me. But if
he be not the Messiah after all? Esora asked. Should I love him
less? he answered her. None is as perfect as he. I have known him
long, Esora, and can say truly that none is worthy to be the carpet
under his feet. I have said naught of this to thee before, but I am
glad to have spoken, for now thou understandest how much thou
hast done for me. Thou and thy balsam and thy ministration. My
balsam, she answered, has done better than I expected it would do.
Thou sawest his back this morning. One can call it cured. His
hands and feet have mended and his strength is returning. In a
222

few days he will be fit to travel. This is the third time, Esora, that thou hast said he'll be able to travel soon — yet thou sayest he is so patient and gentle that it is a pleasure to attend on him; and an awe. But, Master, the danger is great, and every day augments the danger. Secrets, as I've said, take a long time to leak out, but they leak out in time. Her words are wise, he thought to himself, and he overlooked her, guessing her to have shrunken to less than her original size; she seemed but a handful of bones and yellow skin, but when she looked up in his face her eyes were alive, and from under a small bony forehead they pleaded, and with quavering voice she said: Let him go, dear Master, for if the Pharisees seek him here and find him, he will hang again on the cross. Thou wouldst have me tell him, Esora, that rumours are about that he did not die on the cross and that a search may be made for him. I wouldn't have thee speak to him of Pilate or his crucifixion, Master, for we don't know that he'd care to look back upon his troubles; he might prefer to forget them as far as he is able to forget them. But thou canst speak to him of his health, Master, which increases every day, and of the benefit a change would be to him. Speak to him if thou wouldst of a sea-voyage, but speak not of anything directly for fear of perplexing him. Lead rather than direct, for his mind must be a sort of maze at present. A great deal has befallen, and nothing exactly as he expected. Nor would I have thee speak to him of anything but actual things; speak of what is before his eyes as much as possible; not a word about yesterday or of to-morrow, only so far as his departure is concerned. Keep his thoughts on actual things, Master: on his health, for he feels that, and on the dogs about his feet, for he sees them; he takes an interest in them; let him speak to thee of them, which will be better still, and in your talk about dogs many things will happen. The hills about Cæsarea may be mentioned; see that they are mentioned; ask him if they are like the hills above Jericho. I cannot tell thee more, Master, but will pray that thou mayst speak the right words.

A shrewd old thing, Joseph thought, as he went towards Jesus, looking back once to see Esora disappearing into the wood. She'd have me keep his thoughts on actual things, he continued, and seeing that Jesus had called the puppies to him, and was making himself their playmate, he asked him if he were fond of dogs; whereupon Jesus began to praise the bitch, saying she was of better breeding than her puppies, and that when she came on heat again she should be sent to a pure Thracian like herself. Jesus looked up, waiting for Joseph's reply, and Joseph knowing naught of dogbreeding asked if the puppies were mongrels. Mongrels, Jesus repeated, overlooking them; not altogether mongrels, threequarter bred; the dog that begot them was a mongrel, half Syrian, half Thracian; I've seen worse dogs highly prized. Send the bitch to a dog of pure Thracian stock to be lined, and thou'lt get some puppies that will be the sort that I used to seek. Joseph waited, for he expected Jesus to speak of the Essenes and of the time when he was their shepherd; but Jesus's thoughts seemed to have wandered from dogs, and to bring them back to dogs again Joseph interposed: Thou wast then a shepherd? But Jesus did not seem to hear him, and as he was about to repeat his question he remembered that Esora told him to keep to the present time. We do not know, she said, what his thoughts are, or even if he thinks at all; better that he should have nothing to think of except the garden. Soon we shall put a rake in his hand and bid him to the sweeping of dead leaves, and later we'll give him an axe, saying: We need faggots for the kitchen fire. A shrewd old thing, Joseph muttered as he sat by Jesus turning her words over in his mind, thinking how he might lead Jesus to remember that he was a Galilean and unaccustomed to the summer heats of Jerusalem. But his every crafty device came to naught, Jesus listening patiently to all he said but unable to think beyond the present time, replying to Joseph's remarks with a helpless stare or a puzzled and pained expression. He is trying to get back into the past and cannot, Joseph said, and he had no heart to rob Jesus of his harmless, innocent mind, still concerned with nothing but the puppies. It is easy for Esora to say: keep to the present time, but I have to speak to him of the future time and I dare not do it; yet dare it I must, for in this garden his life is in jeopardy. And once more Joseph pondered, thinking that Esora could accomplish the task she had set him better than he could himself. But he would not entrust the task to Esora, and was distraught by day and night, till at last he said: Jesus, sea air is better than mountain air, and none as

224

beneficial as the air that blows up from the sea about Cæsarea, a Roman city.

The word Cæsarea brought a change of expression into Jesus's face, and Joseph, interpreting it to mean that Jesus was prejudiced against those coasts, hastened to say that a sick man is often the best judge of the air he needs. But, Joseph, I have none but thee, Jesus said; and the two men sat looking into each other's eyes, Joseph thinking that if Jesus were to recover his mind he would be outcast, as no man had ever been before in the world: without a country, without kindred, without a belief wherewith to cover himself; for nothing, Joseph said to himself as he sat looking into Jesus's eyes, has happened as he thought it would; and no man finds new thoughts and dreams whereby he may live. I did not foresee this double nakedness, or else might have left him to die on the cross. Will he, can he, forgive me? A moment afterwards he recovered hope, for Jesus did not seem to know that the hills beyond the terrace were the Judean hills, and then, as if forgetting the matter in hand (his projected residence in Cæsarea), he began to speak of Bethlehem, saying he could not think of Bethlehem without thinking of Nazareth, a remark that was obscure to Joseph, who did not know Nazareth. It was to make some answer — for Jesus seemed to be waiting for him to answer — that Joseph said: Nazareth is far from Cæsarea, a remark that he soon perceived to be unfortunate, for it awakened doubts in Jesus that he was no longer welcome in Joseph's house. Why speakest thou of Cæsarea to me? he said. Is it because thou wouldst rid thyself of me? Whereupon Joseph besought Jesus to lay aside the thought that he, Joseph, wished him away. I would have thee with me always, deeming it a great honour; but Esora has charge of thy health and has asked me to say that a change is needed. In Cæsarea thou wilt —— My health? Jesus interrupted. Am I not getting my strength quickly? Do not send me away, Joseph, for I am weak in body and in mind; let me stay with thee a little longer; a few days; a few weeks. If I go to Cæsarea I must learn Greek, for that is the language spoken there, and thou'lt teach me Greek, Joseph. Send me not away. But there is no thought of sending thee away, Joseph answered; my house is thy house for as long as thou carest to remain, and the words were spoken with such an accent of truth that

Jesus answered them with a look that went straight to Joseph's heart; but while he rejoiced Jesus's mind seemed to float away: he was absent from himself again, and Joseph had begun to think that all that could be said that day had been said on the subject of his departure from Judea, when a little memory began to be stirring in Jesus, as Esora would say, like a wind in a field. And Joseph waited. I remember thee, Joseph, as one to whom I did a great wrong, but what that wrong was I have forgotten. Do not try to recall it, Joseph said to him, no wrong was done, Jesus. Thou'rt the rich man's son, Jesus said, and what I remember concerning thee is thy horse, for he was handsomer than any other. His name was Xerxes. Dost still ride him? Is he in the stables of yon house? He was sold, Joseph answered, to pay for our journey in Syria, and some of the price went to pay for thy cloak. The cloak on my shoulders? Jesus asked. The cloak on thy shoulders is one of my cloaks. Thou camest here naked. I was carried here by an angel, Jesus replied, for I felt the feathers of his wings brush across my face. But why that strange look, Joseph? — those curious, inquisitive eyes? It was an angel that carried me hither. No, Jesus, it was I that carried thee out of the sepulchre up the crooked path. What is thy purpose in saying that it was no angel but thou? Jesus asked; and Joseph, remembering that he must not say anything that would vex Jesus, regretted having contradicted him and tried to think how he might mend his mistake with words that would soothe Jesus; but, as it often is on such occasions, the more we seek for the right words the further we seem to be from them, and Joseph did not know how he might plausibly unsay his story that he had carried him without vexing Jesus still further. I felt the angel's wings upon my face! Jesus repeated, and Joseph, not knowing how to answer him, was sorely afflicted, and bethought himself of a vain story in which he had shared the burden with an angel. But he dared not utter it, and whilst thinking that it might be well to say that Bethlehem was like Nazareth, he caught sight of Jesus's face, pale as ashes, more like a dead face than a living, and fearing that he was about to swoon again or die, Joseph called loudly for Esora, who came running down the pathway. Thou mustn't call for me so loudly, Master. If Matred had heard thee and come running —— But, Esora, look. As likely as not it is no

226

more than a little faintness, she said. He has been overdoing it: running after puppies, and talking with thee about Cæsarea. But it was thyself told me to ask him to go to Cæsarea for change of air. Never mind, Master, what I told thee. We must think now how we shall get him back to bed. Do thou take one arm and I'll take the other.

CHAPTER XXII.

JESUS did not speak about angels again, and one morning at the end of the week before going away to Jerusalem to attend to some important business Joseph, after a talk with Esora, turned down the alley with the intention of asking Jesus to leave Judea. It would have been better, she said to herself, if he had waited till evening; these things cannot be settled off-hand; he'll only say the wrong thing again, and she stood waiting at her kitchen door, hoping that Joseph would stop on his way out to tell her Jesus's decision, but he went away without speaking, and she began to think it unlikely that anything was decided. He is soft-hearted and without much will of his own, she said. . . . Jesus is going to stay with us, so we may all hang upon crosses yet, unless, indeed, Master comes to hear something in Jerusalem that will bring him round to my way of thinking. He believes, she continued, that Jesus is forgotten because the apostles have returned to their fishing, but that cannot be; the two young women that came here one Sunday morning with a story about an empty sepulchre have found, I'll vouch, plenty of eager gossips; and a smile floated round her old face at the additions she heard to it yester morning at the gates. But no good would come of my telling him, she meditated, for he'd only say it was my fancies, though he has knowledge that I am always right when I speak out of what he calls my fancies. In about three weeks, she muttered, the stories that are going the round will begin to reach his ears.

The old woman's guess was a good one. It was about that time the camel-drivers, assembled in the yard behind the counting-house, began to tell that Jesus had been raised from the dead, and their stories, being overheard by the clerk, were reported to Joseph. The Pharisees are angry with Pilate for not having put a guard of

soldiers over the tomb, the clerk was saying, when Joseph interjected that a guard of soldiers would be of no avail if God had
wished to raise Jesus from the dead. The point of their discourse,
the clerk continued, is that no man but Jesus died on the cross in
three hours; three days, Sir, are mentioned as the usual time. It
is said that a man, Sir, often lingers on until the end of the fourth
day. Joseph remained, his thoughts suspended, and the clerk, being
a faithful servant, and anxious for Joseph's safety, asked if he
might speak a word of counsel, and reading on Joseph's face that
he was permitted to speak, he said: I would have thee make an
end of these rumours, Sir, and this can be done if thou'lt attend
the next meeting of the Sanhedrin and make plain thy reason for
having gone to Pilate to ask him for the body. As it seemed to
Joseph that his clerk had spoken well, he attended the next meeting of the Council, but the business that the councillors had come
together for did not admit of interruption for the sake of personal
explanation, however interesting, and the hostility of everybody
to him was notable from the first. Only a few personal friends spoke
to him; among them was Nicodemus, who would not be dismissed,
but went away with him at the close of the meeting, beseeching
him not to cross the valley unarmed. And if thou wouldst not
draw attention to thyself by the purchase of arms, he said, I will
give thee the arms thou needest for thyself and will arm some
camel-drivers for thee. I thank thee, Nicodemus, but if I were to
return home accompanied by three or four armed camel-drivers I
should draw the attention of Jerusalem upon me, thereby quicken-
ing the anger of the Pharisées, and my death would be resolved
upon. But art thou sure that the hirelings of the priests haven't
been told to kill thee? Nicodemus asked. Pilate's friendship for
me is notorious, Joseph replied. I'm not afraid, Nicodemus, and it
is well for me that I'm not, for assassination comes to the timorous.
That is true, Nicodemus rejoined, our fears often bring about our
destiny, but thou shouldst avoid returning by the valley; return
by the eastern gate and on horseback. But that way, Joseph answered, is a lonely and long one; and thinking it better to put a
bold face on the matter, though his heart was beating, he began
to speak scornfully of the Pharisees who, seemingly, would have
consented to a desecration of the Sabbath. He had done no more

than any other Jew who did not wish the Sabbath to be desecrated, and remembering suddenly that Nicodemus would repeat everything he said, he spoke again of Pilate's friendship, and the swift vengeance that would follow his murder. Pilate is my friend, and whoever kills me makes sure of his own death. I do not doubt that what thou sayest is true, Joseph, but Pilate may be recalled, and it may suit the next Roman to let the priests have their way. I am going to Egypt to-morrow, he said suddenly. To Egypt, Joseph repeated, and memories awoke in him of the months he spent in Alexandria, of the friends he left there, of the Greek that he had taken so much trouble to perfect himself in, and the various philosophies which he thought had enlarged his mind, though he pinned his faith to none; and reading in his face the pleasure given by the word Egypt, Nicodemus pressed him to come with him. All those who are suspected of sympathy with Jesus, he said, will do well to leave Judea for a year at least. Alexandria, as thou knowest, having lived there, is friendly to intellectual dispute. In this city men live in a kingdom that belongs neither to Cæsar nor to God. But all things belong to God, said Joseph. Yes, answered Nicodemus; but God marks no stint for the mind, though priests do this and in the name of God. Remember Egypt, where thou'lt find me, and glad to see thee, Joseph.

On these words the men parted, and Joseph descended into the valley a little puzzled, for the traditionalism of Nicodemus seemed to have undergone a change. But more important than any change that might have happened in Nicodemus's mind was the journey to Egypt he had proposed to Joseph. Joseph would have liked to go to Egypt, taking Jesus with him, and as he walked he beheld in imagination Jesus disputing in the schools of philosophy, and yet if he were to go away to Egypt the promise to his father would be broken fully. If his father were to fall ill he might die before the tidings of that illness could reach him; a year's residence in Egypt was, therefore, forbidden to him; on the top of the Mount of Olives he stopped, so that he might remember that Nicodemus's disposition was always to hear the clashing of swords. Spears are always glittering in his eyes for one reason or another, he said, and though he would regret a friend's death, he would regard it as being atoned for if the brawl were sufficiently violent. He has gone to
230

Egypt, no doubt, because it is pleasing to him to believe his life to be in danger. He invents reasons. Pilate's recall! Now what put that into his mind? He may be right, but this Mount of Olives is peaceful enough and the road beyond leading to my house seems safe to the wayfarer even at this hour. He followed the road in a quieter mood, and it befell that Esora opened the gates to him, for which he thanked her abruptly and turned away, wishing to be alone; but seeing how overcast was his face, she did not return to her kitchen as she had intended, but remained with him, anxious to learn if the rumours she knew to be current had reached his ears. She would not be shaken off by silence, but followed him down the alley leading to Jesus's cottage, answering silence by silence, certain in this way to provoke him thereby into confidences. They had not proceeded far into the wood before they came upon Jesus in front of a heap of dead leaves that he had raked together. A great many have fallen, he said, and the place was beginning to look untidy, so I thought I would gather them for burning. Thou must not tire thyself, Joseph answered, as he passed on with Esora, asking her as they went through the autumn woods if Jesus found the rake for himself or if she gave it to him. He asked me if he might be allowed to feed the chickens, she said, and I would have let him if Matred's window did not overlook the yard. Master, the hope of getting him out of Judea rests upon the chance that he may recover his mind, and staring at the desert all day won't help him. He mustn't brood, and as there is no work like raking up leaves to keep a man's thought off himself, unless, indeed, it be digging, I thought I'd better let him have the rake. But if Matred should meet him? Joseph asked. She will see the new gardener in him, that will be all. I told her last night, Esora continued, that we were expecting the new gardener, and she said it would be pleasant to have a man about the house again. But he mustn't attempt any hard work like digging yet awhile; he has done enough to-day; I'll go and tell him to put away the rake and pass on to his supper. She waited for Joseph to answer, but he was in no humour for speech, and she left him looking at the hills. A boiling land, he said, hill after hill. A cloud lifts, and we are; another cloud descends, and we are not; so much do we know, but we are without sufficient sight to discover the reason behind all this shaping and reshaping,

231

for like all else we ourselves are changing, as Heraclitus said many years ago. And while thinking of this philosopher, whose wisdom he felt to be more satisfying than any other, he paced back and forth, seeking a little while longer to untie the knot that all men seek to untie, abandoning it at last, saying : Fate tied it securely before the beginning of history, and on these words he ran up the steps of his house, pausing on the threshold to listen, for he could distinguish Esora's voice, and Matred's; afterwards he heard Jesus's voice, and he said : Jesus eats with my servants in the kitchen! This cannot be, and he almost obeyed the impulse of the moment, which was to call Jesus and tell him to come and eat his supper with him. To do this, however, would draw Matred's attention to the fact that Jesus was not of her company but of her master's. And distinctions between servants and master, he continued, are not for him, who thinks in eternal terms.

He sat at table, his thoughts away, till awakening suddenly from a reverie, of which he remembered nothing, he rose from his seat and went to the kitchen door, regretting that he was not with Jesus, for to miss his words, however slight they might be, seemed to him to be a loss that could not be repaired. They are listening to him, he said, and with the same pleasure that I used to listen, watching his eyes lighting his words on their way. But at that moment a shuffling of feet sent him back to his seat again, and he put food into his mouth just in time to escape suspicion of eavesdropping. I thought, Master, thy supper being finished, I might take away the plates. I've hardly begun my supper, Esora. Your voices in the kitchen prevented me from eating. We are sorry for that, Master, she replied. Make no excuses, Esora. I said it was the voices in the kitchen that disturbed me, but in truth it was my own thoughts, for I have heard many things to-day in Jerusalem. Esora's face brightened and she said to herself : My words to him are coming true. Sit here, Esora, and I'll tell thee what I've heard to-day. And while Matred listened to Jesus in the kitchen Esora heard from Joseph that the camel-drivers had been talking of the resurrection in the yard behind the counting-house, and that his clerk's advice to him had been to attend the Sanhedrin, and make plain that his reason for going to Pilate to ask for the body of Jesus was because he did not wish a desecration of the Sabbath. But he

232

had only met a show of dark faces, and left the meeting in company with Nicodemus. Esora, is our danger as great as this young man says it is? Master, I have always told thee that as soon as Jesus leaves Judea he will be safe from violence, from death, and we shall be safe too, but not till then. But how are we to persuade him to leave Judea, Esora? Thou must try, Master, to persuade him, there is no other way. He is talking now with Matred in the kitchen. Ask him to come here, and thou'lt see, Esora, the sad face that up-lifts when I speak to him of Cæsarea. I'll speak for thee, Master, she answered, and going to the door she called Jesus to them, and when he stood before them she said: Have I not proved a good physician to thee? To-day thy back gives thee no trouble. Only aching a bit, he answered, from stooping, but that will pass away. And my balsam having cured thy feet and hands is it not right that I should take a pride in thee? And, smiling, Jesus answered: Had I voice enough I would call the virtue of thy balsam all over the world. My balsam has done well with thee, but a change is needed to restore thee to thyself, and seeing a cloud come into his face, she continued: We weren't talking of sending thee to Cæsarea, for it is of little use to send a man in search of health whither he is not minded to go. Our talk was not of Cæsarea. But of what city then? Jesus asked, and Esora began to speak of Alexandria, and Joseph, thinking that she was but repeating indifferently all she had heard of that city from him, interrupted her and began to discourse about the several schools of philosophy and his eagerness to hear Jesus among the sages. But why should thy philosophers listen to me? Jesus asked. Because thou'rt wise. No man, he replied, is wise but he who would learn, and none is foolish but he who would teach. If there are learners there must be teachers, Joseph said, and he awaited Jesus's answer eagerly, but Esora, fearing their project would be lost sight of in argument, broke in, saying: Neither teaching nor learning avails, but thy health, Jesus, and to-morrow a caravan starts for Egypt, and we would know if thou'lt join it, for one whom thou knowest goes with it, a friend, one Nicodemus, a disciple, whose love for thee is equal to my master's. Jesus's face darkened, but he said nothing, and Esora asked him if he did not care to travel with Nicodemus, and he answered that if he went to Egypt he would like to go with Joseph.

233

But my master has business here, and may not leave it easily. Is this so, Joseph? Jesus asked, and Joseph answered: It is true that I have business here, but there are other reasons, and weightier ones than the one Esora has put before thee, why I may not leave Jerusalem and go to live in Egypt. But wouldst thou have me go to Egypt with Nicodemus, Joseph? Jesus asked, and Joseph could not do else than say that the companion he would choose would not be one whose tongue was always at babble. But wilt thou go to Egypt, he asked, if I tell thee that it is for thy safety and for ours that we propose this voyage to thee? And Jesus answered: Be it so, Joseph; I will undertake the journey. Then, Jesus, we'll make plans together, Esora and myself, for thy departure; and having thanked him, Jesus returned to Matred in the kitchen, and they could hear him talking with her while they debated, and as soon as the kitchen door closed Joseph told Esora that he could not break the promise he gave to his father, and it was this very promise that she strove to persuade him to forgo. For it is the only way, she urged, and he, agreeing with her, said: Though I have promised my father not to keep the company of Jesus, it seems to me that I should be negligent in my duty towards Jesus if I did not go with him to Egypt; and Esora answered: It is well said, Master, and now we will go to our beds. God often counsels us in sleep and warns us against hasty promises. And it was as he expected it would be, for that night he was disturbed by a dream in which his father appeared to him wearing a distressful face, saying: I have a blessing that I would give to thee. There were more words than this, but Joseph could not remember them; but the words he did remember seemed to him a warning that he must not leave Judea; and Jesus was of one mind with him when he heard them related on the terrace. A son, he said, must be always obedient to his father, and love him before other men. Whereupon Esora, who was standing by when these words were spoken, was much moved, for she, too, believed in dreams and their interpretation, and she could put no other interpretation upon Joseph's dream than that he was forbidden to go to Egypt. But Joseph might write, she said, to some of his friends in Egypt, and they could send a friend, if they wished it, who would meet Jesus at Jericho; and this plan was in dispute till all interest in Egypt faded from their minds,

234

and they began to talk of other countries and cities. Of Athens and Corinth we were talking, Joseph said to Esora, who had come again into the room, and of India, of Judea. But if Jesus were to go to India we should never see him again, she answered. It is thy good pleasure, Master, to arrange the journey, and when it is arranged to thy satisfaction thou'lt tell me, though I do not know why thou shouldst consult me again. I came to tell thee that one of thy camel-drivers has come with the news that the departure of the caravan for Egypt has been advanced by two days. But if thou'rt thinking of Egypt no longer I may send him away. Tell him to return to the counting-house, and that there is no order for to-day, Joseph replied. You will settle the journey between you, Esora said, turning back on her way to the kitchen to speak once more. She would have me go, Jesus said. Put that thought out of thy mind, Joseph replied quickly, for it is not a true thought. Thou shouldst have guessed better; it is well that thou goest, but we must find the country and the city that is agreeable to thee, and that will be discovered in our talk in the next few days, to which Jesus answered nothing; and at the end of the next few days, though much had been said, it seemed to Joseph that Jesus's departure was as far away as ever. It has become, he said to Esora, a little dim. I know nothing, he continued, of Jesus's mind.

After speaking these words he went to his counting-house distracted and sad, expecting to hear from his clerk that the story of Jesus's resurrection was beginning to be forgotten in Jerusalem, but the clerk knew nothing more, and was eager to speak on another matter. Pilate had sent soldiers to prevent a multitude from assembling at the holy mountain, Gerizim, for the purpose of searching for some sacred vessels hidden there by Moses, so it was said. Many had been slain in the riot, and the Samaritans had made representations to Vitellius, artfully worded, the clerk said, and dangerous to Pilate, for Vitellius had a friend whom he would like to put in Pilate's place. Joseph sat thinking that it was not at all unlikely he was about to lose his friend and protector, and the clerk, seeing his master troubled, dropped in the words: Nothing has been settled yet. Joseph gave no heed, and a few days afterwards a messenger came from the Prætorium to tell Joseph that Pilate wished to see him. We shall not meet again, Joseph, unless thou comest to Rome, and thou must come quickly to see me there, for my health is declining. We have been friends, such friends as may rarely consist with Roman and Hebrew, he said, and the words stirred up a great grief in Joseph's heart, and when he returned that evening to his house he was overcome by the evil tidings, but he did not convey them to Esora that evening, nor the next day, nor the day afterwards, and they becoming such a great torment in his heart he did not care to go to his counting-house, but remained waiting in his own rooms, or walking in the garden, startled by every noise and affrighted by every shadow. Day passed over day, without news of Pilate, till one of the providers that came to the gates brought the news of his departure to Esora, and when she heard it again she went to Joseph, saying: So thy friend Pilate has been ordered to Rome? He has, indeed, Joseph answered, overcome by the intrigues of the Samaritans, who sought to assemble together, not so much to discover sacred vessels as to bring about a change of government. We are beset with danger, Esora, for it has come to my mind that the stories about the resurrection of Jesus of Nazareth may be kindled again, and it will not be difficult to incite the priests against me; everybody is saying that I was the last man to see Jesus, and must know where his body is hidden; that is enough for the priests, and they will send up a band of Zealots to seek him in this garden. There is no place here where we can hide him from them. That is why I have not been to my counting-house for three days, fearing to leave thee and Matred alone with him, for they would surely choose the time when I was away in Jerusalem to plunder my house. As he was saying these things Matred came into the room with some logs, but before throwing them on the fire she looked at those that Jesus had brought in, and it seeming to Joseph that her eyes were full of suspicion, he said, when the door closed behind her: How is it that she came to us whilst we were talking of Jesus, and of all, why did she say that the logs he had brought in were part of a dead tree that he had felled in the morning?

Esora tried to persuade him that his fears were imaginary, but she too feared that Matred might begin to suspect that Jesus was no ordinary gardener; she had said: Ye speak strangely in Galilee, and to kindle the story again it would only be necessary for some-

236

body to come up to the gates and ask her if one Jesus, a Galilean, was known to her, one that Pilate condemned to the cross. Her answer would be : There is one here called Jesus, he is a Galilean, and may have been on the cross for aught I know. And such answer would be carried back to the priests, who would order their hirelings to make a search for Jesus; and master and servant often sat of an evening listening to the wind in the chimney. Is it warning us of a raid? Esora asked. Ooo-eee! said the wind. If a tree fell it was an omen, and they related their dreams to each other in the alleys of the gardens, till it occurred to them that to be seen in long converse together would awaken Matred's suspicion. The shutters were put up and they sat in the dark afraid to speak lest the walls had ears. Esora, the braver of the two, often said : Master, strive to quell thy fears, for the new procurator has given pause to the story of the resurrection. We have heard little of it lately, and Jesus is beginning to be forgotten. Not so, Esora, for to-day I heard — and Joseph began a long relation which ended always with the phrase : We are beset with danger. We have been saying that now for a long while, Esora answered, yet nothing has befallen us yet, and what cannot be cured must be endured. We must bear with him. If, Esora, I could bring myself to break all promises to my father and go away with him to Egypt this misery would be ended. Master, thou canst not do this thing; thou hast been thinking of it all the winter, and were it possible it would be accomplished already. If it hadn't been for that dream — and Joseph began to relate again the dream related many times before. Forget thy dream, Master, Esora said to him, for it will not help us; as I have said, what cannot be cured must be endured. We must put our trust in time, which brings many changes; and in the spring something will befall; he'll be taken from us. The spring, Esora? And in safety? Tell me, and in safety? Nay, Master, I cannot tell thee more than I have said; something will befall, but what that thing may be, I cannot say. Will it be in the winter or in the spring? It will be in February or March, she said. It was, however, before then, in January (the winter being a mild one, the birds were already singing in the shaws), that a camel-driver came to the house on the hillside to tell Joseph that a camel had been stolen from them on their way from Jericho to Jerusalem during the night or in the early

237

morning, and with many words and movements of the hands, that irritated Joseph, he sought to describe the valley where they pitched their tent. Get on with thy story, Joseph said; and the man told that they had succeeded in tracking the band, a small one, to a cave — Out of which, he said, it will be easy to smoke them if Fadus, the procurator, will send soldiers at once, for they may go on to another cave, not deeming it safe to remain long in the same one. Didst beg the camel back from the robbers? Joseph asked, for he was not thinking of the robbery, but of his meeting with Fadus. No, Master, there was no use doing that. They would have taken our lives. But we followed them, spying them from behind rocks all the way, and the cave having but one entrance they can be smoked to death with a few trusses of damp straw. But care must be taken lest our camel perish with them. If we could get them to give up the camel first, I'm thinking ——

It was a serious matter to hear that robbers had again established themselves in the hills; and while Joseph pondered the disagreeable tidings a vagrant breeze carried the scent of the camel-driver's sheepskin straight into Jesus's nostrils as he came up the path with a bundle of faggots on his shoulders. He stopped at first perplexed by the smell and then, recognising it, he hurried forward, till he stood before the spare frame and withered brown face of the desert wanderer. Hast come from Kerith? he asked. From Kerith truly, the camel-driver answered; and Jesus stood like one in ecstatic vision, and put questions to the camel-driver regarding the quality of the sheep the shepherds led, asking if the rams speeded, if there were many barren yoes in the flock, and if there was as much scab about as formerly, questions that one shepherd might put to another, but which seemed strangely out of keeping with a gardener's interests. And the camel-driver answered Jesus's questions as well as he was able, till, guessing a former shepherd in the gardener, he asked Jesus if he had ever led a flock. Joseph tried to interrupt, but the interruption came too late; Jesus said that for many years he was a shepherd. And who was thy master? the camel-driver asked; Jesus answered that he was in those days an Essene living in the great settlement on the eastern bank of Jordan. Whereupon the camel-driver began to relate that Brother Amos was not doing well with the sheep and that some of the
238

brethren were gone to the Brook Kerith and had taken possession
of a cave in the rocks above it. The camel-driver was about to begin to make plain this Amos's misunderstanding of sheep, but Jesus
interrupted him. Who may their president be? he asked; and with
head bent, scratching his poll, the camel-driver said at last that he
thought it was Hazael. Hazael! Jesus answered, and forthwith his
interest in the camel-driver began to slacken. The anemone is on
the hills to-day, he said, and Joseph looked at him reproachfully;
his eyes seemed to say: Hast forgotten so easily the danger we
passed through by keeping thee here, counting it as nothing, so
great was our love of thee? — and Jesus answering that look
replied: But, Joseph, how often didst thou speak to me of Cæsarea,
Alexandria, Athens, and other cities? Esora, too, was anxious that
I should leave Judea . . . for my sake as well as thine. India was
spoken of, but the Brook Kerith is not twenty odd miles from here
and I shall be safe among the brethren. Why this silence, Joseph?
and whence comes this change of mood? Jesus asked, and Joseph
began to speak of the parting that awaited them. But there'll be
no parting, Jesus interposed. Thou'lt ride thy ass out to meet me,
and we shall learn to know each other, for thou knowest nothing of
me yet, Joseph. Thou'lt bring a loaf of bread and a flagon of wine
in thy wallet, and we shall share it together. I shall wait for thy
coming on the hillside. Even so, Jesus, I am sad that our life here
among the trees in this garden should have come to an end. We
were frightened many times, but what we suffered is now forgotten.
The pleasure of having thee with us alone is remembered. But it
is true we have been estranged here. May we start to-night? Jesus
asked, and Joseph said: If a man be minded to leave, it is better
that he should leave at once.

CHAPTER XXIII.

AN hour later, about two hours before midnight, they were riding into the desert, lighted by a late moon and incommoded by two puppies that Jesus could not be dissuaded from bringing with him: For if Brother Amos give up his flock to me, he argued, I shall need dogs. But Brother Amos will give thee his dogs, Joseph said. A shepherd, Jesus answered, cannot work with any dogs but his own. But what has become of the dogs that were left behind? Joseph asked, and not being able to tell him, Jesus fell to wondering how it was he had forgotten his dogs. At that moment one of the puppies cried to be let down. See how well he follows, Jesus said, but hardly were the words past his lips than the puppy turned tail, and Jesus had to chase him very nearly back to Bethany before he allowed himself to be overtaken and picked up again. The way is long, Joseph cried, more than seven hours to the city of Jericho, and if these chases happen again we shall be overtaken by the daylight. One of my caravans starts from Jericho at dawn; and if we meet it I shall have my camel-drivers round me asking pertinent questions and may be compelled to return with them to Jericho. Come, Jesus, thine ass seems willing to amble down this long incline; and dropping the reins over the animal's withers, and leaning back, holding a puppy under each arm, Jesus allowed the large brown ass he was riding to trot; it was not long before he left far behind the heavy weighted white ass, which carried Joseph. And Joseph, seeing the distance lengthening out between them, said: He rides in a dream! and was tempted to cry to Jesus to stop, but dared not, lest he might awaken robbers (their strongholds having lately been raided by soldiers), and he had in mind the fugitives that might be lurking in the hills, so instead of crying to Jesus to hold hard, he urged his ass forward. But the best speed he could make was not
240

sufficient to overtake the nimbly trotting brown ass, and the pursuit might have been continued into Jericho if Jesus had not been suddenly warned by the silence to stop and wait for Joseph to overtake him, which he did in about ten minutes, whispering: Ride not so fast; robbers may be watching for travellers. Not at this hour, Jesus replied; and he prepared to ride on. This time one of the puppies succeeded in getting away and might have run back again to Bethany had not Joseph leapt from his ass and driven him back to Jesus with loud cries that the ravines repeated again and again. If there were robbers asleep, thy cries would awaken them. True, true, Joseph replied; I forgot; and he vowed he would not utter another word till they passed a certain part of the road, advantageous, he said, to robbers. No better spot between Jerusalem and Jericho for murder and robbery, he continued; cast thine eyes down into the ravine into which he could throw us. But if a robber should fall upon me do not stay to defend me; ride swiftly to the inn for help; and, despite the danger, Joseph rode in front of Jesus, sustained by the hope that the good fortune that attended him so far would attend him to the end. And they rode on through the grey moonlight till a wolf howled in the distance. Joseph bent over and whispered in Jesus's ear: Hold thy puppies close to thy bosom, Jesus, for if one be dropped and start running back to Bethany he will be overtaken easily by that wolf and thou'lt never hear of him again. Jesus held the puppies tighter, but there was no need to do so, for they seemed to know that the howl was not of their kin. The wolf howled again, and was answered by another wolf. The twain have missed our trail, Joseph said, and had there been more we might have had to abandon our asses. If we hasten we shall reach the inn without molestation from robbers or wolves. How far are we from the inn, Jesus? About two hours, Jesus answered, and Joseph fell to gazing on the hills, trying to remember them, but unable to do so, so transformed were they in the haze of the moonlight beyond their natural seeming. They attracted him strangely, the hills, dim, shadowy, phantasmal, rising out of their loneliness towards the bright sky, a white cliff showing sometimes through the greyness; the shadow of a rock falling sometimes across a track faintly seen winding round the hills, every hill being, as it were, a stage in the ascent.

241

As the hills fell back behind the wayfarers the inn began to take shape in the pearl-coloured haze, and the day Joseph rested for the first time in this inn rose up in his memory with the long-forgotten wanderers whom he had succoured on the occasion : the wizened woman in her black rags and the wizened child in hers. They came up from the great desert and for the last fifteen days had had only a little camel's milk, so they said, and like rats they huddled together to eat the figs he distributed. He had seen the inn many times since then and the thought came into his mind that he would never see it again. But men are always haunted by thoughts of an impending fate, he said to himself, which never befalls. But it has befallen mine ass to tire under my weight, he cried. He must be very tired, Jesus answered, for mine is tired, and I've not much more than half thy weight; and the puppies are tired, tired of running alongside of the asses, and tired of being carried, and ourselves are tired and thirsty : shall we knock at the door and cry to the innkeeper that he rouse out of his bed and give us milk for the puppies if he have any? I wouldn't have him know that I journeyed hither with thee, Joseph replied, for stories are soon set rolling. Esora has put a bottle of water into the wallet; the puppies will have to lap a little. We can spare them a little though we are thirstier than they. She had put bread and figs into the wallet, so they were not as badly off as they thought for; and eating and drinking and talking to the puppies and feeding them the while, the twain stood looking through the blue, limpid, Syrian night, till at the end of a long silence Jesus said : The dawn begins; look, Joseph, the stars are not shining as brightly over the Jericho hills as they were. But Joseph could not see that the stars were dimmer. Are they not withdrawing? Jesus asked, and then, forgetful of the stars, his thoughts went to the puppies : See how they crouch and tremble under the wall of the garth. Now there must be a wolf about, he said, and after he had thrown a stone to hasten the animal's departure he began to talk to the puppies, telling them they need have no fear of wolves, for when they were full-grown and were taught by him they would not hold on but snap and snap again. That is how the Thracian dogs fight, like the wolves, he said, turning to Joseph. He is thinking, Joseph said to himself, of sheep and dogs and being a shepherd again. But of what art thou thinking, Joseph? — of that strip of green sky which is the dawn? I can

242

see, now, that thy shepherd eyes did not deceive thee, Joseph answered. The day begins again; and how wonderful is the return of the day, hill after hill rising out of the shadow. An old land, he said, like the end of the world. Why like the end of the world? Jesus asked. Joseph had spoken casually; he regretted the remark, and while he sought for words that would explain it away a train of camels came through the dusk rocking up the hillside, swinging long necks, one bearing on its back what looked like a gigantic bird. A strange burden, Joseph said, and what it may be I cannot say, but the camels are my camels, and thou art safe out of sight under the wall of this garth. A moment after a word was passed up the line that the master had bidden a halt, and one of the camel-drivers said: She stopped half-an-hour ago to drop her young one, and we put him on the dam's back, and she doesn't feel his weight. We shall rest for an hour between this and Jerusalem, and when we lift him down he'll find the dug. But I've a letter for thee, Master, from Gaddi, who wishes to see thee. I thought to deliver it in Jerusalem. It was fortunate to meet thee here. Gaddi will see thee half-a-day sooner than he hoped for. I shall get to him by midday, Joseph said, raising his eyes from the letter. By midday, Master? Why, in early morning I should have thought, unless, indeed, thou'rt biding here till the innkeeper opens his doors. I have business, Joseph answered, with the Essenes that have settled in a cave above the Brook Kerith. About whom, the camel-driver interjected, there is much talk in Jericho. They've disputed among themselves, some remaining where they always were on the eastern bank of the Jordan, but ten or a dozen going to the Brook Kerith, with Hazael for their president. And for what reason? Joseph inquired. I have told thee, Master, all I know, and since thou art going to the Brook Kerith the brethren themselves will give reasons better than I can, even if I had heard what their reasons be for differing among themselves. Whereupon Joseph bade his caravan proceed onward to Jerusalem, and he watched until the camel bearing the youngling lurched out of sight. We shall be discovered if we delay any longer, he said, returning to Jesus, and, mounting their asses, they rode down the hillside into a long, shallow valley out of which the track rose upwards and upwards penetrating into the hills above Jericho.

CHAPTER XXIV.

NOW it is here we leave the track, Jesus said, and he turned his ass into a little path leading down a steeply shelving hillside. We shall find the brethren coming back from the hills, if they aren't back already. It is daylight on the hills though it is night still in this valley; and looking up they saw a greenish moon in the middle of a mottled sky of pink and grey. Over the face of the moon wisps of vapour curled and went out: And the asses, Joseph said, are loth to descend the hillside for fear of this strange moon, or it may be they are frightened by the babble of this brook; it seems to rise out of the very centre of the earth. How deep is the gorge? Very deep, Jesus answered; many hundred feet. But the asses don't fear precipices, and if ours are unwilling to descend the hillside it is because the paths do not seem likely to lead to a stable; so would I account for their obstinacy. I'll not ride down so steep a descent, and Joseph slipped from his ass's back; and, rid of his load, the ass tried to escape, but Jesus managed to turn him back to Joseph, who seized the bridle. Dismount, Jesus, he cried, for the path is narrow, and to please him Jesus dismounted, and, driving their animals in front of them, they ventured on to a sort of ledge.

It passed under rocks and between rocks to the very brink of the precipice as it descended towards the bridge that spanned the brook some hundreds of feet lower down. Already our asses scent a stable, Jesus said; he called after them to stop, and the obedient animals stopped and began to seek among the stones for a tuft of grass or a bramble. I see no place here for a hermitage, Joseph said, only roosts for choughs and crows. There have been hermits here always, Jesus answered. We shall pass the ruins of ancient hermitages farther down on this side above the bridge. The bridge was built by hermits who came from India, Jesus said. And was de-

stroyed, Joseph interjected, by the Romans, so that they might
capture the robbers that infested the caves. But the Essenes must
have repaired the bridge lately, Jesus replied, and he asked Joseph
how long the Essenes had been at the Brook Kerith. My camel-
driver did not say, Joseph answered, and Jesus pointed to the ledge
that the Essenes must have chosen for a dwelling: It cannot be
else, he said; there is no other ledge large enough to build upon in
the ravine; and behind the ledge thou seest up yonder is the large
cave whither the ravens came to feed Elijah. If the brethren are
anywhere they are on that ledge, in that cave; and he asked Joseph
if his eyes could not follow the building of a balcony: Thine eyes
cannot fail to see it, for it is plain to mine. Joseph said he thought
he could discern the balcony. But how do we reach it? We aren't
angels, he said. We shall ascend, Jesus answered, by a path going
back and forth, through many terraces. Lead on, Joseph answered.
But stay, let us admire the bridge they have built and the pepper-
trees that border it. I am glad the Romans spared the trees, for
men that live in this solitude deserve the beauty of these pepper-
trees. Jesus said: Yonder is the path leading to the source of the
brook; fledged at this season with green reeds and rushes. They
have built a mill I see! turned by the brook and fed, no doubt, by
the wheat thy camels bring from Moab. But the Essenes seem
late at work this morning. As he spoke these words an old man
appeared on the balcony, and Joseph said: That must be Hazael,
but his beard has gone very white. It is Hazael, our president,
Jesus answered. Let us go to him at once; and still driving the
asses in front of them and carrying the puppies in their arms they
worked their way up through the many terraces. Not one is more
than three feet wide, yet in every one are fig-trees, Jesus remarked,
and there seem to be vines everywhere, for though the Essenes
drink no wine, they sell their grapes to be eaten or to be turned
into wine, Joseph. Our rule is not to kill, but we sell our sheep,
and alas! some go to the Temple and are offered in sacrifice. I
used to weep for my sheep, he muttered, but in this world —— The
steep ascent checked further speech, and they walked to the east
and then to the west, back and forth, fifty little journeys taking
them up to the cenoby. The great door was opened to them at
once, and Hazael came forward to meet them, giving his left hand

to Joseph and his right to Jesus, whom he drew to his bosom. So, my dear Jesus, thou hast come back to us, Hazael said, and he looked into Jesus's face inquiringly, learning from it that it would not be well to ask Jesus for the story of what had befallen him during the last three years; and Joseph gave thanks that Hazael was possessed of a mind that saw into recesses and appreciated fine shades.

We are glad to have thee back again, Jesus; and thou hast come, perchance to take charge of our flock; it needs thy guidance. Brother Amos will be glad to be relieved of his charge of it. Has it not prospered under Brother Amos? Jesus asked. A long story that is, Hazael answered. Brother Amos will tell it to thee when the time comes. Thou hast brought dogs with thee, and of the breed that our shepherds are always seeking. We had much trouble with them, Jesus replied; and the two Essenes talked together, leaving Joseph to admire the vaulting of the long dwelling, and to wander out through the embrasure on to the balcony, from whence he could see the brethren going to their work along the terraces. Among the ruins of the hermitage on the opposite side above the bridge a brother fondled a pet lamb while he read. He is one, Joseph said to himself, that has found the society of this cenoby too numerous for him, so he retired to a ruin, hoping to draw himself nearer to God. But even he must have a living thing by him; and then, his thoughts changing, he fell to thinking of the day when he would ride out to meet Jesus among the hills. Himself always first at the tryst would espy Jesus from afar, coming from the cenoby to meet him — a happiness too great to be pondered, a too-compelling vision, and to escape from it he watched a flight of doves that had just left their cotes. He lost sight of them among the high rocks, and, listening to the ripple of the brook far away in the abyss, he remembered that Jesus had told him the gorge was never without water. Hazael's voice interrupted his reveries: Would it please thee, Sir, to visit our house? he asked, and he threw open the door and showed a great room, common to all. On either side of it, he said, are cells, six on one side, four on the other, and into these cells the brethren retire after breaking bread, and it is in this domed gallery we sit at food. But Jesus has spoken to thee of these things, for though we do not speak to strangers of our
246

THE BROOK KERITH

rule of life, there would have been no transgression in Jesus speaking of it to thee. Joseph asked for news of Banu, and he heard with sorrow how Banu had been caught by a lion before he could close the entrance of his cave to the beast. The tidings seemed to affect Jesus strangely; he covered his face with his hands, and Hazael repented having spoken of Banu, guessing that the hermit's death carried Jesus's thoughts into a past time that he would shut out for ever from his mind. He atoned, however, for his mistake by an easy transition which carried their discourse into an explanation of the dissidence that had arisen among the brethren —— And which, he said, compelled us to come hither. The Essenes live in single strictness, and it used to be my duty to go in search of young men such as I might judge to be well disposed towards God, and to bring them hither with me so that they might see what our life is, and, discovering themselves to be true servants of the Lord, adopt a life as delightful and easy to those who love God truly as it is hard to them whose thoughts are set on the world and its pleasures. I have travelled through Palestine often in search of such young men, and many who came with me are still with me. It was in Nazareth that we met, he said, and he stretched his hand to Jesus. Dost remember? Well indeed! And without more Hazael pursued his story: The brother, however, who succeeded me as missionary brought back only young men who, after a few months' trial, fell away. It would be unjust for me to say that the fault was with the missionary: times are not as they used to be; the spirit of the Lord is not so rife nor so ardent now as it was once, and the dwindling of our order was the reason given for the proposal that some of us should take wives. The argument put forward was that the children born of these marriages would be more likely than other children to understand our oaths of renunciation of the world and its illusions. It was pleaded, and I doubt not in good faith, that it were better the Essenes should exist under a modified and more worldly rule than not exist at all; and while unable to accept this view we have never ceased to admire the great sacrifice that our erstwhile brethren have made for the sake of our order. That the large majority was moved by such an exalted motive cannot be doubted; but temptations are always about; everyone is the Adam of his own soul, and there may have been a few

247

that desired the change for less worthy motives. There was a brother ——

At that moment an accidental tread sent one of the puppies howling down the dwelling, and Hazael, fearing that he might fall into the well and drown there, sent Jesus to call him back. The puppy, however, managed to escape the well in time, and the pain in his tail ceasing suddenly he ran, followed by his brother, out of the cenoby on to the rocks. I must go after them, for they will roll down the rocks if left to themselves, Jesus cried. A matter of little moment, Hazael replied, compared with the greater calamity of drowning himself in the well, for it is of extraordinary depth and represents the labour of years. Wonderful are the works of man, he added. But greater are the works of God, Joseph replied. Thou didst well to correct me, Hazael answered, for we never should forget that God is over all things, and that man would be without consequence whatsoever were it not for his knowledge of God. But we were speaking of the departure of a few monks from the great cenoby on the eastern side of Jordan. We came hither for the reason that I have told thee. We left protesting that even if it were as our brethren said, and that the children of Essenes would be more likely than the children of Pharisees and Sadducees to choose to worship God according to the spirit rather than to wear their lives away in pursuit of vain conformity to the law — even if this were so, we said, man can only love God on condition that he put women aside, for woman represents the five senses : pleasure of the eyes, of the ears, of the mouth, of the finger-tips, of the nostrils : we did not fail to point out that though our brethren might go in unto them for worthy motives, yet in so doing they would experience pleasure, and sexual pleasure leads to the pleasure of wine and food. One of the brethren said this might not be so if elderly women were chosen, and at first it seemed as if a compromise were possible. But a moment after, a brother reminded us that elderly women were not fruitful. To which I myself added another argument, that a different diet from ours is necessary to those who take wives unto themselves. Thou understandest me, Joseph ? Women have never been a temptation to me, Joseph answered, nor to Jesus ; and he related how Jesus had saved the wild man of the woods above Capernaum from the villagers who had followed him to his cave.

248

And how did he do that? Hazael asked; and when Joseph had told him, he answered: Better that a man should wound himself than sin. And they talked of Jesus, Joseph saying that he had suffered cruelly for teaching that the Kingdom of God is in our own hearts — For to teach that religion is no more than a personal aspiration is to attack the law, which, though given to us by Moses, existed beforetimes in heaven, always observed by the angels, and to be observed by them for time everlasting. Jesus, then, set himself against the Temple? Hazael said slowly, looking into Joseph's eyes. In a measure, Joseph answered, but it was the priests who exasperated the people against him, and what I have come here for, beyond his companionship on the journey, is to beg of thee to put no questions to him. A day may come when he will tell his story if he remain with thee. Here he is safe, Hazael said, and I pray God that he may remain with us. But where is Jesus? Hazael asked, and they sought him in the terraces, where the monks were at work among the vines. See our fig-trees already in leaf. Without our figs we should hardly be able to live here, and it is thy transport that enables us to sell our grapes and our figs and the wine that we make, for we make wine, though there are some who think it would be better if we made none. It was thou that urged Pilate to free these hills from robbers, and hadst thou not done so we could not have lived here in peace. But I'm thinking of so many things that I have lost thought of him whom we seek. He cannot have passed this way, unless, indeed, he descended the terrace towards the bridge, and he could hardly have done that. He has gone up the hills, and they will help to put the past out of his mind. And, talking of Jesus's early life in the cenoby, and of his knowledge of flocks and suchlike, Hazael led Joseph through the long house and up some steps on to a rubble path. The mountain seems to be crumbling, Joseph said, and looked askance at the quiet room built on the very verge of the abyss. That is where thou'lt sleep when thou honourest us with a visit, Hazael said, which will be soon, we trust, he continued; for we owe a great deal to thee, as I have already explained, and now thou com'st with a last gift — our shepherd.

On these words they passed under an overhanging rock, which Joseph said would fall one day. One day, replied the Essene, all the

world will fall, and I wish we were as safe from men as we are from
this rock. Part of the bridge over the brook is of wood and it can
be raised. But the ledge on which we live can be reached from the
hills by this path, and it would be possible to raid us from this
side. Thou seest here a wall, a poor one, it is true; but next year
we hope to build a much stronger wall, some twenty feet high and
several feet in thickness, and then we shall be secure against the
robbers if they should return to their caves. We have little or
nothing to steal, but wicked men take pleasure in despoiling even
when there is nothing to gain: our content would fill them with
displeasure, he said, as he sought the key. But on trying the door
it was found to be unlocked, and Joseph said: It will be no use
building a wall twenty feet high to secure yourselves from robbers
if you leave the door unlocked. It was Jesus that left the door
unlocked, Hazael answered; he must have passed this way. We
shall find him on the hillside; and Joseph stood amazed at the
uprolling hills and their quick descents into stony valleys. Beyond
that barren hill there is some pasturage, Hazael said; and in search
of Jesus they climbed summit after summit, hoping always to catch
sight of him playing with his dogs in the shadow of some rocks,
but he was nowhere to be seen, and Hazael could not think else
than that he had fallen in with Amos and yielded to the beguilement of the hills — For he has known them, Hazael continued,
since I brought him here from Nazareth, a lad of fifteen or sixteen
years, not more. We shall do better to return and wait for him.
He will remember us presently. To which Joseph answered, that
since he was so near Jericho he would like to go thither; a great
pile of business awaited his attention there, and he begged Hazael
to tell Jesus that he would return to bid him good-bye on his way
back to Jerusalem that evening, if it were possible to do so.

CHAPTER XXV.

IT was as Hazael had guessed : the puppies had scampered up the loose pathway leading to the hills. Jesus had let them through the door, and had followed them up the hills, saying to himself : They have got the scent of sheep. The stubborn, unruly ground lay before him just as he remembered it, falling into hollows but rising upwards always, with still a little grass between the stones. But not enough to feed a flock, he remarked, as he wandered on, watching the rosy clouds about the sun's rim, thinking the while that Amos should be down by the Jordan — And would be there, he said to himself, no doubt, but for the wild beasts that have their lairs in the thickets. Whoever redeems the shepherd from the danger of lions will be a great benefactor ; and he, too, will be a benefactor who rids us of wolves, that kill more sheep than lions do, being more numerous. It was in these words that his life on the hills returned to him, and it was then that Brother Amos came in sight, walking at the head of a lame, lank, withering flock.

Why, Jesus, it is thou, as I'm alive, come back to us at last ! Well, we've been expecting thee this long while. And thou hast not come back too soon, as my poor flock testifies. I'm ashamed of them ; but thou'lt not speak too harshly of my flock to Hazael, who thinks if he complains enough he'll work me up into a good shepherd despite my natural turn for an indoor life. But I'd not have thee think that the flock perished through my fault, and see in them a lazy shepherd lying always at length on the hillside. I walk with them in search of pasture from daylight till dark, wearing my feet away, but to no purpose, as any man can see though he never laid eyes on a sheep before. But it was thou, Brother, that recommended me for a shepherd, and I can think of naught but my love of wandering with thee on the hills, and listening to thee prating of rams and

yoes, that put it into my head that I was a shepherd by nature and thy successor. Thou wast brought up to the flock from thy boyhood, and a ram's head has more interest for thee than a verse of Scripture; thy steady, easy gait was always the finest known on these hills for leading a flock; but my feet pain me after a dozen miles, and a shepherd with corny feet is like a bird with a torn wing. Thou understandest the hardship of shepherding, and that one isn't a shepherd for willing it; and I rely on thee, Brother, to take my part and to speak up for me when Hazael puts questions to thee. So thou wouldst be freed from the care of the flock? Jesus said. My only wish, he answered. But thou'lt make it clear to Hazael that it was for lack of a good ram the flock fell away. I gave thee over a young ram with the flock, one of the finest on these hills, Jesus said. Thou didst; and he seemed like coming into such a fine beast, Amos answered, that we hadn't the heart to turn him among the yoes the first year but bred from the old fellow. An old ram is a waste, Jesus replied, and he would have said more if Amos had not begun to relate the death of the fine young beast that Jesus had bred for the continuance of the flock. We owe the loss of him, he said, to a yoe that no shepherd would look twice at, one of the ugliest in the flock, she seemed to me to be and to everybody that laid his eyes on her, and she ought to have been put out of the flock, but though uninviting to our eyes she was longed for by another ram, and so ardently that he could not abide his own yoes and became as a wild sheep on the hills, always on the prowl about my flock, seeking his favourite, and she casting her head back at him nothing loth. It would have been better if I had turned the evil yoe out of the flock, making him a present of her, but I kept on foiling him; and my own ram, taking rage against this wild one, challenged him, and one day, seeing me asleep on the hillside, the wild ram came down and with a great bleat summoned mine to battle. It seemed to me that heaven was raining thunderbolts, so loud was the noise of their charging; and looking out of my dreams I saw the two rams backing away from each other, making ready for another onset. My ram's skull was the softer, he being a young-ling; it was already shaken in several charges, and was broken in this last charge — a terrible one, the worst known on the hills. I can still hear the two rams; and the yoes, too, are in my mind,
252

those of both flocks gathered on different sides to look on. But thy dogs? Where were thy dogs all this while? Jesus inquired. My dogs! If I'd had a Thracian he never would have suffered that the sheep killed each other. A Thracian would have awakened me. My dogs are of the soft Syrian breed given to growling and no more. The wild ram might have become tame again, and would doubtless have stayed with me as long as I had the yoe; but he might have refused to serve any but her. No man can say how it would have ended if I had not killed him in my anger. So thou wast left, Jesus remarked, without a serviceable ram. With naught, Amos sighed, but the old one, and he was that weary of jumping that he began to think more of his fodder than yoes. Without money one can't get a well-bred ram, as I often said to Hazael, but he answered me always that he had no money to give me, and that I must do as well as I could with the ram I had. . . . He is gone now, but before he died he ruined my flock. It is true that the shepherd's labour is wasted without a good ram, Jesus repeated. Thou speakest but the truth, Amos replied; and knowing the truth, forget not to speak well of me to Hazael as a shepherd, and find a reason that will satisfy him for the dwindling of the flock that henceforth will be in thy charge. Jesus said that he was willing to resume his charge, but did not know if Hazael and the brethren would receive him back into the order after his long absence. Amos seemed to think that of that there could no doubt. All will be glad to have thee back . . . thou'rt too useful for them to slight thee, he cried back, and Jesus returned to the cenoby dreaming of some grand strain that would restore the supremacy of the flock.

As he passed down the gallery Hazael, who was sitting on the balcony, cried to him. Joseph, he said, waited an hour and has gone; he had business to transact in Jericho. But, Jesus, what ails thee? It seems strange, Jesus answered, he should have gone away like this. But have I not told thee, Jesus, that he will return this evening to wish thee good-bye? But he may not be able to return this evening, Jesus replied. That is so, Hazael rejoined. He said that he might have to return to Jerusalem at once, but he will not fail to ride out to meet thee in a few days. But he will not find me on the hills; no tryst has been made, Jesus said, as he turned away; and guessing his intention to be to leave at once for

253

Jericho, Hazael spoke of Joseph's business in Jericho, and how displeased he might be to meet Jesus in the middle of his business and amongst strangers. The Essenes are not well looked upon in Jerusalem, he said. We do not send fat rams to the Temple. Fat rams, Jesus repeated. Amos has been telling me that what lacks is a ram, and the community had not enough money to buy one. That is true, Hazael said. Rams are hard to get even for a great deal of money. Joseph might lend us the money; he is rich. He will do that, Jesus answered, and be glad to do it. But a ram must be found, and if thou'lt give me all the money thou hast I'll go in search of one. Joseph will remit to thee the money I have taken from thee when he returns. It will be a surprise for him to find in the flock a great fine ram of the breed that I remember to have seen on the western hills. I'll start at daybreak. Thou shalt have our shekels, Hazael said; they are few, but the Lord be with thee and his luck.

CHAPTER XXVI.

ALTHOUGH the day was still young the sun was warm, and the sky told him that before noon his tongue would be cleaving to the sides of his mouth. A fair prediction this was, for long before the oak wood came into sight he was thinking of the well at the end of the wood, indulging in hopes that the shepherds had not forgotten to replace the stopper, leaving fouled water for the next comer, which they sometimes did. He remembered one, often execrated for his carelessness, and as he walked his comrades of old time kept rising up in his mind, their faces, hands, and gait, the stories they told of their dogs and of losses suffered from wolves and lions in the jungles along the Jordan. In old times these topics were the substance of his life, and he wished to hear the shepherds' rough voices again, to look into their eyes, to talk sheep with them, to plunge his hands once more into the greasy fleeces, yes, and to vent his knowledge, so that if he should happen to come upon new men they would see that he had been at the job before. Now the day seems like keeping up, he said; but there was a boding in his heart that the valleys would be close and hot in the afternoon and the hill-tops uninviting. But his humour was not for fault-finding; and with the ram in view always — not a long-legged brute with a face like a yoe upon him, but a broad, compact animal with a fine woolly head — he stepped out gaily, climbing hill after hill, enjoying his walk and interested in his remembrance of certain rams he had once seen near Cæsarea, and in his hope of possessing himself of one of these. With money enough upon me to buy one, he kept saying to himself, I shouldn't come back empty-handed. The day burns like a fire, he cried at the end of the fourth hour. But yonder is the oak wood. He stopped to think out the whereabouts of the well, and as he was thinking he caught sight of a shepherd — Who is, no doubt, by the well, he said; he is trying to lift out the stopper; and the shepherd, catching sight of Jesus, called him to come to his help, saying that it would need their united strength to get it out. We're moving it, the shepherd cried after a bit. We are, Jesus replied. How is the water? Fair enough if thy thirst be fierce, the shepherd replied. There is better about a mile from here, but I see thou'rt thirsty.

As soon as the men had quenched their thirst, the sheep came forward, each waiting his turn, as is their wont; and when the flock was watered it sought the shade of a great oak, and the twain, sitting under the burgeoning branches, began to talk. It was agreed between them that it would not do to advise anybody to choose shepherding as a trade at present, for things seemed to be going more than ever against the shepherd; the wild animals in the thickets along the Jordan had increased, and the robbers, though many had been crucified, were becoming numerous again; these did not hesitate to take a yoe or wether away with them, paying little for it, or not paying at all. But art thou a shepherd? Jesus answered: A shepherd in time past, a one-time Essene shepherd, that has returned to the brethren. The Essenes are good to the poor, the shepherd said, and glad to hear he was talking to a mate, he continued his complaint, to which Jesus gave heed, knowing well that it would not be long before they would be speaking of the breed of sheep best suited to the hills; the which came to pass, for, like Jesus, he lacked a good ram, and for the lack of one, he said, his flock had declined. The better the breed, he continued, the more often it required renewing, and his master would not pay money for new blood, so he was thinking of leaving him; and to justify himself he pointed out to Jesus the ram that was to serve the flock that autumn, asking him how with such a one a shepherd could earn the few lambs he receives in payment if the flock increase under his care. He's four years old if he's a day, Jesus muttered. He is that, the shepherd answered; yet Master told me yesterday he must serve another season, rams being so dear; but nothing, say I, is dearer than an old ram. I'm with thee in that, Jesus answered; and my plight is the same as thine. I'm searching for a ram, and have a friend who would pay a great sum of money for one if one of the sort and kind I am looking for can be found. Well, luck will be

256

with thee, but I know no ram on these hills that I'd pay money for, the shepherd answered; none we see is better than yon beast, and he is what thou seest him to be, a long-backed, long-legged, ugly ram that would be pretty tough under the tooth, and whose fleece a shepherd would find thin in winter-time. But there were once fine sheep on these hills, Jesus answered, and I remember a ram —— Ay, mate, thou mayst well remember one, and I think I know the shepherd that thou'rt thinking of, but he that owns the breed will not sell a ram for the great sums of money that have been offered to him, for his pride is to keep the breed to himself. We've tried to buy, and been watching this long while for a lucky chance to drive one away, for a man that has more than he needs and will not sell aught thereof calls the thief down into his house, as it were, creating the thief out of an honest man, for which he deserves to be punished. But the rich are never punished, and this man's shepherds are wary, and his dogs are fierce, and none has succeeded yet in getting a sample of the breed. But where may this man be found? Jesus asked, and the shepherd mentioned a village high up on the mountains over against the sea. But go not thither, for twenty miles is a long walk if the end of it be but jeers and a scoffing. A scoffing! Jesus returned. Ay, and a fine one in thine ears; and a fine thirst upon thee, the shepherd continued, and turning to the oak-tree he began to cut branches to feed his goats. Twenty miles uphill in front of me, Jesus meditated, with jeers and scoffings at the end of the journey, of which I have had plenty; and he began to walk quickly and to look round the hills in search of pasture for a flock, for these hills were but faintly known to him. It isn't reasonable that a man will not part with a ram for a great sum of money, he said, and though he may not sell the lamb to his neighbours, whom he knows for rascals, he may sell to the Essenes, whose report is good. And he continued his way, stopping very often to think how he might find a bypath that would save him a climb; for the foot-hills running down from west to east, off the main range, formed a sort of giant ridge and furrow broken here and there, and whenever he met a shepherd he asked him to put him in the way of a bypath; and with a word of counsel from a shepherd and some remembrance he discovered many passes; but despite these easy ways the journey began to seem very long,

257

so long that it often seemed as if he would never arrive at the village he was seeking. He told me I'd find it on the last ridge looking seaward. He said I couldn't miss it; and shading his eyes with his hand, Jesus caught sight of some roofs that he had not seen before. The roofs, maybe, he said, of the village in which I shall find my ram, and maybe he who will sell me the ram sits under that sycamore. If such be my fortune he will rise to meet me, Jesus continued, and he strove against the faintness coming over him. Is there a fountain? he asked. By that arch the fountain flows; drink thy fill, wayfarer. His sight being darkened he could not see the arch but stumbled against it and stood there, his face white and drawn, his hand to his side. At last, unable to bear up any longer, he fell, and was without sense till somebody came to him with water; and after drinking a little he revived, and said he could walk alone. But as soon as they loosed him he fell again, and when lifted from the ground a second time he asked for the inn, saying he had come a long way. Whereupon a man said: Thou shalt rest in my house; I guess thee to be a shepherd from thy garb, though thy garb isn't altogether a shepherd's. But my house is open to him who needs food and shelter. Lean on my arm. . . .

Let me untie thy sandals, were the next words Jesus heard, and when his feet were bathed and he had partaken of food and drink, and was rested, he asked the villager if he could reach Cæsarea before nightfall. With a knowledge of the hills that would keep thee in the path thou mightest trudge far enough to see Cæsarea by daybreak. I have no knowledge of these hills, Jesus answered. Whence comest thou — from the hills over against Jordan? From Kerith, from the Brook Kerith, an hour and a half from Jericho. A shepherd I guessed thee to be. And a fair guess, Jesus said; a shepherd I am, and in search of a ram of good breeding, sent hither by another shepherd. He did but make sport of thee, the villager answered, for it is I who own the breed that all men would have. So a shepherd sent thee hither to buy a ram from me? He said thou wouldst not sell. Then he was an honester shepherd than I thought for: he was minded to save thee a vain journey, and it would have been well hadst thou listened to his counsel, for I will not part with the breed; and my hope is that my son will not be tempted, for it is through our breed that we have made our riches — such small
258

riches as we possess, he added, lest he should appear too rich in the eyes of a stranger. If thou'lt not sell I must continue my journey farther, Jesus answered. In quest of a ram? the shepherd said. But thou'lt not find any but long-backed brutes tucked up in the belly that offend the eye and are worse by far than a hole in the pocket. With such rams the hills abound. But get thee the best, though the best may be bad, for every man must work according to his tools. If thou hadst asked me for anything but my breed of sheep I would have given it, for thy face and thy speech please me, but as well ask me for my wife or my daughter as for my rams. Be it so, Jesus answered, and he rose to continue his way, but his host said that having taken meat and drink in his house he must sleep in it too, and Jesus, being tired, accepted the bed offered to him. He could not have fared farther; there was no inn nor public guest-room, and in the morning his host might be in the humour to part with a ram for a great sum of money. But the morning found his host in the same humour regarding his breed of sheep — determined to keep it; but in all other things willing to serve his guest. Jesus bade him good-bye, sorry he could not persuade him but liking him all the same, and fared on for two hours, till he was near the cultivated lands of Cæsarea, and it seemed to him then that his best chance of getting news of a ram would be to turn westward, and finding bed and board in every village, he travelled far and wide in search of the fine rams that he had once caught sight of in those parts. But the rams of yore seemed to have disappeared altogether from the country. Thou mayst journey to Cæsarea and back again, but thou'lt not find anything better than that I offer thee, one man said to Jesus, whereupon Jesus turned his back upon Cæsarea and began the return journey sad and humble, but with hope still a-flutter in his heart, for he continued to inquire after rams all the way till he came one bright morning to the village in which lived the owner of the great breed of sheep that he coveted, honourably coveted, he muttered to himself, but coveted heartily.

The sun was well up at the time, and Jesus had come by the road leading up from the coast. He had passed over the first ridge, and had begun to think that he must be near the village in which the man lived who owned the great breed of sheep when his thoughts were interrupted by a lamb bleating piteously, and, looking round,

259

he saw one running hither and thither, seeking his dam. Now the lamb seeming to him a fine one, he was moved to turn back to the village to tell the man he had lodged with that a lamb of his breed had lost the yoe. Thou sayest well, the man answered, and that lamb will seek vainly, for the yoe hurt her hoof, and we kept her in the garden so that she might be safer than with my shepherd out on the hills, and the luck we have had is that a panther broke into the garden last night. We thought he had killed the lamb as well, but he took only the yoe, and the lamb thou bringest me tidings of will be dead before evening. My thanks to thee, shepherd, for thy pains. But, said Jesus, thou'lt sell me the lamb that runs bleating after yoe, on the chance that I shall rear him? Whereat the villager smiled and said : It seems hard to take thy money for naught, for thou hast a pleasant face; but who knows what luck may be with thee. For a shekel thou shalt have the lamb. Jesus paid the shekel, and his eyes falling upon a bush in whose stems he knew he should find plenty of sap, he cut some six or seven inches, and, having forced out the sap, showed it to the villager, and asked him for a rag to tie round the end of it. I hardly know yet what purpose thou'lt put this stem to, the shepherd said, but he gave Jesus the rag he asked for, and Jesus answered : I've a good store of yoe's milk drawn from the udder scarce an hour ago. Thou hast yoe's milk in thy bottle ! the villager said. Then it may be I shall lose my breed through thoughtlessness. And it was with a grave face that he watched Jesus tie a rag around the hollow stem, put the stem into the lamb's jaws and pour milk down it, feeding the lamb as well as the yoe could have done. It may be I shall get him home alive, Jesus muttered to himself. Thou'lt do it, if luck be with thee, and if thou canst rear him my breed has passed from me. Thou'lt be rewarded for taking my shekel, Jesus answered. A fine lamb for a month, the villager remarked. One that will soon begin to weigh heavy in my bosom, Jesus answered; a true prophecy, for after a few miles Jesus was glad to let him run by his side; and knowing now no other mother but Jesus, he trotted after him as he might after the yoe — Divining perhaps, Jesus said to himself, the leathern bottle at my girdle. But the lamb was laggard, and fearing a wolf Jesus carried him again, and despite his weight they were at noon by the well at the end of the oak wood.

Lamb, we'll sleep awhile together in a pleasant hollow at the edge of the wood. Lay thyself down and doze. The lamb was obedient, but before long he awoke Jesus with his bleating. He wants some milk, he said, and undid the leather girdle and placed the feeding-pipe in the lamb's mouth. But before giving him milk he was moved to taste it: For if the milk be sour —— The milk has soured, he said, and the poor bleating thing will die in the wood, his bleatings growing fainter and fainter. He'll look into my face, wondering why I do not give him the bottle from which he took such a good feed only a few hours ago; and while Jesus was think-ing these things the lamb began to bleat for his milk, and as Jesus did not give it to him he began to run round in search of the yoe, and Jesus let him run, hoping that a wild beast would seize and carry him away and with his fangs end the lamb's sufferings quicker than hunger could. But no wolf or panther was in the thicket, and the lamb returned to him — Brought back, he said, by a memory of the bottle. But, my poor wee lamb, there is no sweet milk in my bottle, only sour, which would pain thee. Think no more of life, but lie down and die : we shall all do the same some day. . . . Thy life has been shorter than mine, and perhaps better for it. I've no milk for thee and cannot bear to look in thy face : run again in search of the yoe and find instead the panther that took her; and the lamb went as bidden, to return soon after bleating — Come back to me, having found neither yoe nor panther. Go, and seek a wolf; he will be a better friend to thee than I. And turning his face aside, he asked how it was that he should feel more pain at this lamb's death than another's, he who had watched the death of so many. But it was so; and now all his hopes and fears centred in this one thing that Fate had confided to his bosom. A little milk would save it, but he had no milk. He might pick him up and run, calling to the shepherds, but none would hear. I cannot listen to his bleating any longer, he said, and tried to escape from the lamb, but he was followed round the trees, and just as he was about to climb into one out of the lamb's sight his nostrils caught the scent of fleeces coming up the hillside. A shepherd is leading his flock to the well-head, he said, so, wee lamb, thou wilt not die to-day; and, addressing himself to the shepherd, he said : I've got a lamb of the right breed, but have no milk to give him. Canst thou pay for it?

the shepherd asked, and Jesus said : I can ; and the shepherd called
a yoe and the lamb was fed.

Well, luck is in thy way, the shepherd said, for I was on my way
to another well, and cannot tell what came into my mind and turned
me from it and brought me up here. Every life, Jesus said, is in
the hands of God, and it was not his will to let this lamb die.
Dost believe, the shepherd answered, that all is ordered so?
And Jesus answered him : Thou'lt fill my bottle with milk?
The shepherd said : I will; but thou hast still a long way before
the lamb can be fed again. Hide thy bottle under a cool stone in
yon forest and in the evening the milk will still be sweet and thou
canst feed thy lamb again and continue thy journey by starlight.
But these hills are not my hills ; mine are yonder, Jesus said, and at
night all shapes are different. No matter, the way is simple from
this well, the shepherd answered, and he gave Jesus such directions
as he could follow during the night. Now mind thee, he continued,
look round for a shepherd at daybreak. He'll give thee fresh milk
for thy lamb and by to-morrow evening thou'lt be by the Brook
Kerith. And this advice appearing good to Jesus, he turned into
the shade of the trees with his lamb, and both slept together side
by side till the moon showed like a ghost in the branches of the
trees. It was time then to feed the lamb, and the milk being sweet
in the bottle, the lamb drank it greedily ; and when he had drunk
enough Jesus was tempted to drink what the lamb could not drink,
for he was thirsty after eating his bread, but he went to the well
and took a little water instead, and lay down, telling the lamb that
he might sleep but a little while, for they must be ready at midnight
to travel again. If we meet a shepherd thou livest, if he fail us
thou diest, Jesus said, and seeing a shepherd leaving a cavern at
dawn with his flock, Jesus called to him and bought milk from him,
and once more the twain continued their journey, the lamb so
quaintly watchful of his shepherd that Jesus took pleasure sometimes in hiding himself behind a rock, and as soon as the lamb
missed him he would run to and fro bleating in great alarm till he
found Jesus ; and when he came upon him he thrust his nozzle into
Jesus's hand. It was then more than at any time he delighted in
being carried. No, my good lamb, I've carried thee far and now
can barely carry myself to the bridge ; and the lamb had to follow
262

THE LITTLE RAM

to the bridge, and they began to ascend the terraces together, but the steep ascents very soon began to tire him, and the lamb lay down and bleated for Jesus to take him up in his arms, which he did, but, overcome with the weariness of a long journey, he had to lay him down after a few paces. Yet he would not surrender the lamb to the brethren who came and offered to carry him, saying: I have carried him so far and will carry him to the end, but ye must let me rest on your arms. Meanwhile, fetch me a little milk, for the lamb has had all that I could buy from the shepherds on the hills, and do not ask how I became possessed of this lamb, for I am too tired to tell the story. So did he speak, holding the lamb to his bosom; and leaning on the arm of one of the brethren while another pushed from behind, overworn he reached the cenoby.

Now I must feed my lamb; go to Brother Amos and ask him to bring some yoe's milk at once. But the brethren were loth to go, saying: Brother Amos is feeding his sheep far from here, but will return in the evening. But the lamb must be fed every three or four hours, Jesus answered, and do ye go at once to Amos and tell him to bring the milk at once. He must not be kept waiting for his milk. Now look at him and say which among you has seen a finer lamb. I can speak no more, but will sleep a little as soon as I have placed him in a basket. But wake me up as soon as the milk comes, for I will trust none to feed him but myself; and he dropped off to sleep. The Essenes standing by, understanding that the lamb had caused Jesus a long search, went after Amos as they were bidden, and finding him not as far as they thought for with his flock, they related to him Jesus's request that he should bring some yoe's milk at once, which he did, and seeing Jesus in deep sleep he said: It is a pity to waken him, for I know how to feed a lamb as well as he does. May I not? But the Essenes said: He'll be vexed indeed if the lamb be fed by any but him. So be it, Amos answered; and they roused Jesus with difficulty, for his sleep was deep, and when he opened his eyes he knew not where he was for some time. At last memory returned to him, and, struggling from the couch, he said: I must feed my lamb. The milk is fresh from the yoe? he asked. Yes, Jesus, Amos answered, I have just drawn it from the udder. As soon as he is old enough to run with the flock I'll bring him, Jesus said, and thou'lt be free to return to the

Scriptures. And having asked that he might be awaked in four hours his eyes closed, which is not to be wondered at, he having slept hardly at all for four days. Does he put his lamb before the Scriptures? the Essenes asked each other, and they withdrew, shaking their heads.

CHAPTER XXVII.

JESUS fell back into sleep as soon as the lamb was fed, and it was in this second sleep of more than six hours that he regained his natural strength. Has Joseph returned? he asked on awakening, and the brother nearest him answered that he had not; where-upon Jesus asked that Hazael should come to him, and he said to him: Hazael, Joseph told thee that as soon as his business was transacted in Jericho he would return hither, and if that were not possible the delay would not be long. But four days have passed and we haven't seen him nor have we news of him. Now how is this? News could not have reached him in Jericho nor in Jerusalem of my faring among the hills of Cæsarea in search of a lamb; only there I might find a lamb that would recover for us the strength that has gone out of the flock. And I would that Joseph were here to see him that I've brought back. My heart misgives me. Thou'lt feed him in my absence, he said to one of the brethren, and I'll go down on to the terraces and wander across the bridge, for on the hills over yonder I may catch sight of Joseph coming to meet me. Can none tell me if he will come from Jericho or Jerusa-lem? A brother cried that he would feed the lamb as Jesus directed, and the brethren at work among the fig-trees spoke to each other of the grief visible on Jesus's face as he passed them and questioned each other and sought a reason for it. Has the lamb fallen sick? one asked, and on that thought they ran up the terraces to inquire for the lamb, who, that day, had been given the name of Cæsar. The lamb sleeps in peace, Hazael answered, but Jesus, his saviour, has gone out in great disorder of mind to get tidings of Joseph, the great trader in figs and dates. He promised to return the same eve-ning after transacting his business in Jericho, Hazael continued. Four days have passed away without news of him; some misfortune may have befallen him. May have! Hazael repeated under his breath as he walked away. And the brethren waited for Jesus to return, but he did not return to them. At nightfall a watch was set at the bridge head, and the same was done for many succeeding days, till the story reached the Brook Kerith that Joseph had been killed in the streets of Jerusalem by order of the Zealots. Priests never forget to revenge themselves on those that do not submit to their ideas and exactions, Hazael muttered, thereby stirring the curiosity of the brethren; but he could not tell them more, Joseph's story having been insufficient to make plain the truth that Joseph, as Jesus's friend, must have earned the High Priest's displeasure. A very little suspicion, he said to himself, is enough to bring about the death of a man in our days; and the priests were always jealous and afraid of prophets. Is then our Jesus a prophet? Saddoc asked, and Manahem's eyes were full of questions. I can tell ye no more than I've said already, Hazael answered, and the brethren forgot their curiosity, for their hearts were stirred with pity. A great grief it surely will be, they said to one another, when Jesus returns and hears that his friend is dead, and they asked which among them should be the one to tell him of this great loss that had befallen him. Not I, said one; Nor I, another answered, and as they passed into their cells it was in the mind of all that Hazael should tell him.

Next morning, after giving thanks for the returning light, with one accord they waited on the hillside, hoping that every minute would bring them sight of Jesus. At last a shepherd came through the dusk, but it was Amos, and the news he brought was that he had met Jesus overnight wandering, his mind distraught. Tidings of Joseph's death must have reached him on the hills, said Manahem, and the brethren concurred. But what hast thou done with thy sheep? Eleazar asked. I left them with Jesus; the flock alone could bring back his senses to him. Thou wast always a fool, Amos, and the years have not given thee sense! the brethren cried as they returned to the cenoby to mourn for Jesus and for the sheep, till some shepherds came, and they leading Jesus by the hand were followed by the few sheep that had escaped the wolves. How many sheep have ye brought back? Caleb asked. Eleven, a shepherd answered, and Jesus's eyes wandered over the dimin-

266

ished flock —— Without counting them, for he does not see them, exclaimed Saddoc. His heart is broken, were Benjamin's words; and just as if he were among strangers whose company he would escape from, Jesus wandered up the path leading to the hills. Manahem went after him and brought him back, but Jesus stood like a stock before the cavern. It was here he saw Joseph last, said Manahem, and we would do well to leave him to himself, to wander anywhither, nowhither, giving him food if his grief allows him to come for it. Restraint would estrange him from us, change indifference to hate; and we would do well to take our eyes from him, for when the mind is away man is but an animal — animals do not like watchful eyes. We·must watch lest he do himself bodily harm, Eleazar said. He can but walk over a cliff in a dream and so end his misery, Manahem answered. We would not that the crows and vultures fed on Jesus, Caleb muttered. Behold him now! He sees not the cliffs above him, nor the cliffs beneath him. A wonderful thing is grief whilst it lasts, said Saddoc, more powerful than the love of God; but it wears away, and in this it is unlike the love of God, which does not change. It is strange that one who loves God as truly as Jesus should abandon himself to grief, for where God is, grief is not. Saddoc's words caused the brethren to drop into reveries and dreams, and when they spoke out of these their words were : His grief is more like despair. And in speaking these words they were nearer to the truth than they knew, for Joseph's death had quickened in Jesus an almost dead memory, and as he sat gazing across the abyss his thoughts were that God held him accursed, else he would not have taken Joseph from him. He forgot to take food and drink, and his life would have passed from him if Cæsar had not broken away from his keeper and run bleating among the rocks till he came upon Jesus, whom he recognised at once and refused to leave, thrusting his nozzle into Jesus's hand. Give me the feeding bottle and I will feed him; and on the feeding bottle being passed to Jesus Cæsar began to bleat, and so cheerfully that all conceived a new affection for him. But he had thought only for Jesus, whom he followed about the cliffs as a dog might, lying down at his side.

Jesus and Cæsar go together in safety, said the brethren, where there is scarce foothold for either. Sheep and goats never lose their

267

footing, a brother answered. It is fortunate, said another, that Cæsar should love Jesus, and it may be that his happy disposition will react on Jesus and win him out of his melancholy. And it seemed as if the brother had guessed rightly, for though Jesus's face showed no interest in the brethren, nor in the cenoby, he seemed to enjoy the sympathy of the dumb animal. He liked to call to Cæsar and to lay his hand upon Cæsar's head, and to look into his eyes, and in those moments of sympathy the brethren said : He forgets his grief. But Cæsar is coming into ramhood, Saddoc answered, and will have to go away with the flock. There were brethren who cried out against this : Let the flock perish rather than Jesus should be deprived of Cæsar. Wouldst have him remain when he is a great ram? Manahem asked, and the others answered : Yes, for Jesus takes no thought for anything but Cæsar; and the brethren conferred together, and spent much thought in trying to discover a remedy other than Cæsar for Jesus's grief.

But one day Jesus said to the brethren : Cæsar is coming into ramhood, and I must take him away to the hills; he must come with me and join the yoes. Art thou going to be our shepherd again? said they. If ye will entrust the flock to me. My thoughts will never wander from it again. Jesus spoke the words significantly, and many of the brethren believed that he would prove himself to be the great shepherd that he was of yore, but others said : His grief will break out upon him on the hills; but these counsels were overruled by Manahem and Saddoc. Jesus, Saddoc said, never smiles and his words are few, but he is himself again, and the best shepherd that ever walked these hills is worse than he, so it is said. He lost a few sheep, Manahem said, in the first days of his great grief, but his mind is altogether now on the encouragement of the flock and Amos is wearied of it and would return to the reading of the Scriptures. Thou speakest well, Manahem, Saddoc returned, for it was in his mind as it was in Manahem's that the sight of men and the sound of men's voices were a torture to Jesus, and that he longed for solitude and silence and the occupation of the flock. The cenoby will never be the same again without our pet, some of the brethren cried, but others said : It must be so. We'll go to see Cæsar's lambs, they cried, as he was being led away. There will be no lambs by Cæsar this spring, Jesus answered. He'll run with

268

the yoes and that's about all; for a ram is not fit for service till he is two years old. Whereupon the distraction of Jesus's grief being removed from the cenoby, the Essenes fell to talking again of the great schism and what came of it. Are our brothers happier in wedlock than we are in celibacy? was the question they often put to each other on the balcony; and a sudden meeting of thoughts set them comparing the wives beyond Jordan with the yoes of the hills. Which are the most fruitful? they asked themselves; and it was averred that though twin lambs were of equal worth, it might fall out in the strange destinies that beset human life that one of human twins might be a robber and the other a devout Essene.

On the balcony overhanging an abyss, through which a brook sings a monotonous song, men may dream a long while on destiny, and rise up from their different meditations moved to speak of the hardships the brethren by the lake would meet with when they set themselves to discover women who would accept the rule of life of the Essenes, without thought of enjoyment, only that the order might not perish, and with it holiness pass out of the world. Of what women will they possess themselves? a brother often asked. Not Jewish women, who would prefer to join themselves with Pharisees or Sadducees rather than with Essenes; and the converts, the brother continued, that might be made among the Gentile women from Mesopotamia and Arabia could not be counted upon to produce pious children, though the fathers that begot the children might be themselves of great piety. These words put the thought into another brother's mind, that a woman is never faithful to one man, an abiding doctrine among the Essenes: and the group of three, Caleb, Eleazar and Benjamin, began to speak of the stirs and quarrels that these converts would provoke in the cenoby. For even amongst those who have renounced women, there are always a few that retain a longing for women in their heart, and the smouldering embers will burst into flame at the sight of woman. Is not that so, Benjamin? There is much truth in thy words, Caleb, Benjamin answered, and I would know if they partition off the women into an enclosure by themselves, and only take them out at a time judged to be the fruitfullest, for it is not lawful for us to experience pleasure, and as soon as the women are with child, the

269

brethren we have left behind, I trust, withdraw from the company of their wives. Unless, said Eleazar, all the rules of our order be abolished. We did well to leave them, Caleb answered. And then, posing his small fat hands on the parapet, he said: Women have ever been looked upon as man's pleasure, and our pleasures are as wolves, and our virtues are as sheep, and as soon as pleasure breaks into the fold the sheep are torn and mangled. We're better here with our virtues than they by the lake with their pleasures. Trouble has begun amongst them already, Eleazar said, and Benjamin turned to ask him if he had gotten news of the brethren by the lake; and he answered that yesterday a shepherd told him that many brothers had left the settlement. We did well, Caleb said, to cherish our celibacy, and the price of living on this rock was not too high a price for it. But tell us what thou hast heard, Eleazar. Eleazar had heard that troubles were begun, but he hoped children would bring peace to all. But all women aren't fruitful, Caleb said, and Benjamin was vexed with Eleazar because he hadn't asked how many women were already quick. And they fell to talking scandal, putting forward reasons why some of the brethren should separate themselves from their wives. Perhaps we shall never know the why and the wherefore, Eleazar said, seeing it is against our rules to absent ourselves without permission from the cenoby, and if we were to break this rule, Hazael might refuse to receive us again. We should wander on the hills seeking grass and roots, for our oaths are that we take no food from strangers. Yet I'd give much to hear how our brethren, for they are our brethren, fare with their wives. And when they met on the balcony, the elder members of the community, Hazael, Mathias, Saddoc and Manahem, like the younger members, conferred together as to whether any good could come to those that had taken wives to themselves for their pleasure. Not for their pleasure, Hazael said, but that holiness may not pass out of the world for ever. But as holiness, Mathias was moved to remark, is of the mind, it cannot be affected by any custom we might impose upon our bodily nature. Whereupon a disputation began in which Manahem urged upon Mathias that if he had made himself plain it would seem that his belief was that holiness was not dependent upon our acts: And if that be so, he asked, why do we live on this ledge of rock? To
270

which question Mathias answered that the man whose mind is in order need not fear that he will fall into sin, for sin is but a disorder of the mind. But may we keep our minds pure and be wived? Saddoc asked. I would have Mathias answer me this question. Thy question is without sense, Saddoc. As well mightst thou ask if a man can keep his temper and have a sore finger; some can, and some cannot. Mathias, said Manahem, has answered thee, Saddoc, and answered well. But I would have him tell me if we are not justified in considering marriage as philosophers may, no subject being alien from philosophy. Is not that so, Mathias? Mathias agreed that no subject was alien from philosophy, to which Saddoc answered : We would be able to consider the wiving of our brethren with profit if we knew which of the brothers had taken to himself a wife; but only rumour reaches us here; and the brethren looked across the chasm, their thoughts crossing it easily, passing over the intervening hills down into the plains and over Jordan. We should no doubt be content, said Manahem, with our own beliefs, and abide in the choice that we have made without questioning it further, as Hazael has said. Yet it is hard to keep thoughts of the brethren we have left out of our minds. How are we, Hazael, to remain unmoved when rumours touching on the lives of those we have left behind reach us? Is it not merely natural that we should desire to hear how our brethren fare in married life? Dost think, Hazael, that those we left behind never ask each other how we fare in our celibacy? Man is the same all the world over inasmuch as he would like to hear that he has avoided the pitfall his brother has fallen into. It is said, Manahem continued, that the elders yonder are disturbed now as to whether they too should be wived, though in the great disputation we took part in, it was decided that marriage should be left to the younger and more fruitful. Wherefore, if it be said that trouble has come, Hazael answered, we should be sorry for our weak brethren; and if stories reach us, he continued, we should receive them with gravity; we should not go out to seek stories of the misfortunes of those who have not been as wise as we, and of all we should not wish to go down to Jordan to inquire out the truth of these stories. Caleb and Benjamin ask bytimes for leave to visit them; Eleazar, too, has asked; but I have refused them always, knowing well whither

271

their curiosity would lead them. Lest, Mathias interposed, they bring back the spirit and sense of women with them.

A flock of doves crossing over the chasm on quick wings put an end to the discourse, and as no more stories reached them in their cavern above the Brook Kerith about the behaviour of the wives to their husbands and of the husbands towards their wives, the thoughts of the younger brethren reverted to Cæsar, and to the admiration of the yoes for his beauty. A year later, when Jesus came down from the hills, he was met with cries of : How fares it with Cæsar? Does he tire on the hills? When will the yoes begin to drop their lambs? A buzz of talk began at once in the cenoby when the tidings arrived that Cæsar's lambs were appearing, but the brethren could not hide their rue that these should but look like the lambs they had seen before. We expected the finest lambs ever seen on these hills, they said, and thou hast no more word to say in praise of them than that they are good lambs. Jesus answered that in two months he would be better able to judge Cæsar's lambs, and to choose amongst them some two or three that would continue the flock worthily. Which? the brethren asked, but Jesus said a choice would be but guess-work at present; none could pick out the making of a good ram till past the second month. Caleb marked one which he was sure would be chosen later, and Benjamin another, and Eleazar another; but when the time came for Jesus to choose, it was none of these that he chose, and on hearing of their mistakes, the brethren were disappointed, and thought no more of the flock, asking but now and then for Cæsar, and forgetting to mourn his decease at the end of the fourth year. His successor coming to them without romantic story, the brethren were from henceforth satisfied to hear from time to time that the hills were free from robbers; that the shepherds had banded together in great wolf hunts; and that freed from their natural enemies, wolves and robbers, the flock had increased in numbers beyond the memory of the oldest shepherd on the hills.

CHAPTER XXVIII.

THE brethren waxed rich, and after their midday meal they talked of the exceeding good fortune that had been vouchsafed to them, dwelling on the matter so earnestly that a scruple sometimes rose up in their hearts. Did we do well to forgo all troubles? Do the selfish find favour in God's sight? they were asking, when Caleb said: We have visitors to-day, and looking across the chasm they saw three men emerging from the shadow of the high rock. They may be robbers, Benjamin cried, and we would do well to tell the brethren working along the terraces to pass the word down to him who stands by the bridge head that he is to raise the bridge and refuse to lower it till the strangers speak to him of their intentions and convince him that they are peaceful. That is well said, Benjamin, Eleazar replied: Amos, who is standing by the fig-tree yonder, will pass on the word. They cried out to him and watched the warning being passed from Essene to Essene till it reached the brother standing by the bridge-head. He looked in the direction of the strangers coming down the path, and then in haste set himself to pull the ropes and press the levers whereby the bridge was raised and lowered. Now they are speaking across the brook to each other, Benjamin said: and the group on the balcony saw the bridge being let down for the strangers to cross over. It seems to me, Benjamin continued, Bartholomew might have spent more time inquiring out their intentions. But we are many and they are few, Caleb answered, and the Essenes on the balcony watched somewhat anxiously Bartholomew conducting the strangers back and forth through the terraces. Is not Bartholomew as trustworthy as any amongst us? Eleazar asked. It isn't likely that he would mistake robbers for pilgrims; and as if Bartholomew divined the anxiety of those above him he called up the rocks that the visitors he was bringing were Essenes from the lake. Essenes from the lake!

273

Caleb cried. Then we shall learn, Eleazar replied, which is preferable, celibacy or marriage. But we mustn't speak at once to them of such matters. We must prepare food for them; they will need it after their long journey. Our president will be with you in a moment, Bartholomew said, addressing Shallum, a tall thin man, whose long neck, sloping shoulders and dark round eyes reminded his brethren of an ungainly bird. His companions, Shaphan and Eleakim, were of different appearances. Shaphan's skull, smooth and glistening, rose, a great dome above a crumpled face; he moped like a sick monkey, dashing tears from his eyes continually, whereas Eleakim, a sprightly little fellow with half-closed eyes like a pig, agreed that Shallum should speak for them. Shallum began : We are, as you have already heard, from the great cenoby at the head of the lake, and, therefore, I need not tell you the reason why you are here and why the residue are yonder, but will confine myself to the story of our flight from the lake to the brook. Honourable President and Brethren, it is known unto you that the division of our order was not brought about by any other reason than a dispute on both sides for the maintenance of the order. We know that, Hazael answered, and attribute no sinfulness to the brethren that differed from us. Our dream, Shallum continued, was to perpetuate holiness in this world, and our dream abides, for man is a reality only in his dreams; his acts are but a grotesque of his dream.

At these words the Essenes gathered close together, and with brightening eyes listened, for they interpreted these words to mean that the brethren by the lake had fallen headlong into unseasonable pleasures, whereof they were now reaping the fruit : no sweet one, if the fruit might be judged by the countenances of their visitors. As I have said, Shallum continued, it was with us as it has been with men always — our acts became a mockery of our dreams almost from the beginning, for when you left us we gave out that we were willing to receive women who would share our lives and with us perpetuate holiness. We gave out that we were willing to view all who came and consider their qualifications, and to take them as wives if they should satisfy us they would obey our rule and bear children; but the women that came in response to our advertisement, though seemingly of pious and honourable demeanour, were
274

not satisfied with us. Our rule is, as you brethren know well, to wear the same smock till it be in rags, and never to ask for a new pair of sandals till the last pieces of the old pair have left our feet. We presented, therefore, no fair show before the women who came to us, and when our rule was told to them, they withdrew, dissatisfied with our outward show, with the food we ate, and the hours we kept, and of all with the rule that they should live apart from us, only keeping company with us at such times when women are believed to be most fruitful. Such was the first batch in brief; the second batch (they came in batches) pleaded that they could not be wives for us, inasmuch as we were held in little esteem by the Sadducees and the Pharisees, and we were reproved by them for not sending animals for sacrifice to the Temple, a thing that we must do if we would have them live with us. But it being against our rule to send animals to the Temple for sacrifice, we bade them farewell and sent forth messengers into other lands, inviting the Gentiles to come to us to receive instruction in the Jewish religion, with promises to them that if our rule of life was agreeable to them, and they were exact in the appointments of all rites and ceremonies, we should be willing to marry them after their time of probation was over. On this second advertisement, women came to us from Arabia and Mesopotamia, and though we did not approve of the rich garments they wore and the sweet perfumes that trailed after them, we liked these things, as all men do, with our senses; and our minds being filled with thoughts of the children that would continue the order of the Essenes, we spoke but little against the fine linen these women wore and the perfume they exhaled, whereby our ruin was brought about. Joazabdus, our president, himself fell into the temptation of woman's beauty and was led into sinful acquiescence of a display of the images she had brought with her; for without a display of them on either side of the bridal bed she would not permit his embraces. She was of our religion in all else, having abjured her gods and goddesses at every other moment of the day and night; but licence of her body she could not grant except under the eyes of Astarte, and Joazabdus, being a weak man, allowed the images to remain. As soon as the news spread that these images were among us, we went in deputation to our president to beg him to cast them out, but he answered

275

us : Only one image remains — that of Astarte : none looks upon it but she, and if I cast out the image that she reverences she will go hence and with the fruit of my body within her body, and a saint may be lost to us. But we answered him that even as Jacob set up parti-coloured rods before the conceiving yoes that they might bear parti-coloured lambs, so to gaze in the marriage-bed upon the image of Astarte would surely stamp upon the children that might come the image of that demon. But he was not to be moved, whereupon we withdrew, saying to one another : We shall not move him out of his wickedness; and that was why we went to his brother Daddeus and asked him to accept the headship of the community in his brother's place. And seeing that he was unwilling to set himself against his brother, we said : Our God comes before all things, and here we have heathen goddesses among us; and the end of it was that Cozby, that was the Chaldean woman's name, put poison into Daddeus's food, thinking to establish her rule thereby; but as soon as the death of Daddeus became known many left the cenoby polluted in their eyes by heathenism and murder.

So it always falls out, Hazael cried, wine and women have lost the world many saints. Wine deceives the minds of those that drink it, and it exalts men above themselves, and leads them into acts that in any other moment they would shrink from, leaving them more stupid than the animals. Nor is the temptation of women less violent than that of wine. Women's beauty is even more potent, for once a man perceives it he becomes as if blind to all other things; his reason deserts him, he broods upon it by day, and falls at last, as our brother has told us, into unseasonable pleasures, like Solomon himself, about whom many things are related, but not so far as I know that he became so intoxicated with women's various beauty that he found his pleasure at last in his own humiliation. If Solomon did not, others have; for there is a story of a king that allowed his love of a certain queen to take so great a hold upon him that he asked her to come up the steps of his throne to strike him on the face, to take his crown from his head and set it upon her own. This was in his old age, and it is in old age that men fall under the unreasonable sway of women — he was once a wise man, so we should refrain from blame, and pity our brethren who have fallen headlong into the sway of these Chaldean and Arabian

276

women. I might say much more on this subject, but words are useless, so deeply is the passion for women ingrained in the human heart. Proceed, therefore, Brother: we would hear the trouble that women have brought on thee, Brother Eleakim. At once all eyes were turned towards the little fellow whose wandering odours put into everybody's mind thoughts of the great price he must have paid in bracelets and fine linen, but Eleakim told a different story — that he was sought for himself alone, too much so, for the Arabian woman that fell to his lot was not content with the chaste and reasonable intercourse suitable for the begetting of children, the reason for which they had met, but would practise with him heathen rites, and of a kind so terrible that one night he fled to his president to ask for counsel. But the president, who was absorbed in his own pleasures, drove him from his door, saying that every man must settle such questions with his wife. Hazael threw up his hands. Say no more, Brother Eleakim, thou didst well to leave that cenoby. We welcome thee, and having heard thee in brief we would now hear Brother Shaphan. At once all eyes were turned towards the short, thick, silent man, who had till now ventured into no words; and as they looked upon him their thoughts dwelt on the strange choice the curator had made when he chose Brother Shaphan for a husband; for though they were without knowledge of women, their sense told them that Brother Shaphan would not be pleasing to a woman. But Eleakim's story had prepared them for every strange taste, and they waited eagerly for Shaphan. But Shaphan had not spoken many words when tears began to roll down his cheeks, and the brethren of the Brook Kerith bethought themselves that it might be a kindly act to avert their eyes from him till he recovered his composure; but as his grief continued they sought to comfort him, telling him that his troubles were now ended. He would not, however, lift his face from his hands at their entreaty, and his companions said that the intervals between his tears since he was married were never long. At these words Shaphan lifted his face from his hands and dashed some tears from his eyelids. He will tell us now, the brethren said to themselves, but he only uttered a few incoherent words, and his face sank back into his hands. And it was then that Jesus appeared at the end of the domed gallery.

277

Hazael signed to one of the brethren to bring a chair, and when Jesus was seated Hazael told him who the strangers were in these words: Great trouble has fallen upon our order; the wives the brethren have taken unto themselves against my counsel have not obeyed their husbands. Wilt tell our Brother Jesus the trouble that has befallen those that stayed by the lake, Shallum? I will, Shallum replied, for it will please him to hear my story and it will be a satisfaction to me to tell the quarrels that set my wife and me apart till at last I was forced to send her back to her own people. My story will be profitable to you, though you are without wives, for to err is human. The brethren were at once all ears for the new story, but Shallum was so prolix in his telling of his misfortunes that the brethren begged him to tell them again of the ranging of the gods and goddesses on either side of the president's marriage-bed. He paid no heed to them, however, but proceeded with his own story, and so slow was his procedure that Hazael had to interrupt him again. Shallum, he said, it is clear to me that our shepherd has come with some important tidings to me, and it will be kind of thee to forgo the rest of thy story for the present at least, till I have conferred with our shepherd. I should have been loth, Jesus interposed, to interrupt a discourse which seems to be pleasing to you all and which would be to me too if I had knowledge of the matters which concern you, but the differences of men with their wives and wives with their husbands are unknown to me, my life having been spent on the hills with rams and yoes. As he said these words a smile came into his eyes. The first smile I have seen on his face for many years, Hazael said to himself, and Jesus continued: I have left my flock in charge of my serving boy, for I have come to tell the president that he must not be disappointed if many sheep are lost on the hills this year; robbers having hidden themselves again in the caves and fortified themselves among cliffs so difficult that to capture them soldiers must be let down in chests and baskets — a perilous undertaking this is, for the robbers are armed and determined upon revolt against Herod, who they say is not a Jew, and holds his power in Judea from the Romans. They are robbers inasmuch as they steal my sheep, but they are men who value their country higher than their lives. This I know, for I have conferred with them: and Jesus told the Essenes a story of an old

278

man who lived in a cave with his family of seven, all of whom besought him to allow them to surrender to the Romans. Cowards, he said, under his breath, and made pact with them that they should come out of the cave one by one, which they did, and as they came he slew them and threw their bodies into the precipice, sons and daughters, and then he slew his wife, and after reproaching Herod with the meanness of his family, although he was then a king, he threw himself from the cliff's edge.

It is a great story that thou tellest, Jesus, Manahem said, and it is well to hear that there are great souls still amongst us, as in the days of the Maccabees. However this may be, Saddoc interposed, these men in their strife against the Romans must look to our flocks for food. Three sheep were taken from me last night, Jesus answered, and the rest will go one by one, two by two, three by three, unless the revolt be quelled. And if the revolt be not quelled, Saddoc continued, the robbers will need all we have gotten, which is little; they may even need our cave here, and unless we join them they will cast us over the precipices. It was to ask : Are we to take up arms against these robbers? that I came hither, Jesus said. You will confer amongst yourselves, Brethren, Hazael said, and will forgive me if I withdraw : Jesus would like to speak with me privately. The Essenes bowed, and Hazael walked up the domed gallery with Jesus, and as soon as they disappeared at the other end Shallum began : Your shepherd tells you the truth; the hills are once more infested with the remains of Theudas's army. But who may Theudas be? one of the brethren asked. So you have not heard, Shallum cried, of Theudas, and you living here within a few miles of the track he followed with his army down to Jordan. Little news reaches us here, Saddoc said, and he asked Shallum to tell of Theudas, and Shallum related how Theudas had gathered a great following together in Jerusalem and provoked a great uprising of the people whom he called to follow him through the gates of the city, which they did, and over the hills as far as Jordan. The current of the river, he said, will stop, and the water rise up in a great wall as soon as I impose my hands. We have no knowledge if the waters would have obeyed his bidding, for before the waters had time to divide a Roman soldier struck off the prophet's head and carried it to Jerusalem on a spear, where the sight of it was well

279

received by the priests, for Theudas preached against the Temple, against the law, and the traditions, as John and his disciples had done beforetimes. A great number, he continued, were slain by the Roman soldiers, and the rest dispersed, having hidden themselves in the caves, and become robbers and rebels. Nor was Theudas the last, he began again; there was another, an Egyptian, a prophet or a sorcerer of great repute, at whose bidding the people assembled when he announced that the walls of the city would fall as soon as he lifted up his hands. They must follow him through the breach into the desert to meet the day of judgment by the Dead Sea. And what befell this last prophet? Saddoc asked. He was pursued by the Roman soldiers, Eleakim cried, starting out of a sudden reverie. And was he taken prisoner? Manahem asked. No, for he threw a rope into the air and climbed out of sight, Eleakim answered. He must have been a great prophet or an angel more like, for a prophet could not climb up a rope thrown into the air, Caleb said. No, a prophet could not do that. But it is easier, Shaphan snorted, to climb up a rope thrown into the air than to return to a wife, if the flesh be always unwilling. At the words all eyes were turned to Shaphan, who seemed to have recovered his composure. It is a woeful thing to be wedded, he cried. But why didst thou accept a wife? Manahem asked. Why were ye not guided by our counsels? We hoped, Shaphan said, to bring saints into the world and we know not yet that robbers may not be the fruit of our wives' wombs. But if the flesh was always unwilling, Manahem answered, thou hast naught to fear. It would be better, Shallum interrupted, to turn us adrift on the hills than that we should return to the lake where all is disorder now.' Ye are not many here, Eleakim said, to defend yourselves against robbers, and we have hands that can draw swords. Our president alone can say if ye may remain, Manahem said; he is in the gallery now and coming towards us. Our former brethren, Hazael, have renounced their wives, Manahem began, and would return to us and help to defend our cave. You come submissive to our wisdom? Hazael asked. The three strangers replied that they did so, and Hazael stood, his eyes fixed on the three strangers. We will defend you against robbers if these would seek to dispossess you of your cave, Eleakim cried. We have but two cells vacant, Hazael said. It
280

matters not to us where we sleep if we sleep alone; and the president smiling at Shaphan's earnestness said : But three more mouths to feed will be a strain upon our stores of grain. Even though there be three more mouths to feed, Shallum answered, there will be six more hands to build a wall against the robbers. To build a wall against robbers? Hazael said. It is a long while we have been dreaming of that wall; and now it seems the time has come to hold a council. We have been speaking of a wall to protect us against robbers ever since we came here, Manahem cried, and Saddoc answered : We have delayed too long, we must build : the younger brethren will reap the benefit of our toil. We all seem to be in favour of the wall, Hazael said. Are there no dissentients? None. For the next year or more we shall be builders rather than interpreters of the Scriptures. Mathias will come to the wall to discourse to us, Caleb interjected, and Saddoc answered him : Whatsoever may befall us, we are certain of one thing, we shall always be listening to Mathias. But Mathias is a man of great learning, Caleb replied. Of Greek learning may be, Saddoc answered. But even that is not sure; some years ago —— But if Greek wisdom be of no value why is it taught here? Caleb interrupted, and the old Essene answered that Greek wisdom was not taught in the Brook Kerith, but Greek reasoning was applied to the interpretation of Scripture. But there will be no occasion for Mathias's teaching for some years. Years, sayest thou, Saddoc? Amos interjected. I spoke plainly, did I not? Saddoc answered. If it will take us years to build the wall, Amos said, we may as well save ourselves the trouble of becoming builders, for the robbers will be upon us before it is high enough to keep them out; we shall lose our lives before a half-finished wall, and methinks I might as well have been left to my flock on the hills. Thou speakest truly, Saddoc replied, for I doubt if thou wilt prove a better builder than thou wast a shepherd. If my sheep were poor, thy interpretations of the Scriptures are poorer still, Amos said, and the twain fell to quarrelling apart, while the brethren took counsel together. If this mischief did not befall them, and a wall twenty feet high and many feet in thickness were raised, would they be able to store enough food in the cave to bear a three-months' siege? And would they be able to continue the cultivation of their figs along the terrace if robbers were at the gates? But a siege, Manahem answered these disputants, cannot well be, for the shepherds on the hills would carry the news of the siege to Jericho, whence troops would be sent to our help, and at their approach the robbers would flee into the hills. What we have to fear is not a siege, but a sudden assault; and from a successful assault a wall will save us. That is true, Saddoc said. And to defend the wall we must possess ourselves of weapons, Caleb, Benjamin and Eleakim cried; and Shallum told them that a certain hard wood, of which there was an abundance in Jericho, could be shaped into cutlasses whereby a man's head might be struck off at a blow.

At these words the brethren took heart, and Hazael selected Shallum for messenger to go to Jericho for the wood, and a few days afterwards the Essenes were busy carving cutlasses for their defence, and designing a great wall with towers, whilst others were among the cliffs hurling down great masses of stone out of which a wall would soon begin to rise. And every day, an hour after sunrise, the Essenes were quarrying stone and building their wall, and though they had designed it on a great scale, it rose so fast that in two months they were bragging that it would protect them against the great robber, Saulous, a pillager of many caravans, of whom Jesus had much to say when he came down from the hills. The wall will save you, Jesus said, from him. But who will save my flock from Saulous, who is besieged in a cave, and comes forth at night to seek for food for himself and his followers? But if the cave is besieged? Caleb said, laying down his trowel. The cave has two entrances, Jesus answered, and he told them that his belief now was that what remained of the flock should be sent to Jerusalem for sale. The rams, of course, should be kept, and a few of the best yoes for a flock to be raised in happier times. These were his words one sad evening, and they were so convincing that the builders laid down their trowels and repaired to the vaulted gallery to sit in council. But while they sat thinking how they might send representatives to the procurator the robbers were preparing their own doom by seizing a caravan of more than fifty camels laden with wheat for Jerusalem — a very welcome booty. But booty was not the one object of the robbers; they had in mind an uprising against Roman rule by means of bread riots, and to thwart this design the procurator sent many troops of soldiers with orders to bring all that could be taken alive to Jerusalem for crucifixion, saying: Pilate's method of lighting trusses of damp straw at the entrance of the caves has not subdued these hillsides. And when the news of the first captures were brought to him, he said: We shall wait until we have fifty-three — the number of camels stolen. The renown of this hanging will spread through Judea, and for three days at least malefactors will be seen dying at distances of half-a-mile, and lest their sufferings should inspire an attempt at rescue, a decree shall be placed over every cross that rescuers will be punished by crucifixion; and that there shall be no meddling with Roman justice, the soldiers on guard shall be given extra crosses to be used if a comrade should cut down a robber or give him drugs to mitigate his agony. And all this was done as had been commanded, the robbers being exposed at once on the road from Jerusalem; and it was on the first day of the great crucifixion that Jesus, coming round the shoulder of the hill with his flock, was brought to a sudden stop before a group of three.

These, about six or seven hours, a Roman soldier said, in answer to Jesus's question as to the length of time they had been on their crosses, not more than six hours, the soldier repeated, and he turned to his comrade for confirmation of his words. Put a lance into my side, a robber cried out, and God will reward thee in heaven. Thou hast not ceased to groan since the first hour. But put a lance into my side, the robber cried again. I dare not, the soldier answered. Thou'lt hang easier to-morrow. But all night I shall suffer; put a lance into my side, for my heart is like a fire within me. And do the same for me, cried the robbers hanging on either side. All night long, cried the first robber, the pain and the ache and the torment will last; if not a lance, give me wine to drink, some strong, heady wine that will dull the pain. Thy brethren bear the cross better than thou. Take courage and bear thy pain. I was not a robber because I wished it; my house was set on fire as was many another to obtain recruits. Yon shepherd is no better than I. Why am I on the cross and not he? His turn may come, who knows, though he stands so happy among his sheep. To-night he will sleep in a cool cavern, but I shall linger in pain. Give me drink and I will tell thee where the money we have robbed

283

is hidden. The money may not be in the cave, and if it be we might not be able to find it, the soldier answered; and the crucified cried down to him that he could make plain the spot. The soldier was not, however, to be bribed, and they told the crucified that the procurator was coming out to visit the crosses on the morrow, and would be disappointed if he found dead men upon them instead of dying men. Shepherd, the soldiers will not help us; canst thou not help us? Happy shepherd, that will sleep to-night amongst thy sheep. Come by night and give us poison when these soldiers are asleep. We will reward thee. Lift not thy hand against Roman justice, the soldier said to Jesus, lest thou take his place on the cross. Such are our orders. Go thy way. And horror-stricken, Jesus hurried through the hills, pursued by memories of the crucified robbers, and he went on and on, with the intent of escaping from their cries and faces, till, unable to walk farther, he stopped, and, looking round, saw the tired sheep, their eyes mutely asking him why he had come so far, passing by so much good herbage without halting. Poor sheep, he said, I had forgotten you, but there is yet an hour of light before folding-time. Go, seek the herbage among the rocks. My dogs, too, are tired, he added, and want water, and when he had given them some to drink he sat down, hoping that the crucified might not return to his eyes and ears. But he need not have hoped: he was too tired to think of what he had seen and heard, and sat in peace watching the sunset till, as in a vision, a man in a garden, in an agony of doubt, appeared to him. He was betrayed by a disciple and taken before the priests and afterwards before Pilate, who ordered him to be scourged and crucified, and beneath his cross the multitude passed, wagging their heads, inviting him to descend if he could detach himself from the nails. A veil fell and when it was lifted Joseph was bending over him, and soon after was carrying him to his house. The people of that time rose up before him: Esora, Matred, and the camel-driver, the scent of whose sheepskin had led him back to his sheep, and he had given himself to their service with profit to himself, for it had kept his thoughts from straying backwards or forwards, fixing them in the present. He had lived in the ever-fleeting present for many years — how many? The question awoke him from his reverie, and he sat wondering how it was he could think so quietly

of things that he had put out of his mind instinctively, till he seemed
to himself to be a man detached as much from hope as from regret.
It was through such strict rule that I managed to live through the
years behind me, he said. I felt that I must never look back, but
in a moment of great physical fatigue the past returned, and it lies
before me now, the sting taken out of it, like the evening sky in
tranquil waters. Even the memory that I once believed myself
to be the Messiah promised to the Jews ceases to hurt; what we
deem mistakes are part and parcel of some great design. Nothing
befalls but by the will of God. My mistakes! Why do I speak of
them as mistakes? for like all else they were from the beginning
of time, and still are and will be till the end of time, in the mind
of God. His thoughts continuing to unroll, it was not long before
he felt himself thinking that the world was right to defend itself
against those that would repudiate it. For the world, he said to
himself, cannot be else than the world, a truth that was hidden
from me in those early days. The world does not belong to us, but
to God. It was he that made it, and it is for him to unmake it when
he chooses and to remake us if he chooses. Meanwhile we should
do well to accept his decrees and to talk no more of destroying the
Temple and building it up again in three days. Nor should we
trouble ourselves to reprove the keepers of the Temple for having
made themselves a God according to their own image and likeness,
with passions like a man and angers like a man, thereby falling into
idolatry, for what else is our God but an Assyrian king who sits on a
throne and metes out punishments and rewards? It may be that
the priest will some day come into the knowledge that all things are
equal in God's sight, and that he is not to be won by sacrifices,
observances or prayers, that he has no need of these things, not
even of our love, or it may be that they will remain priests. But
though God desires neither sacrifices, observances, nor even love,
it cannot be that we are wholly divorced from God. It may be that
we are united to him by the daily tasks which he has set us to
perform. All around him were his sheep picking the herbage in the
last glowing light of the sunset, and putting his pipes to his lips he
blew the tune that the sheep knew well, and they followed him into
the cavern in which they were to sleep that night.

CHAPTER XXIX.

IT is a great joy to return to thought after a long absence from it, and Jesus was not afraid, though once his conscience asked him if he were justified in yielding himself unreservedly to reason. A man's mind, he answered, like all else, is part of the Godhead; and at that moment he heard God speaking to him out of the breeze. My beloved son, he said, we shall never be separated from each other again. And Jesus replied: Not again, Father, for thou hast given back to me the God that I knew in Nazareth and in the hills above Jericho, but lost sight of in the Book of Daniel. How many, he asked himself, have been led by reading that book into the belief that they were the precursors of the Messiah? We know of Theudas and the Egyptian, and there were many others whose names have not reached us. But I alone believed myself to be the Messiah. He was astonished he could remember so great a sin and not fear God. But I cannot fear God, for I love God, he said; my God neither forgives nor punishes, and if we repent it should be for our own sakes and not to please God. Moreover, it must be well not to waste too much time in repentance, for it is surely better to understand than to repent. We learn through our sins. If it had not been for mine, I should not have learnt that quires and scrolls lead men from God, and that to see and hear God we have only to open our eyes and ears. God is always about us. We hear him in the breeze, and we find him in the flower. He is in these things as much as he is in man, and all things are equal in his sight; Solomon is no greater than Joshbekashar.

He had not remembered the old shepherd, who had taught him all he knew about sheep, for many a day. It is nigh on five and forty years, he said to himself, since he called me to hold the yoes while he made them clean for the winter. It was in yon cave the flock was folded when I laid hands on the yoes for the first time and dragged them forward for him to clip the wool from the rumps. He could see in his memory each different yoe trotting away, looking as if she were thankful for the shepherd's kind office towards her. There was something extraordinarily restful in his memory of old Joshbekashar, and to prolong it Jesus fell to recalling the old man's words; and every little disjointed sentence raised up the old man before him. It was but three times that I held the yoes for him, so it cannot be much more than forty years since that first clipping. Now I come to think on it, the clipping befell on a day like to-day. We'll clip our yoes to-day, and it was with a sense of commemoration in his mind that he called to young Jacob to come to his aid, saying: Joshbekashar's flock was always folded in yon cave for this clipping; the only change is that I am the clipper and thou'rt holding them for me. There are forty-five to be clipped, and just the same as before each yoe will trot away into the field looking as if she were thankful at having been made clean for the winter. On these words both fell to their work, and the cunning hand spent no more than a minute over each. Stooping over yoes makes one's back ache, he said, rising from the last one, using the very same words he heard forty years before from Joshbekashar: Time brings back the past! he said. We repeat the words of those that have gone before while doing their work; and it is likely we are doing God's work as well by making the yoes clean for the winter as by cutting their throats in the Temple. All the same stooping over yoes makes one's back ache, he repeated, for the words evoked the old shepherd, and he waited for Jacob to answer in the words spoken by him forty years ago to Joshbekashar. Himself had forgotten his words, but he thought he would recognise them if Jacob were inspired to speak them. But Jacob kept silence for shame's sake, for his hope was that the flock would be given to his charge as soon as old age obliged Jesus to join his brethren in the cenoby. Thou'lt be sorry for me, lad, I know that well, but thou hast begun to look forward to the time when thou'lt walk the hills at the head of the flock like another; it is but proper that thou shouldst, and it is but natural that the time should seem long to thee; but take on a little patience. This much I can vouch for: every bone in me was aching when I left the cavern this morning,

and my sight is no longer what it was. Master Jesus, I'd as lief wait; the hills will be naught without thee. Dost hear me, Master? Jesus smiled and dropped back into his meditations, and from that day onward very little sufficed to remind him that he would end his days in the cenoby reading the Scriptures and interpreting them. In the cenoby, he said, men do not think, they only read, but in the fields a shepherd need never lose sight of the thought that leads him. A good shepherd can think while watching his sheep; and as the flock was feeding in good order, he took up the thread of a thought to which he had become attached since his discovery that signs and sounds of God's presence are never lacking on earth. As God's constant companion and confidant he had come to comprehend that the world of nature was a manifestation of the God he knew in himself. I know myself, he said one day, but I do not know the God which is above, for he seems to be infinite; nor do I know nature, which is beyond me, for that, too, seems to run into an infinite, but an infinite that is not that of God. A few moments later it seemed to him he might look upon himself as an islet between two infinities. But to which was he nearer in eternity? Ah, if he knew that! And it was then that a conviction fell upon him that if he remained on the hills he would be able to understand many things that were obscure to him to-day. It will take about two years, he said, and then many things that are dark will become clear. Two infinites, God and nature. It was just then that his eyes fell on a yoe wandering near some scrub. A wolf, he said, may be lurking there. I must bring her back; and he put a stone into his sling. A wolf is lurking there, he continued, else Gorbotha would not stand growling. Gorbotha, a golden-haired dog, like a wolf in build, stood snuffing the breeze, whilst Thema, his sister, sought her master's hand. A moment after the breeze veered, bringing the scent to her, and the two dogs dashed forward into the scrub without finding either wolf or jackal lying in wait. All the same, he said, a wolf or a jackal must have been lying there and not long ago, else the dogs would not have growled and rushed to the onset as they did. Gorbotha lays his nose to the scent; Thema is running it; I must get them back. Obedient to his call the dogs lifted their heads, hesitated, and returned perplexed and anxious to their master, who resumed his meditation, saying to himself
288

CLIPPING THE YOES

that if aching bones obliged him to return to the cenoby he would
have to give up thinking. For one only thinks well in solitude and
when one thinks for oneself alone; but in the cenoby the brethren
think together. All the same my life on the hills is not over yet,
and an hour later he put his pipes to his lips and led his flock to
different hills, for, guided by some subtle sense, he seemed to divine
the springing up of new grass; and the shepherds, knowing of this
instinct for pasturage, were wont to follow him, and he was often at
pains to elude them, for on no hillside is there grass enough for
many flocks.

My poor sheep, he said, as he watched them scatter over a
grassy hillside. Ye're happy this springtime for ye do not know that
your shepherd is about to be taken from you. But he has suffered
too much in the winter we've come out of to remain on the hills
many more years. Before leaving you he must discover a shepherd
that will care for you as well as he has done. Amos is dead; there is
no one in the cenoby that understands sheep. Would ye had speech
to counsel me. But tell me, what would ye say were I to leave you
in Jacob's charge? As if weary of grass a sad sheep walked a little
way, and it was then that it began to seem to Jesus that he might
do well to entrust his flock to Jacob. He had sent him out that
morning with twenty lambs too young to run with the flock, and
he now stood waiting for him, thinking that if Jacob lost none
between this day and the end of the summer, the flock might be
given over to him. Every young man's past is tarnished, he continued, for he could not forget that Jacob had begun by losing his
master's dogs; two had been killed by panthers. And since that
luckless night Jacob had believed evil to be with him, and not without cause. On hearing that rain had fallen in the west, he set out
for Cæsarea to redeem his credit, but at the end of the fourth day
he could find no cavern in which to fold his sheep, and lay down in
the open, surrounded by his flock, unsuspicious that a pack of
wolves had trailed him from cavern to cavern since he left the Jordan valley, the animals divining that their chance would come at
last. It would have been better, Jacob said, if they had rushed over
him, for after this disaster no one would employ him; he had wandered an outcast, living on the charity of shepherds, sharing a little
of their bread, and charity being perishable stuff, he would have

had to sit with the beggars by the wayside above Jericho if Jesus had not given his lambs into his charge — by this act unwittingly restoring to Jacob some of his lost faith in himself. He had gone away muttering: Jesus, who knows more than all the other shepherds on the hills, holds me to be no fool, and one day I'll be trusted again with a flock. I'm young and can wait, and Jesus, mayhap, will tell me his cure for the scab, and by serving him I may get a puppy when Thema has a litter. In such wise Jacob looked to Jesus and Thema for fortune, and as he came over the ridge and caught sight of Jesus waiting for him, he said: Call up thy dogs, Master, lest they should fall upon mine and upon me. Gorbotha has already risen to his feet and Thema is growling. Jesus laid his staff across their backs. What, will ye attack Jacob? he cried, and what be your quarrel with his dogs? Poor Syrian dogs, Jacob answered, that would be quickly killed by thine. If I had had dogs like Gorbotha and Thema the wolves would not —— But, Jacob, thou wouldst have lost thy dogs as well as thy sheep. What stand could any dogs make against a pack of wolves, and a shepherd without dogs is like a bird without wings, as Brother Amos used to say. Yes, that is just it, Jacob replied, struck by the aptness of the comparison. Thou art known, Jesus, to be the most foreseeing shepherd on the hills; but the flock would not have increased without thy dogs. Abdiel is great in his knowledge of dogs, and he told me that he had never known any like thine, Master. Come now, Thema, Jesus cried. Come, lie down here; lay thy muzzle against my knee. And growl not at Jacob or I'll send thee away. So Abdiel spoke of my dogs! They are well enough; one can work with them. But I've had better dogs. Whereupon Jesus told a story how one night he had lain under a fair sky to sleep and had slept so soundly that the rain had not wakened him: But Boreth — that was the dog's name — distressed at the sight of me lying in the rain, began to lick my face, and when I had wrung out my cloak he led me to a dry cave unknown to me, though I thought I knew every one in these hills. He must have gone in search of one as soon as it began to rain, and when he found a dry one he came back to awaken me. More faithful dogs, he said, there never were than these at my feet, but I've known stronger and fiercer. But I'd tell thee another story of Boreth; and he related how one night in
290

December as he watched, having for his protection only Boreth (his other dogs, Anos and Torbitt, being at home, one with a lame paw, the other with puppies), he had fallen asleep, though he knew robbers were about in the hills — especially in the winter months, he said. But I knew I could count on Boreth to awake me if one came to steal the sheep. Now what I'm about to say, Jacob, happened at the time of the great rain of December, when the nights are dark about us. I was sleeping in a sheltered place in the coign of a cliff, the flock was folded and Boreth was away upon his rounds, and it was then that two robbers stole into the cave. One was about to plunge his dagger into me, but I had time to catch his wrist and to whistle; and in a few seconds Boreth leapt upon the robber that was seeking to stab me. He bit his neck and shoulder; and then, leaving that robber disabled, he attacked the robber's mate, and it was wonderful how he crept round and round in the darkness, biting him all the time, and then pursuing the two he worried them up the valley until his heart misgave him and he thought it wouldn't be safe to leave me alone any longer. But Gorbotha would defend thee against a robber, Jacob said, and he called to the dog, but Gorbotha only growled at him. Have patience with them, Jesus rejoined; I'll not feed them for three days, and after feeding them thou'lt take them to the hills, and when they have coursed and killed a jackal for thee it may be that they'll accept thee for master. But these Thracians rarely love twice. Come, Jacob, and we'll look into thy flock of lambs and take counsel together. They seem to be doing fairly well with thee — a bit tired; I dare say thou hast come a long way with them. We walked too fast, Jacob answered, saying he had had to go farther than he thought for in search of grass, and had found some that was worth the distance they had journeyed, for the lambs had fallen to nibbling at once. Fell to nibbling at once, did they? Jesus repeated. When they're folded with the yoes, thou'lt put into their jaws a stick to keep them from sucking. And without waiting for Jacob to answer he asked which of all these lambs he would choose to keep for breeding from. Jacob pointed out first one and then another; but Jesus shook his head and showed him a lamb which Jacob had not cast his eyes over and said: I would not prophesy anything of sheep, but shall be surprised if he doesn't come into a

291

broad-shouldered ram, strong across the loins and straight on his legs, of the kind and sort to get lambs that do well on these hills. And to advise thee well, I say : leave him on his dam another hundred days; shear him, for it will give him strength to take some wool from him, but do not take it from his back, leaving him unprotected from the sun. And all the first year he will skip about with the yoes and jump upon them, but it will be only play, for his time has not yet come; in two more years he'll be at his height, serving ten yoes a day; but keep him not overlong; thou must always have some new rams preparing, else thy flock will decline. The ram thou seest on the right is old, and must soon be replaced. But the white ram yonder is still full of service : a better I've never known. The white ram is stronger than the black, though the black yoe will turn from him and seek a ram of her own colour. I've known a white ram so ardent for a black yoe that he fought the black ram till their skulls cracked. Master, it is well to listen to thee, Jacob interrupted, for none knoweth sheep like thee, but as none will ever give me charge of a flock again, thy teaching is wasted upon me. Look to the yoes' teeth, Jacob, and to their udders; see that the udders are sound. Master, never before didst thou mock at me, who am for my misfortunes the flouting-stock of all these fields. In what have I done wrong? That my lambs are a bit tired is all thou hast to blame me for to-day. Jacob, I'm not mocking at thee, but looking forward a little, for time is on thy side and will soon put thee in charge of a flock again. Time is on my side, Jacob repeated. If I understand thee rightly, Master, thy meaning is, that the hills are beginning to weary thee. Look into my beard, Jacob, and see how much grey hair is in it, and my gait is slower than it used to be; a stiffness has come upon my joints that will not wear out, and my eyes are not as keen as they were, and when I see in thee a wise shepherd, between the spring and autumn, it may be that Hazael, our president, at my advice, will entrust my flock to thy charge.

CHAPTER XXX.

SO thou thinkest, Eliab, that the autumn rains will make an end of him. And maybe of thee too, Bozrah, Eliab returned. A hard life ours is, even for the young ones. Hard bread by day and at night a bed of stones — a hard life from the beginning, one that doesn't grow softer; and to end in a lion's maw at fifty is the best we can hope for. For us, perhaps, Bozrah answered; but Jesus will go up to the cenoby among the rocks and die amongst the brethren reading the Scriptures. If the autumn rains don't make an end of him, Eliab interjected testily, as if he did not like his forecast of Jesus's death to be called into question. As I was saying, a shepherd's life is a hard one, and when the autumn rains make an end of him, the brethren will be on the look-out for another shepherd, and there's not one amongst them that would bring half the flock entrusted to him into the fold at the end of the year. The best of us lose sheep : what with —— The flock will go to Jacob, the lad he's been training to follow him ever since his friend was killed, Havilah remarked timidly. Eliab and Bozrah raised their eyes, and looked at Havilah in surprise, for a sensible remark from Havilah was an event, and to their wonder they found themselves in agreement with Havilah. The flock would go to Jacob without doubt. Of course, Havilah cried, excited by the success of his last remark, he be more than fifty. Thou mightst put five years more to the fifty and not be far wrong, Bozrah interposed. Havilah was minded to speak again, but his elders' looks made him feel that they had heard him enough. Now, Bozrah, how many years dost thou make it since Joseph of Arimathea was killed? How many years? Bozrah repeated. I can't tell thee how many years, but many years. . . . Stay, I can mark the date down for thee. It was about ten years before Theudas (wasn't that his name?) led the multitude over these hills. A great riot that was surely — fires lighted at the side of the woods for the roasting of our lambs, and many's the fine wood that was turned to blackened stems and sad ashes in those days. It comes back to me now, Eliab interjected. Theudas was the name. I'd forgotten it for the moment. He led the multitude to Jordan, and while he was bidding the waters divide to let him across the Romans had his head off. It was nigh ten years before that rioting that Gaddi's partner was killed in Jerusalem. I believe thee to be right, Bozrah replied, and they talked of the different magicians and messiahs that were still plaguing the country, stirring them up against the Romans. But, cried Bozrah suddenly, the story comes back to me. Not getting any news of his friend, Jesus left his flock with Amos, and came down to the pass between the hills where the road descends to the lake to inquire from the beggars if they had seen Gaddi's partner on his way to Jerusalem or Jericho; and seeing the lepers and beggars gathering about Jesus, I came down to hear what was being said, but before I got as far I saw Jesus turn away and walk into the hills. It was from the beggars and lepers that I heard that Joseph had been killed in the streets of Jerusalem. Thou knowest how long beggars take to tell a story; Jesus was far away before they got to the end of it, simple though it was. I'd have gone after him if they'd been quicker. More of the story I don't know. It was just as thou sayest, mate, Eliab answered, and thou'lt bear me out that it was some months after, maybe six or seven, that Jesus was seen again leading the flock. I remember the day I saw him, for wasn't I near to rubbing my eyes lest they might be deceiving me — I remember, Eliab continued, it comes back to me as it does to thee, for within two years he had gathered another handsome flock about him. A fine shepherd, Havilah said. None better to be found on the hills. Thou speakest well, Eliab answered him, and for thee to speak well twice in the same day is well-nigh a miracle. Belike thou'lt awake one morning to find thyself the Messiah Israel is waiting for, so great is thy advancement of late in good sense. Havilah turned aside, and Eliab, divining his wounded spirit, sought to make amends by offering him some bread and garlic, but Havilah went away, a melancholy, heavy-shouldered young man, one that, Eliab said, must feel life cruelly, knowing himself

294

as he must have done from the beginning to be what is known as a good-for-nothing.

And it was soon after Havilah's departure that Jesus returned to the shepherds and, stopping in front of Eliab and Bozrah, he said: I've come back, mates, to give you my thanks for many a year of good-fellowship. So the time has come for us to lose thee, mate, Eliab answered. We are sorry for it, though it isn't altogether unlooked for. We were saying not many moments ago, Bozrah interjected, that the life on the hills is no life for a man when he has gone fifty, and thou'lt not see fifty again. No, and not by three years, Jesus answered. About three years ago the feeling began to come over me that I couldn't fight another winter out on these hills, and then Jacob, waiting for a flock, was remembered, and he may as well have mine during my life as wait for my death to get it. Better so, said Eliab, whose wont it was to strike his word in whenever the speaker paused. He did not always wait for the speaker to pause, and this trick being known to Bozrah, he said: And by all accounts thou hast made a true shepherd of him, passing over to him all thy knowledge. A lad of good report, Jesus answered, who had fallen on a hard master —— A thing that has happened to all of us in our time, Bozrah interjected. He's not the first that fell out of favour for that his yoes hadn't given as many lambs as they might have done. Nor was there anything of neglect in it, but such a bit of ill luck as might run into any man or any man might run up against. He was told, said Eliab, who could not bear anyone to tell a story but himself, that though he were to bring the parts of the sheep the wolf had left behind to his master he would have to seek another master. Such severity frightens the shepherd, and the wolf smells out the frightened shepherd, Jesus said, and he told his mates that he had not found Jacob lacking in truthfulness nor in natural discernment, and he asked them to give all their protection to Jacob: Who will, he said, go forth in charge of our flock tomorrow. The shepherds answered that they were sorry to lose Jesus, and that the hills would not seem like the hills without him, and Jesus answered that he, too, would be lonely among the brethren reading the Scriptures. When one is used to sheep one misses them sorely, Eliab said, there's always something to learn from them; and he began to tell a story; but before he came to the end

295

of it Jesus's thoughts had strayed from the story he was listening
to, and he turned away, leaving the shepherd with his half-finished
story, and walked absorbed in his thoughts, immersed in his own
mind, till he had reached the crest of the next hill and was within
some hundred yards of the brook. It was then that he remembered
he had left them abruptly in the middle of a half-finished tale, and
he stopped to consider if he should return to them and ask for the
end of the story. But fearing they would think he was making a
mocking-stock of them, he sighed, and was vexed that they had
parted on a seeming lack of courtesy: On no seeming lack, on a
very clear lack, he said to himself; but it would be useless to return
to them; they would not understand, and a man had always better
return to his own thoughts. Repent, repent, he said, picking up
the thread of his thoughts, but acknowledgment comes before
repentance, and of what help will repentance be, for repentance
changes nothing; it brings nothing unless grief peradventure. I
was in the hands of God then just as I am now, and everything
within and without us is in his hands, the things that we look upon
as evil and the things that we look upon as good. Our sight is not
his sight, our hearing is not his hearing; we must despise nothing,
for all things come from him, and return to him. I used, he said,
to despise the air I breathed, and long for the airs of paradise, but
what did these longings bring me? — grief. God bade us live on
earth and we bring unhappiness upon ourselves by desiring heaven.
Jesus stopped, and looking through the blue air of evening, he
could see the shepherds eating their bread and garlic on the hillside.
Folding-time is near, he said to himself, but I shall never fold a
flock again. . . .

His thoughts began again, flowing like a wind, as mysteriously,
arising he knew not whence, nor how, his mind holding him as fast
as if he were in chains, and he heard from within that he had passed
through two stages — the first was in Jerusalem, when he preached
against the priests and their sacrifices. God does not desire the
blood of sheep, but our love, and all ritual comes between us and
God. . . . God is in the heart, he had said, and he had spoken as
truly as a man may speak of the journey that lies before him on the
morning of the first day. In the desert he had looked for God in
the flowers that the sun called forth and in the clouds that the wind

shepherded, and he had learnt to prize the earth and live content among his sheep, all things being the gift of God and his holy will. He had not placed himself above the flowers and grasses of the earth, nor the sheep that fed upon them, nor above the men that fed upon the sheep. He had striven against the memory of his sin, he had desired only one thing, to acknowledge his sin, and to repent. But it seemed to him that anger and shame and sorrow, and desire of repentance, had dropped out of his heart. It seemed to him as he turned and pursued his way that some new thought was striving to speak through him. Rites and observances, all that comes under the name of religion, estranges us from God, he repeated. God is not here, nor there, but everywhere : in the flower, and in the star, and in the earth underfoot. He has often been at my elbow, God or this vast Providence that upholds the work; but shall we gather the universal will into an image and call it God? — for by doing this do we not drift back to the starting-point of all our misery? We again become the dupes of illusion and desire; God and his heaven are our old enemies in disguise. He who yields himself to God goes forth to persuade others to love God, and very soon his love of God impels him to violent words and cruel deeds. It cannot be other, for God is but desire, and whosoever yields to desire falls into sin. To be without sin we must be without God. Jesus stood before the door of the cenoby, startled at the thoughts that had been put into his mind, asking himself if any man had dared to ask himself if God were not indeed the last uncleanliness of the mind.

CHAPTER XXXI.

IF thou wouldst not miss Mathias's discourse, Brother Jesus, thou must hasten thy steps. He is telling that the Scriptures are but allegories. Some of us are opposed to this view, believing that Adam and Eve are —— Yea, Brother, and my thanks to thee for thy admonishment, Jesus said, for he did not wish to discredit Mathias's reputation for theological argument; but no sooner was he out of sight of the gate-keeper than he began to consider the great rock that Joseph had predicted would one day come crashing down, and, being no wise in a hurry, fell to wondering how much of the mountain-side it would bring with it when it fell. At present it projected over the pathway for several yards, making an excellent store-house, and, his thoughts suspended between the discussion that was proceeding regarding Adam and Eve — whether the original twain had ever lived or were but allegories (themselves and their garden) — he began to consider if the brethren had laid in a sufficient stock of firewood, and how long it would take him to chop it into pieces handy for burning. He would be glad to relieve the brethren from all such humble work, and by taking it upon himself he would be able to plead an excuse for absenting himself from Mathias's discourses. Hazael would not refuse to assign to him the task of feeding the doves and the cleaning out of their coops; he would find occupation among the vines and fig-trees — he was something of a gardener — and Hazael would not refuse him permission to return to the hills to see that all was well with the flocks. Jacob will need to be looked after; and there are the dogs; and if they cannot be brought to look upon Jacob as master their lives will be wasted, he said. I seem to read supper in their eyes, he added, and having tied them up supperless he visited the bitch and her puppies. Brother Ozias hasn't forgotten to feed her. There

298

is some food still in the platter. But they must submit, he continued, his thoughts having returned to his dogs, Theusa and Tharsa, and then he stood listening, for he could hear Mathias's voice. The door of the lecture-room is closed; if I step softly none will know that I have returned from the hills, and I can sit unsuspected on the balcony till Mathias's allegories are ended, and watching the evening descending on the cliff it may be that I shall be able to examine the thoughts that assailed me as I ascended the hillside; whether we pursue a corruptible or an incorruptible crown the end is the same, he said. It was not enough for me to love God, I must needs ask others to worship him, at first with words of love, and when love failed I threatened, I raved; and the sin I fell into others will fall into, for it is natural to man to wish to make his brother like himself, thereby undoing the work of God. Myself am no paragon; I condemned the priests whilst setting myself up as a priest, and spoke of God and the will of God, though in all truth I had very little more reason than they to speak of these things. God has not created us to know him, or only partially through our consciousness of good and evil. Good and evil do not exist in God's eyes as in our eyes, for he is the author of all, but it may be that our sense of good and evil was given to us by him as a token of our divine nature. If this be true, why should we puzzle and fret ourselves with distinctions like Mathias? It were better to leave the mystery and attend to this life, casting out desire to know what God is or what nature is, as well as desire for particular things in this world which long ago I told men to disregard. . . . A flight of doves distracted his attention, and a moment after the door of the lecture-room opened and Saddoc and Manahem appeared, carrying somebody dead or who had fainted.

As they came across the domed gallery towards the embrasure Jesus heard Manahem say: He will return to himself as soon as we get him into the air. And they placed him where Jesus had been sitting. A little water, Saddoc cried, and Jesus ran to the well, and returning with a cup of water he stood by sprinkling the worn, grey face. The heat overcame me, Hazael murmured, but I shall soon be well and then you will bear me back to hear —— The sentence did not finish, and Jesus said: Thou'lt be better here with me, Hazael, than listening to discourses that fatigue the mind.

Mathias is very insistent, Manahem muttered. He is indeed, Saddoc answered. And while Jesus sat by Hazael, fearing that his life might go out at any moment, Manahem reproved Saddoc, saying that whereas duty is the cause of all good, we have only to look beyond our own doors to see evil everywhere. Even so, Saddoc answered, what wouldst thou? That the world, Manahem answered, was created by good and evil angels. Whereupon Saddoc asked him if he numbered Lilith, Adam's first wife, among the evil angels. A question Manahem did not answer, and, being eager to tell the story, he turned to Jesus, who he guessed did not know it, and began at once to tell it, after warning Jesus that it was among their oldest stories though not to be found in the Scriptures. She must be numbered among the evil angels, he said, remembering that Saddoc had put the question to him, for she rebuked Adam, who took great delight in her hair, combing it for his pleasure from morn to eve in the garden, and left him, saying she could abide him no longer. At which words, Jesus, Adam sorrowed, and his grief was such that God heard his sighs and asked him for what he was grieving, and he said : I live in great loneliness, for Lilith, O Lord, has left me, and I beg thee to send messengers who will bring her back. Whereupon God took pity on his servant Adam and bade his three angels, Raphael, Gabriel and Michael, to go away at once in search of Lilith, whom they found flying over the sea, and her answer to them was that her pleasure was now in flying : And for that reason I will not return to Adam, she said. Is that the answer we are to bring back to God? they asked. I have no other answer for him, she answered, being in a humour in which it pleased her to anger God, and the anger that her words put upon him was so great that to punish her he set himself to the creation of a lovely companion for Adam. Be thou lonely no more, he said to Adam. See, I have given Eve to thee. Adam was never lonely again, but walked through a beautiful garden, enjoying Eve's beauty unceasingly, happy as the day was long, till tidings of their happiness reached Lilith, who by that time had grown weary of flying from sea to sea : I will make an end of it, she said, and descending circle by circle she went about seeking the garden, which she found at last, but failing to find the gate or any gap in the walls she sat down and began combing her hair. Nor was she long combing it
300

before Lucifer, attracted by the rustling, came by, saying: I would be taken captive in the net thou weavest with thy hair, and she answered: Not yet; for my business is in yon garden, but into it I can find no way. Wilt lend me thy sinewy shape, Lucifer? for in it I shall be able to glide over the walls and coil myself into the tree of forbidden fruit, and I shall persuade Eve as she passes to eat of it, for it will be to her great detriment to do so. But of what good will that be to me? Lucifer answered, wouldst thou leave me without a shape whilst thou art tempting Eve? Thy reward will be that I will come to thee again when I have tempted Eve and made an end of her happiness. We shall repeople the world with sons and daughters more bright and beautiful and more supple than any that have ever been seen yet. All the same! Lucifer answered, not liking to part with his shape. But as his desire could not be gainsaid, he lent his shape to Lilith for an hour. And it was in that hour our first parents fell into sin, and were chased from the garden. Did she return to Lucifer and fulfil her promise or did she cheat him? Saddoc asked. As Manahem was about to answer Saddoc intervened again: Manahem, thou overlookest the fact that Mathias holds that the Garden of Eden and Adam and Eve, to say nothing of Lilith, are a parable, and his reason for thinking thus is, as thou knowest well, that the Scriptures tell us that after eating of the forbidden fruit Adam and Eve sought to hide themselves from God among the trees. He holds as thou sayest, Saddoc, that the garden means the mind of man as an individual; and he who would escape from God flees from himself, for our lives are swayed between two powers: the mind of the universe, which is God, and the separate mind of the individual. Then, if I understand thee rightly, Manahem, and thy master, Mathias, the Scriptures melt into imagery? What says Jesus? This, Saddoc, that it was with such subleties of discourse and lengthy periods that Mathias fatigued our Father till he fainted away in his chair. Jesus is right, Manahem answered; it was certainly Mathias's discourse that fatigued our Father, so why should we prolong the argument in his face while he is coming back to life? It was not the length of Mathias's discourse, nor his eloquence, Hazael said, that caused my senses to swoon away. My age will not permit me to listen long. I would be with Jesus, and I would that ye, Saddoc and Manahem, return to the lecture-room at once, else our brother will think his discourse has failed. Jesus is here to give the attendance I require. Go, hasten, lest ye miss any of his points.

The brethren were about to raise a protest, but at a sign from Jesus they obeyed; Mathias's voice was heard as soon as the door of the lecture-room was opened, but the brethren did not forget to close it, and when silence came again Hazael said: Jesus, come hither, sit near me, for I would speak to thee, but cannot raise my voice. Thou'lt sleep here to-night, and to-morrow we shall meet again. And this is well, for my days are numbered. I shall not be here to see next year's lambs and to agree that this new shepherd shall be recompensed by a gift of eighteen, as is the custom. And Jesus, understanding that the president was prophesying his own death, said: Why speakest thou like this to me who have returned from the hills to strangers? for all are strangers to me but thou. I shall be sorry to leave thee, Jesus, for our lives have been twisted together, strands of the same rope. But it must be plain to thee that I am growing weaker; month by month, week by week, my strength is ebbing. I am going out; but for what reason should I lament that God has not chosen to retain me a few months longer, since my life cannot be prolonged for more than a few months? My eighty odd years have left me with barely strength enough to sit in the doorway looking back on the way I have come. Every day the things of this world grow fainter, and life becomes to me an unreal thing, and myself becomes unreal to those around me; only to thee do I retain anything of my vanished self. So why should I remain? For thy sake, lest thou be lonely here? Well, that is reason enough, and I will bear the burden of life as well as I can for thy sake. A burden it is, and for a reason that thou mayst not divine, for thou art still a young man in my eyes, and, moreover, hast not lived under a roof for many years listening to learned interpretations of Scripture. Thou hast not guessed, nor wilt thou ever guess, till age reveals it to thee, that as we grow old we no longer concern ourselves to love God as we used to love him. No one would have thought, not even thou, whose mind is always occupied with God, and who art more conscious of him perhaps than anyone I have known, no one, I say, not even thou, would have thought that as we approach death our love of God should

302

grow weaker, but this is so. In great age nothing seems to matter, and it is this indifference that I wish to escape from. Thou goest forth in the morning to lead thy flock in search of pasture, if need be many hours, and God is nearer to us in the wilderness than he is among men. Which means, Jesus said, that under this roof I, too, may cease to love God? Not cease to love God : one doesn't cease to love God, Hazael answered. But, Hazael, this night I've yielded up the flocks to a new shepherd, for my limbs have grown weary, and what thou tellest me of old age frightens me. Thou wouldst warn me that God is loved only on the hills under the sky —— I am too weak to choose my thoughts or my words, and many things pass out of my mind, Hazael answered. Had I remembered I shouldn't have spoken. But why not speak, Father? Jesus asked, so that I may be prepared in a measure for the new life that awaits me. Life never comes twice in the same way, Hazael replied; nor do the same things befall any two men. I know not what may befall thee : but the sky, Jesus, will always be before thine eyes and the green fields under thy feet, even while listening to Mathias. But thou didst live once under the sky, Jesus said. Not long enough, Hazael murmured, but the love of God was ardent in me when I walked by day and night, sleeping under the stars, seeking young men who could give up their lives to the love of God and bringing them back hither into the fold of the Essenes. In those days there was little else in me but love of God, and I could walk from dusk to dusk without wearying; twelve and fifteen hours were not too many for my feet : my feet bounded along the road while my eyes followed white clouds moving over the sky; I dreamed of them as God's palaces, and I saw God not only in the clouds but in the grass, and in the fields, and the flower that covers the fields. I read God in the air and in the waters : and in every town in Palestine I sought out those that loved God and those that could learn to love God. I could walk well in those days, fifteen hours were less than as many minutes are now. I have walked from Jerusalem to Joppa in one day, and the night that I met thy father outside Nazareth I had walked twelve hours, though I had been delayed in the morning : eight hours before midday, and after a rest in the wood I went on again for several hours more, how many I do not know, I've forgotten. I did not know the distance that I had walked

303

till I met thy father coming home from his work, his tools in the bag upon his shoulder. His voice is still in my ear. But if it be to Nazareth thou'rt going, come along with me, he said. And I can still hear ourselves talking, myself asking him to direct me to a lodging, and his answering: There's a house in the village where thou'lt get one, and I'll lead thee to it. But all the beds in that house were full; we knocked at other inns, but the men and women and children in them were asleep and not to be roused; and if by chance our knocking awakened somebody we were bidden away with threats that the dogs would be loosed upon us. Nazareth looks not kindly on the wayfarer to-night, I said. Yet it shall not be said that a stranger had to sleep in the streets of Nazareth, were thy father's very words to me, Jesus. Come to my house, he said; though it be small and we have to put somebody out of his bed, it will be better than that our town should gain evil repute. Thou canst not have forgotten me coming, for thy father shook thee out of thy sleep and told thee that he wanted thy bed for a stranger. I can see thee still standing before me in thy smock, and though the hours I'd travelled had gone down into my very marrow, and sleep was heavy upon my eyes, yet a freshness came upon me as of the dawn when I looked on thee, and my heart told me that I had found one that would do honour to the Essenes, and love God more than any I had ever met with yet. But I think I hear thee weeping, Jesus. Now, for what art thou weeping? There is nothing sad in the story, only that it is a long time ago. Our speech next day still rings in my ear — my telling thee of the Pharisees that merely minded the letter of the law, and of the Sadducees that said there was no life outside this world except for angels. It is well indeed that I remember our two selves sitting by the door on two stools set under a vine, and it throwing pretty patterns of shadow on the pavement whilst we talked — whilst I talked to thee of the brethren, who lived down by the Bitter Lake, no one owning anything more than his fellow, so that none might be distracted from God by the pleasures of this world. I can see clearly through the years thy face expectant, and Nazareth — the deeply rutted streets and the hills above. The days that we walked in Nazareth are pleasant memories, for I could never tell thee enough about the Essenes: their contempt of riches, and that if there were one among
304

them who had more than another, on entering the order he willingly shared it. We were among the hills the day that I told thee about the baker; how he put a platter with a loaf on it before each of the brethren, how they broke bread, deeming the meal sacred, and it was the next day that we bade farewell to thy father and thy mother and started on our journey; a long way, but one that did not seem long to us, so engaged were we with our hopes. It was with me thou sawest Jerusalem for the first time; and I remember telling thee as we journeyed by the Jordan seeking a ford that the Essenes looked upon oil as a defilement, and if any one of them be anointed without his approbation it is wiped off, for we think to be sweaty is a good thing, and to be clothed in white garments, and never to change these till they be torn to pieces or worn out by time. And of the little band that came with us that day from Galilee there remain Saddoc, Manahem and thyself. All of you learnt from me on the journey that we laboured till the fifth hour and then assembled together again clothed in white veils, after having bathed our bodies in cold water. But, Jesus, why this grief? Because I am going from thee? But, dear friend, to come and to go is the law of life, and it may be that I shall be with thee longer than thou thinkest for; eighty odd years may be lengthened into ninety; the patriarchs lived till a hundred and more years, and we believe that the soul outlives the body. Out of the chrysalis we escape from our corruptible bodies, and the beautiful butterfly flutters Godward. Grieve for me a little when I am gone, but grieve not before I go, for I would see thy face always happy, as I remember it in those years long ago in Nazareth. Jesus, Jesus, thou shouldst not weep like this! None should weep but for sin, and thy life is known to me from the day in Nazareth when we sat in the street together to the day that thou wentest to the Jordan to get baptism from John. But a year of my life is unknown to thee, Hazael. We will not speak of it, Hazael answered, nor of thy transgression of our rules atoned for on the hills. Since God has forgiven thee why should we be laggards in forgiveness? Thy hand heals the sick —— I pray thee, Father, not to say another word, for none is less worthy than I am. The greatest sinner amongst us is sitting by thee, one that has not dared to tell his secret to thee. . . . The memory of my sin has fed upon me and grown stronger, becoming a devil within

305

me, but till now I have lacked courage to come to thee and ask thee to cast it out. But now since thou art going from us this year or the next, I wouldn't let thee go without telling it; to none may I tell it but to thee, for none else would understand it. I am listening, Jesus, Hazael answered.

The mutter of the water in the valley below them arose and grew louder in the silence; as Jesus prepared to speak his secret the doors of the lecture-room opened and the monks came out singing:

> In the Lord put I my trust:
> How say ye to my soul, Flee
> As a bird to your mountain?
> For, lo, the wicked bend their
> Bow, they make ready their arrow
> Upon the string, that they may privily
> Shoot at the upright in heart.
> If the foundations be destroyed, what
> Can the righteous do?
> For the righteous Lord loveth
> Righteousness; his countenance
> Doth behold the upright.

These words of the psalmist were meant for me, Jesus whispered, and now that the brethren are here I may not speak, but to-morrow—— There may be no to-morrow for us, the president answered. Even so, Jesus answered, I cannot speak to-night. It is as if I were bidden to withhold my secret till to-morrow. We know not why we speak or why we are silent, but silence has been put upon me by the words of the psalm. Be it so, the president answered, and he was helped by Saddoc and Manahem to his feet. Our Brother Jesus, he said, has given over the charge of our flocks to a young shepherd in whom he has confidence, and Jesus sleeps under a roof to-night, the first for many years, for, like us, he is getting older, and the rains and blasts of last winter have gone into his bones. All the cells, Father, Saddoc replied, are filled. I know that well, Saddoc, Hazael answered, and Jesus can sleep here on these benches; a mattress and a cloak will be sufficient for him who has slept in caverns, or in valleys on heaps of stones that he piled so that he might not drown in the rains. Manahem will get thee a mattress, Jesus; he knows where to find one. I am strong enough to walk alone, Saddoc. And disengaging himself from Saddoc's

306

arm, Hazael walked with the monks towards his cell, joining them
in the psalm:

> All the powers of the Lord
> Bless ye the Lord; praise and
> Exalt him above all for ever.

As the doors of the cell closed Saddoc approached Jesus, and,
breaking his reverie, he said: Thou hast returned to us at last;
and it was not too soon, for the winter rains are cold on bones as
old as thine. But here comes Manahem with a mattress for thee.
On the bench here, Manahem; on the bench he'll lie comfortably,
and we'll get him a covering, for the nights are often chilly though
the days be hot; we must try to make a comfortable resting-place
for him that has guarded our flocks these long years. Wilt tell us
if thou beest glad to yield thy flock to Jacob and if he will sell yoes
and rams to the Temple for sacrifice? Ask me not any questions
to-night, Brother Saddoc, for I'm troubled in mind. Forgive me
my questioning, Jesus, Saddoc answered, and the three Essenes,
leaning over the edge of the gorge, stood listening to the mutter of
the brook. At last, to break the silence that the brook rumpled
without breaking, Jesus asked if a wayfarer never knocked at the
door of the cenoby after dark asking for bed and board. None
knows the path well enough to keep to it after dark, Saddoc said;
though the moon be high and bright the shadows disguise the path
yonder. The path is always in darkness where it bends round the
rocks, and the wayfarer would miss his footing and fall over into
the abyss, even though he were a shepherd. Thyself wouldst miss it.
Saddoc speaks well; none can follow the path, Manahem said, and
fortunately, else we should have all the vagrants of the country
knocking at our door. We shall have one to-night — vagrant or
prophet, Jesus said, and asked his brethren to look yonder; for
it seemed to him that a man had just come out of the shadow of
an overhanging rock. Manahem could see nobody — For, he said,
none could find the way in the darkness; and if it be a demon, he
continued, and fall, it will not harm him: the devil will hold him
up lest he dash himself at the bottom of the ravine. But if it be a
man of flesh and blood like ourselves he will topple over yon rock,
and Manahem pointed to a spot, and they waited, expecting to see
the shadow or the man they were watching disappear; but the

man or the shadow kept close to the cliffs, avoiding what seemed to be the path so skilfully that Saddoc and Manahem said he must know the way. He will reach the bridge safely, cried Saddoc, and we shall have to open our doors to him. Now he is crossing the bridge, and now he begins the ascent. Let us pray that he may miss the path through the terraces. But would you have him miss it, Saddoc, Jesus asked, for the sake of thy rest? He shall have my mattress; I'll sleep on this bench in the window under the sky, and shall be better there : a roof is not my use nor wont. But who, said Saddoc, can he be? — for certainly the man, if he be not an evil spirit, is coming to ask for shelter for the night; and if he be not a demon he may be a prophet or robber : once more the hills are filled with robbers. Or it may be, Jesus said, the preacher of whom Jacob spoke to me this evening; he came up from the Jordan with a story of a preacher that the multitude would not listen to and sought to drown in the river, and our future shepherd told me how the rabble had followed him over the hills with the intent to kill him. Some great and terrible heresy he must be preaching to stir them like that, Manahem said, and he asked if the shepherd had brought news of the prophet's escape or death. Jesus answered that the shepherd thought the prophet had escaped into a cave, for he saw the crowd dispersing, going home like dogs from a hunt when they have lost their prey. If so, he has been lying by in the cave. Who can he be? Saddoc asked. Only a shepherd could have kept to the path. Now he sees us . . . and methinks he is no shepherd, but a robber.

The Essenes waited a few moments longer and the knocking they had expected came at their door. Do not open it! Saddoc cried. He is for sure a robber sent in advance of his band, or it may be a prisoner of the Romans, and to harbour him may put us on crosses above the hills. We shall hang! Open not the door! If it be a wayfarer lost among the hills a little food and water will save him, Jesus answered. Open not the door, Jesus; though he be a prophet I would not open to him. A prophet he may be, and no greater danger besets us, for our later prophets induced men to follow them into the desert, promising that they should witness the raising of the dead with God riding the clouds and coming down for judgment. I say open not the door to him, Jesus! He may be one of the followers of the prophets, of which we have seen enough in these last years, God knows! The cavalry of Festus may be in pursuit of him and his band, and they have cut down many between Jerusalem and Jericho. I say open not the door! We live among terrors and dangers, Jesus; open not the door! Hearken, Saddoc, he calls us to open to him, Jesus said, moving towards the door. He is alone. We know he is, for we have seen him coming down a path on which two men pass each other with difficulty. He is a wayfarer, and we've been safe on this ledge of rock for many years; and times are quieter now than they have been since the dispersal of the great multitude that followed Theudas and were destroyed, and the lesser multitude that followed Banu; they, too, have perished. Open not the door, Jesus! Saddoc cried again. There are Sicarii who kill men in the daytime, mingling themselves among the multitude with daggers hidden in their garments, their mission being to stab those that disobey the law in any fraction. We're Essenes, and have not sent blood offerings to the Temple. Open not the door. Sicarii or Zealots travel in search of heretics through the cities of Samaria and Judea. Open not the door! Men are for ever fooled, Saddoc continued, and will never cease to open their doors to those who stand in need of meat and drink. It will be safer, Jesus, to bid him away. Tell him rather that we'll let down a basket of meat and drink from the balcony to him. Art thou, Manahem, for turning this man from the door or letting him in? Jesus asked. There is no need to be frightened, Manahem answered; he is but a wanderer, Saddoc. A wanderer he cannot be, for he has found his way along the path in the darkness of the night, Saddoc interjected. Open not the door, I tell thee, or else we all hang on crosses above the hills to-morrow. But, Saddoc, we are beholden to the law not to refuse bed and board to the poor, Manahem replied, returning from the door. If we do not open, Jesus said, he will leave our door, and that will be a greater misfortune than any that he may bring us. Hearken, Saddoc! He speaks fair enough, Saddoc replied; but we may plead that after sunset in the times we live in —— But, Manahem, Jesus interjected, say on which side thou art. . . . We know there is but one man; and we are more than a match for one. Put a sword in Saddoc's hand. No, Manahem! for I should seem like a fool with a sword in my hand. Since thou sayest there is but

309

one man and we are three, it might be unlucky to turn him from our doors. May I then open to him? Jesus asked, and he began to unbar the great door, and a heavy, thick-set man, weary of limb and mind, staggered into the gallery, and stood looking from one to the other, as if trying to guess which of the three would be most likely to welcome him.

His large and bowed shoulders made his bald, egg-shaped skull (his turban had fallen in his flight) seem ridiculously small; it was bald to the ears, and a thick black beard spread over the face like broom, and nearly to the eyes; thick black eyebrows shaded eyes so piercing and brilliant that the three Essenes were already aware that a man of great energy had come amongst them. He had run up the terraces despite his great girdlestead and he stood before them like a hunted animal, breathing hard, looking from one to the other, a red, callous hand scratching in his shaggy chest, his eyes fixed first on Saddoc and then on Manahem and lastly on Jesus, whom he seemed to recognise as a friend. May I rest a little while? he asked. If so, give me drink before I sleep. No food, but drink. Why do ye not answer? Do ye fear me, mistaking me for a robber? or have I wandered among robbers? Where am I? Hearken: I am but a wayfarer and thou'rt a shepherd of the hills, I know thee by thy garb, thou'lt not refuse me shelter. And Jesus, turning to Saddoc and Manahem, said: He shall have the mattress I was to sleep upon. Give it to him, Manahem. Thou shalt have food and a coverlet, he said, turning to the wayfarer. No food! he cried; but a drink of water. There is some yoe's milk on the shelf, Manahem. Thou must be footsore, he said, giving the milk to the stranger, who drank it greedily. I'll get thee a linen garment so that thou mayst sleep more comfortable; and I'll bathe thy feet before sleep; sleep will come easier in a fresh garment. But to whose dwelling have I come? the stranger asked. A shepherd told me the Essenes lived among the rocks. . . . Am I among them? He told me to keep close to the cliff's edge or I should topple over. We watched thee, and it seemed every moment that thou couldst not escape death. It will be well to ask him his name and whence he comes, Saddoc whispered to Manahem. The shepherd told thee that we are Essenes, and it remains for thee to tell us whom we entertain. I am Paul of Tarsus, a prisoner of the Romans —— A
310

JESUS MEETS PAUL

prisoner of the Romans! Saddoc cried. Then indeed we are lost; a prisoner of the Romans with soldiers perhaps at thy heels! A prisoner fled from Roman justice may not lodge here. . . . Let us put him beyond our doors. And becoming suddenly courageous Saddoc went up to Paul and tried to lift him to his feet. Manahem, aid me! But neither singly nor together could they manage Paul, and when Jesus, who had gone to fetch a basin of water and a garment, returned, he asked Saddoc and Manahem the cause of their unseemly struggle with the guest; and these, replying to him, said that the guest had told them he was a prisoner of the Romans. Even so, Jesus answered, we cannot turn him from our doors. These men have little understanding, Paul answered. I'm not a criminal fled from Roman justice, but a man escaped from Jewish persecution. Why then didst thou say, cried Saddoc, that thou'rt a prisoner of the Romans? Because I would not be taken to Jerusalem to be tried before the Jews. I appealed to Cæsar, and while waiting on the ship to take me to Italy, Festus gave me leave to come here, for I heard that there were Jews in Jericho of great piety, men unlike the Jews of Jerusalem, who though circumcised in the flesh are uncircumcised in heart and ear. Of all of this I will tell you tomorrow, and do you tell me now of him that followed me along the cliff. We saw no one following thee; thou wast alone. He may have missed me before I turned down the path coming from Jericho. I speak of Timothy, my beloved son in the faith. What strange man is this that we entertain for the night? Saddoc whispered to Manahem. And if any disciple of mine fall into the hands of the Jews of Jerusalem —— We know not of what thou'rt speaking, Jesus answered; and it is doubtless too long a story to tell tonight. I must go at once in search of Timothy, Paul said, and he turned towards the door. The moon is setting, Jesus cried, and returning to-night will mean thy death over the cliff's edge. There is no strength in thy legs to keep thee to the path. I should seek him in vain, Paul answered. Rest a little while, Jesus said, and drink a little yoe's milk, and when thou hast drunken I'll bathe thy feet. Without waiting for Paul's assent he knelt to untie his sandals. We came from Cæsarea to Jericho to preach the abrogation of the law. What strange thing is he saying now? The abrogation of the law! Saddoc whispered to Manahem. The people would not listen to us, and, stirred up by the Jews, they sought to capture us, but we escaped into the hills and hid in a cave to which the spirit of the Lord directed us. Hark, an angel pointed out a cave to him! Manahem whispered in Saddoc's ear. Then he must be a good man, Saddoc answered, but we know not if he speaks the truth. We have had too many prophets; he is another, and of the same tribe, setting men by the ears. We have had too many prophets! We will leave him to Jesus, who will understand him better than we. . . . Now let me bathe thy feet, which are swollen; and after bathing Paul's feet Jesus relieved him of his garment and passed a white robe over his shoulders. Thou'lt sleep easier in it. They would have done well to hearken to me, Paul muttered. Thou'lt tell us thy story of ill treatment to-morrow, Jesus said, and he laid Paul back on his pillow, and a moment after he was asleep.

CHAPTER XXXII.

JESUS feared to awaken him, but was constrained at last to call after him: Thou'rt dreaming, Paul. Awake! Remember the Essenes . . . friends, friends. But Paul did not hear him, and it was not till Jesus laid his hand on his shoulder that Paul opened his eyes. Thou hast been dreaming, Paul, Jesus said. Where am I? Paul inquired. With the Essenes, Jesus answered. I was too tired to sleep deeply, Paul said, and it would be useless for me to lie down again. I am afraid of my dreams; and together they stood looking across the abyss watching the rocks opposite coming into their shapes against a strip of green sky. The ravine was still full of mist, and a long time seemed to pass before the bridge and the ruins over against the bridge began to appear. As the dawn advanced sleep came upon Paul's eyelids. He lay down and dozed awhile, for about an hour, and when he opened his eyes again Jesus's hand was upon his shoulder and he was saying: Paul, it is now daybreak; at the Brook Kerith we go forth to meet the sunrise. To meet the sunrise, Paul repeated, for he knew nothing of the doctrine of the Essenes. But he followed Jesus through the gallery and received from him a small hatchet with instructions how he should use it, and a jar which he must fill with water at the well. We carry water with us, Jesus said, for the way is long to the brook; only by sending nearly to the source can we reach it, and we are mindful not to foul the water we drink. But come, we're late already. Jesus threw a garment over Paul's shoulder and told him of the prayers he must murmur. We do not speak of profane matters till after sunrise. He broke off suddenly and pointed to a place where they might dig: And as soon as we have purified ourselves, he continued, we will fare forth in search of shepherds, who, if we tell them, will be watchful for a young man lost on the hills and will direct him to

313

the Essene settlement above the Brook Kerith. Be of good courage, he will be found. Hadst thou come before today myself would be seeking him for thee, but yesterday I gave over my flock to Jacob, a trustworthy lad, who will give the word to the next one, and he will pass it on to another, and so the news will be carried the best part of the way to Cæsarea before noon. It may be that thy companion has found his way to Cæsarea already, for some can return whither they have come, however long and strange the way may be. Pause, we shall hear Jacob's pipe answer mine. Jesus played a few notes, which were answered immediately, and not long afterwards the shepherd appeared over a ridge of hills. Thy shepherd, Paul said, is but a few years younger than Timothy and he looks to thee as Timothy looks to me. Tell him who I am and whom I seek. Jacob, Jesus said, thou didst tell me last night of a preacher to whom the multitude would not listen, but sought to throw into the Jordan. He has come amongst us seeking his companion Timothy. The twain escaped from the multitude, Jacob interjected. That is true, Jesus answered, but they ran apart above the brook, one keeping on to Cæsarea; this man followed the path round the rocks (how he did it we are still wondering) and climbed up to our dwelling. We must find his companion for him. Jacob promised that every shepherd should hear that a young man was missing. As soon as a shepherd appears on yon hillside, Jacob said, he shall have the word from me, and he will pass it on. Jesus looked up into Paul's anxious face. We cannot do more, he said, and began to speak with Jacob of rams and yoes just as if Timothy had passed out of their minds. Paul listened for a while, but finding little to beguile his attention in their talk, he bade Jesus and Jacob goodbye for the present, saying he was returning to the cenoby. I wonder, he said to himself, as he went up the hill, if they'd take interest in my craft; I could talk to them for a long while of the thread which should always be carefully chosen, and which should be smooth and of equal strength, else, however deftly the shuttle be passed, the woof would be rough. But no matter, if they'll get news of Timothy for me I'll listen to their talk of rams and yoes without complaint. It was kind of Jacob to say he did not think Timothy had fallen down a precipice, but what does he know? and on his way back Paul tried to recall the ravine that he had seen in

314

the dusk as he leaned over the balcony with Jesus. And as he passed through the domed gallery he stopped for a moment by the well, it having struck him that he might ask the brother drawing water to come with him to look for Timothy. If my son were lying at the bottom of the ravine, he said, I should not be able to get him out without help. Come with me.

The Essene did not know who Paul was, nor of whom he was speaking, and at the end of Paul's story the brother answered that there might be two hundred feet from the pathway to the brook, more than that in many places — But thou'lt see for thyself; I may not leave my work. If a man be dying the Essene, by his rule, must succour him, Paul said. But I know not, the Essene answered, that any man be dying in the brook. We believe thy comrade held on to the road to Cæsarea. So it may have been, Paul said, but it may well be otherwise. It may be, the Essene answered, but not likely. He held on to the road to Cæsarea, and finding thee no longer with him kept on — Or rolled over the cliff, Paul interrupted. Well, see for thyself; and if he be at the bottom I'll come to help thee. But it is a long way down, and it may be that we have no rope long enough, and without one we cannot reach him, but forgive me, for I see that my words hurt thee. But how else am I to speak? I know thy words were meant kindly, and if thy president should ask to see me thou'lt tell him I've gone down the terraces and will return as soon as I have made search. This search should have been made before. That was not possible; the mist is only just cleared, the brother answered, and Paul proceeded up and down the terraces till he reached the bridge, and after crossing it he mounted the path and continued it, venturing close to the edge and looking down the steep sides as he went, but seeing nowhere any traces of Timothy. Had he fallen here, he said to himself, he would be lying in the brook. But were Timothy lying there I could not fail to see him, nor is there water enough to wash him down into Jordan. It must be he is seeking his way to Cæsarea. Let it be so, I pray God; and Paul continued his search till he came to where the path twisted round a rock and came out on the hillsides. We separated here, he said, looking round, and then remembering that they had been pursued for several miles into the hills and that the enemy's scouts might be lurking in the neighbourhood, he turned back and descended the path, convinced of the uselessness of his search. We parted at that rock, Timothy keeping to the left and myself turning to the right, and if anything has befallen he must be sought for by shepherds, aided by dogs. Only with the help of dogs can he be traced, he said, and returning slowly to the bridge, he stood there lost in feverish forebodings, new ones rising up in his mind continually : For it might well be, he reflected, that Timothy has been killed by robbers, for these hills are infested by robbers and wild beasts, and worse than the wild beasts and the robbers are the Jews, who would pay a large sum of money for his capture. And his thoughts running on incontinently, he imagined Timothy a prisoner in Jerusalem and himself forced to decide whether he should go there to defend Timothy or continue his mission.

A terrible choice it would be for him to have to choose between his duty towards men and his love of his son, for Timothy was more to him than many sons are to their fathers, the companion of all his travels and his hope, for he was falling into years and needed Timothy now more than ever. But it was not likely that the Jews had heard that Timothy was travelling from Jericho to Cæsarea, and it was a feverish imagination of his to think that they would have time to send out agents to capture Timothy. But if such a thing fell out how would he account to Eunice for the death of the son that she had given him in her wish that somebody should be near him to protect and to serve him. He had thought never to see Eunice again, but if her son perished he would have to see her. But no, there would be no time — he had appealed to Cæsar. He must send a letter to her telling that he had started out for Jericho. A dangerous journey he knew it to be, but he was without strength to resist the temptation of one more effort to save the Jews : a hard, bitter, stiff-necked, stubborn race that did not deserve salvation, that resisted it. He had been scourged, how many times, at the instigation of the Jews ? and they had stoned him at Lystra, a city ever dear to him, for it was there he had met Eunice ; the memories that gathered round her beautiful name calmed his disquiet, and the brook murmuring under the bridge through the silence of the gorge disposed Paul to indulge his memory, and in it the past was so pathetic and poignant that it was almost a pain to remember. But
316

he must remember, and following after a glimpse of the synagogue and himself preaching in it there came upon him a vision of a tall, grave woman, since known to him as a thorn in his flesh, but he need not trouble to remember his sins, for had not God himself forgiven him, telling him that his grace was enough? Why then should he hesitate to recall the grave, oval face that he had loved? He could see it as plainly in his memory as if it were before him in the flesh, her eyes asking for his help so appealingly that he had been constrained to relinquish the crowd to Barnabas and give his mind to Eunice. And they had walked on together, he listening to her telling how she had not been to the synagogue for many years, for though she and her mother were proselytes to the Jewish faith, neither practised it since her marriage, for her husband was a pagan. She had indeed taught her son the Scriptures in Greek, but no restraint had been put upon him; and she did not know to what god or goddess he offered sacrifice. But last night an angel had visited her and told her that that which she had always been seeking (though she had forgotten it) awaited her in the synagogue. So she had gone thither and was not disappointed. I've always been seeking him of whom thou speakest. Her very words, and the very intonation of her voice in these words came back to him; he had put questions to her, and they had not come to the end of their talk when Lois, calling from the doorstep, said : Wilt pass the door, Eunice, without asking the stranger to cross it? Whereupon she turned her eyes on Paul and asked him to forgive her for her forget-fulness, and Barnabas arriving at that moment, she begged him to enter. And they had stayed on and on, exceeding their apportioned time, Barnabas reproving the delay, but always agreeing that their departure should be adjourned since it was Paul's wish to adjourn it. . . . Lois seemed to love Barnabas as a mother, and Lois and Eunice were received by me into the faith, Paul said, and on these words his thoughts floated away and he became absorbed in recol-lections of the house in Lystra. The months he had spent with these two women had been given to him, no doubt, as a recompense for the labours he had endured to bring men to believe that by faith only in our Lord Jesus Christ could they be saved. He would never see Lystra again with his physical eye, but it would always be before him in his mind's eye : that terrible day the Jews had dragged him

317

and Barnabas outside the town rose up before him. Only by feigning death did they escape the fate of Stephen. In the evening the disciples brought them back. Lois and Eunice sponged their wounds, and at daybreak they left for Derbe, Barnabas saying that perhaps God was angry at their delay in Lystra and to bring them back to his work had bidden the Jews stone them without killing them. Eunice was not sure that Barnabas had not spoken truly, and Paul remembered with gratitude that she always put his mission before herself. Thou'lt be safer, she said, in Derbe, and from Derbe thou must go on carrying the glad tidings to the ends of the earth. But thou must not forget thy Galatians, and when thou returnest to Lystra Timothy will be old enough to follow thee. He had fared for ever onwards over seas and lands, ever mindful of his faithful Galatians and Eunice and her son whom she had promised to him, and whom he had left learning Greek so that he might fulfil the duties of amanuensis.

The silence of the gorge and the murmur of the brook enticed recollections, and he was about to abandon himself to memories of his second visit to Lystra when a voice startled him from his reverie, and, looking round, he saw a tall, thin man who held his head picturesquely. I presume thou art our guest, he said, and seeing thee alone, I laid my notes aside and have come to offer my help to thee. Thy help? Paul repeated. To do thee service shouldst thou need it, Mathias replied; and if not, I will withdraw, excusing myself to thee. Excusing thyself? I am thy guest, and the guest of the Essenes, for last night Timothy and myself were assailed by the Jews. By the Jews? Mathias replied, but we are Jews. Whereupon Paul told him of his journey from Cæsarea, and that he had barely escaped drowning in the Jordan. In the escape from drowning Mathias showed little interest, but he was curious to hear the doctrine that had given offence. I spoke of the Lord Jesus Christ, Paul answered, the one Mediator between God and man who was sent by his Father to redeem the world. Only by faith in him the world may be saved, and the Jews will not listen. A hard, bitter, cruel race they are, that God will turn from in the end, choosing another among the Gentiles, since they will not accept him whom God has chosen to redeem men by the death and resurrection from the dead of the Lord Jesus Christ, raised from the dead by his
318

Father. Mathias raised his eyes at the words: resurrection from the dead. Of whom was Paul speaking? He could still give his mind to miracles, but had wearied of the question whether the corruptible body could be raised from earth to heaven, and was now ready to rail against the little interest the Jews took in certain philosophical questions — the relation of God to the universe, and suchlike — and he began to speak to Paul of his country, Egypt, and of Alexandria's schools of philosophy, continuing in this wise till Paul asked him how it was that he had left a country where the minds of the people were in harmony with his mind to come to live among people whose thoughts were opposed to his. That would be a long story to tell, Mathias answered. My life has gone by, he said, in talking to these Essenes who stand midway between Jerusalem and Alexandria. Why I remained with them so long is a question I have often asked myself. Why I came hither with them from the cenoby on the eastern bank, that, too, is a matter that mocks me often. . . . Thou hast heard, he continued, of the schism of the Essenes, how those on the eastern bank believe that the order can be preserved only by marriage, while those on the western bank, the traditionalists up there on that rock in that aerie, would rather the order died than that any change should be made in the rule of life. In answer to a question from Paul he said he did not believe that the order would survive the schism, and whilst speaking of his return to Alexandria, where he might meet his death, his thoughts left the future for the present, and turning to Paul he said: If thou'rt minded to hear my lecture, I will reserve a place where my words are audible; there is a troublesome echo in the cavern. My mind is distracted, Paul replied, by fears for Timothy's safety, but I will give ear to thy words, for the Essenes are near to my own doctrine. The words: my own doctrine, brought a smile into Mathias's face, and Paul, catching sight of his smile, said: Smiling at my Greek, Mathias! Thy Greek is not the Greek of Alexandria, Mathias replied — lacking in construction, maybe, but not in vigour of thought. And I would hear of thy wanderings and preachings in thine own tongue. My wanderings and preachings are but an idle tale if the Lord Jesus Christ was not raised from the dead by the power of his Father, Paul answered, and the words had hardly passed his lips when his

319

great knowledge of men warned him that to engage Mathias in a philosophical disputation would be vain; but he might win him with a story. Wherefore he began to tell that on his return from his mission to Cyprus with Barnabas he had preached in Derbe and Lystra. It was in Lystra, he cried, that I met Timothy, whom I after circumcised with my own hand; he was then a boy of ten, and his mother, who was a pious, God-fearing woman, foresaw in him a disciple, and said when we left, after having been cured by her and her mother of our wounds: When thou returnest to the Galatians he will be nearly old enough to follow thee; but tarry not so long, she added. But it was a long while before I returned to Lystra, and then Timothy was a young man, and our lives ever since have been spent in the Lord's service, suffering tortures from robbers that sought to obtain ransom. We have been scourged and shipwrecked. But, said Mathias, interrupting him, I know not of what thou art speaking, and Paul was obliged to go over laboriously in words the story that he had dreamed in a few seconds. And when it was told Mathias said: Thy story is worth telling. After my lecture the brethren will be glad to hearken to thee. But, said Paul, what I have told thee is nothing to what I could tell; and Mathias answered: So much the better, for I shall not have to hear a twice-told story. And now, he added, I must leave thee, for I have matter that must be carefully thought out, and in those ruins yonder my best thinking is done.

Speak to the Essenes; tell them of my conversion? Paul repeated. Why not? he asked himself, since he was here and could not leave till nightfall. Festus had given him leave to go to Jericho to preach while waiting for the ship that was to take him to Rome, and he had found in Jericho the intolerance that had dragged him out of the Temple at Jerusalem; circumcision of the flesh but no circumcision of the spirit. . . . But here! He had been led to the Essenes by God, and all that had seemed dark the night before was now clear to him. There was no longer any doubt in his mind that the Lord wished his chosen people to hear the truth before his servant Paul left Palestine for ever. He had been led by the Lord among these rocks, perhaps to find twelve disciples, who would leave their rocks when they heard the truth of the death and ascension of Jesus of Nazareth and would carry the joyful tidings to the ends of the earth.

320

CHAPTER XXXIII.

THE Essenes, ten in number, were seated in an embrasure. A reader had been chosen (an elder) to read the Scriptures, and the attention of the community was now engaged in judgment of his attempt to reconcile two passages, one taken from Numbers in which it is said that God is not as man, with another passage taken from Deuteronomy in which God is said to be as man. He had just finished telling the brethren that these two passages were not in contradiction, the second being introduced for the instruction of the multitude and not because the nature of man is as God's nature, and, on second thoughts, he added : Nor must it be forgotten that the Book of Deuteronomy was written when we were a wandering tribe come out of the desert of Arabia, without towns or cities, without a Temple, without an Ark — ours having fallen into the hands of the Philistines. He continued his gloss till Mathias held up his hand and asked Hazael's permission to speak : The words that have been quoted from Deuteronomy, those in which the Scriptures speak of God as if he were a man, attributing to him the acts and motives of man, were addressed, as our reader has pointed out, to men who had hardly advanced beyond the intelligence of childhood, whose minds were still simple and unable to receive any idea of God except the primitive notion that God is a greater man. Now the reason for my interruption is this : I should like to point out that for those who have passed beyond this stage, whose intelligence is not limited to their imagination, and whose will is not governed by selfish fears and hopes, there is another lesson in the words : we can rise to the consciousness of God as an absolute Being, of whom we know only that he is, and not what he is, and this is what is meant when God is spoken of by the name I am that I am.

Eleazar was minded to speak : Mathias begged of him not to withhold his thoughts, but to speak them, and it was at this moment that Paul entered, walking softly, lest his footsteps should interrupt Eleazar, whom he heard say that he disagreed with the last part of Mathias's speech, inasmuch as it would be against the word of the Scriptures and likewise against all tradition to accept God as no more than the absolute substance, which strictly taken would exclude all differences and relation, even the differences and relation of subject and object in self-consciousness. I shall not be lacking in appreciation of the wisdom of our learned brother, Paul heard him say, if I venture to hold to the idea of a God whom we know at least to be conscious, for he says : I am — a statement which had much interest for Paul; and while considering it he heard Manahem say : It is hard to conceive of God except as a high principle of being and well-being in the universe, who binds all things to each other in binding them to himself. Then there are two Gods and not one God, Saddoc interposed quickly, an objection to which Manahem made this answer : Not two Gods but two aspects, thereby confuting Saddoc for the moment, who muttered : Two aspects which have nevertheless to be reduced to unity. Paul's eyes went from Saddoc to Mathias, and he thought that Mathias's face wore an expression of amused contempt as he listened and called upon other disputants to contribute their small thoughts to the discussion. Encouraged by a wave of his hand, Caleb ventured to remark : There is God and there is the word of God, to which Hazael murmured this reply : There is only one God; one who watches over his chosen people and over all the other nations of the earth. But does God love the other nations as dearly as the Hebrew people? Manahem asked, and Hazael answered him : We may not discriminate so far into the love of God, it being infinite, but this we may say, that it is through the Hebrew people that God makes manifest his love of mankind, on condition, let it be understood, of their obedience to his revealed will. And if I may add a few words to the idea so eloquently suggested by our Brother Mathias, I would say that God is the primal substance out of which all things evolve. But these words must not be taken too literally, thereby refusing to God a personal consciousness, for God knows certainly all the differences and all the relations, and we should overturn all the teaching of Scripture and lose ourselves in the errors of Greek philosophy if we held to the belief

322

of a God, absolute, pure, simple, detached from all concern with his world and his people. But in what measure, Manahem asked, laying his scroll upon his knees and leaning forward, his long chin resting on his hand, in what measure, he asked, speaking out of his deepest self, are we to look upon God as a conscious being? If Mathias could answer that question we should be grateful, for it is the question which torments every Essene in the solitude of his cell.

Has any other brother here a word to say? I turn to thee, Brother Caleb. I am sure there is a thought in thy heart that we would all like to hear. No? Wherefore, Brother Saddoc, I call upon thee! Brother Saddoc seemed to have no wish to speak, but Mathias continued to press him, saying : Brother Saddoc, for what else hast thou been seeking in thy scroll but for a text whereon to base an argument? And after seeking vainly a crevice whereby he might escape from Mathias, Brother Saddoc answered that he took his stand upon Deuteronomy. Do we not read that the Lord thy God that goeth before thee shall fight for thee, and in the desert thou hast seen that he bore thee, as a man bears his sons, all the way that ye went till ye came unto this place. But Saddoc, Eleazar interrupted, has forgotten that one of the leading thoughts in this discourse is that the words in Deuteronomy were written for starving tribes that came out of Arabia rather than for us to whom God has given the land of Canaan. We were then among the rudiments of the world and man was but a child, incapable, as Mathias has said, of the knowledge of God as an absolute being. But then, answered Saddoc, the Scriptures were not written for all time. Was anything, Mathias murmured, written for all time? Paul was about to ask himself if Mathias numbered God among the many things that time wastes away when his thought was interrupted by Manahem asking how we are to understand the words : the heavens were created before the earth. Do the Scriptures mean that intelligence is prior to sense? Mathias's face lighted up, and then, taking occasion to make show of his Greek proficiency, he began : Heaven is our intelligence and the earth our sensibility. The spirit descended into matter, and God created man according to his image, as Moses said and said well, for no creature is more like to God than man : not in bodily form (God is without body), but in his intelligence; for the intelligence of every man is in small the intelligence of the

323

universe, and it may be said that the intelligence lives in the flesh that bears it as God himself lives in the universe, being in some sort a God of the body, which carries it about like an image in a shrine. Thus the intelligence occupies the same place in man as the great President occupies in the universe — being itself invisible while it sees everything, and having its own essence hidden while it penetrates the essences of all other things. Also, by its arts and sciences, it finds its way through the earth and through the seas, and searches out everything that is contained in them. And then again it rises on wings and, looking down upon the air and all its commotions, it is borne upwards to the sky and the revolving heavens and accompanies the choral dances of the planets and stars fixed according to the laws of music. And led by love, the guide of wisdom, it proceeds still onward till it transcends all that is capable of being apprehended by the senses, and rises to that which is perceptible only by the intellect. And there, seeing in their surpassing beauty the original ideas and archetypes of all the things which sense finds beautiful, it becomes possessed by a sober intoxication, like the Corybantian revellers, and is filled with a still stronger longing, which bears it up to the highest summit of the intelligible world till it seems to approach to the great king of the intelligible world himself. And while it is eagerly seeking to behold him in all his glory, rays of divine light are pouring forth upon it which by their exceeding brilliance dazzle the eyes of the intelligence. . . . Whilst he spoke, his periods constructed with regard for every comma, Mathias's eyes were directed so frequently towards Paul that Paul could not but think that Mathias was vaunting his knowledge of Greek expressly, as if to reprove him, Paul, for the Aramaic idiom that he had never been able to wring out of his Greek, which he regretted, but which, after hearing Mathias, he would not be without; for to rid himself of it he would have to sacrifice the spirit to the outer form; as well might he offer sacrifice to the heathen gods; and he could not take his eyes off the tall, lean figure showing against the blue sky, for Mathias spoke from the balcony, flinging his grey locks from his forehead, uncertain if he should break into another eloquent period or call upon Paul to speak. He was curious to hear Paul, having divined a quick intelligence beneath an abrupt form that was withal not without beauty;
324

he advanced towards Hazael and, leaning over his chair, whispered to him. He is telling, Paul said to himself, that it would be well to hear me as I am about to start for Rome to proclaim the truth in that city wherein all nations assemble. Well, let it be so, since it was to this I was called hither.

Hazael raised his eyes and was about to ask Paul to speak, but at that moment the bakers arrived with their bread baskets, and the Essenes moved from the deep embrasure in the wall into the domed gallery, each departing for his cell and returning clothed in white garment and veil. Paul was about to withdraw, but Hazael said to him : None shares this repast with us ; it is against the rule ; but so many of the rules of the brethren have been set aside in these later days that, with the consent of all, I will break another rule and ask Paul of Tarsus to sit with us though he be not of our brotherhood, for is he not our brother in the love of God, which he has preached, travelling over sea and land with it for ever in his mouth for the last twenty years. Preaching, Paul answered, the glad tidings of the resurrection, believing myself to have been bidden by the same will of God that called me hither and saved me from death many times that I might continue to be the humble instrument of his will. I will tell how it was laid upon me to preach in Jericho — called out of myself — God knowing well they would not hear me and would drive me into the mountains and turn my feet by night to this place. Be it so, Paul, thou shalt tell thy story, the president answered, and the cook put plates of lentils before the brethren and the baker set by each plate a loaf of bread, and everyone waited till the grace had been repeated before he tasted food. The peace, concord and good will, all that he had recommended in his epistles, Paul saw around him, and he looked forward to teaching the Essenes of the approaching end of the world, convinced that God in his great justice would not allow him, Paul, to leave Palestine without every worthy servant hearing the truth. So he was impatient to make an end of the food before him, for the sustenance of the body was of little importance to him, its only use being to carry the spirit and to fortify it. He took counsel therefore with himself while eating as to the story he should tell, and his mind was ready with it when the president said : Paul, our meal is finished now ; we would hear thee.

CHAPTER XXXIV.

YESTERDAY the Jews would have thrown me into the Jordan or stoned me together with Timothy, my son in the faith, who instead of following me round the hill shoulder kept straight on for Cæsarea, where I pray that I may find him. These things ye know of me, for three of the brethren were on that balcony yesternight when, upheld by the will of God, my feet were kept fast in the path that runs round this ravine. The Jews had abandoned their hunt when I arrived at your door, awakening fear in Brother Saddoc's heart that I was a robber or the head of some band of robbers. Such thoughts must have disturbed his mind when he saw me, and they were not driven off when I declared myself a prisoner to the Romans; for he besought me to depart lest my presence should bring all here within the grip of the Roman power. A hard and ruthless power it may be, but less bitter than the power which the Jews crave from the Romans to compel all to follow not the law alone, but the traditions that have grown about the law. But ye brethren who send no fat rams to the Temple for sacrifice, but worship God out of your own hearts, will have pity for me who have been persecuted by the Jews of Jerusalem (who in their own eyes are the only Jews) for no reason but that I preach the death and the resurrection from the dead of our Lord Jesus Christ, whose apostle I am, being so made by himself when he spoke to me out of the clouds on the road to Damascus. Of this great wonder ye shall hear in good time, but before beginning the story ye have asked me to relate I would calm Brother Saddoc's fears: I am no prisoner as he imagines me to be, but am under bond to return to Cæsarea, having appealed to Cæsar as was my right to do, being a Roman citizen long persecuted by the Jews; and I would thank you for the blankets I enjoyed last night and for the bread I have
326

broken with you. Also for the promise that I have that one of you shall at nightfall put me on the way to Cæsarea and accompany me part of the way, so that I may not fall into the hands of my enemies the Jews, of Jerusalem, but shall reach Cæsarea to take ship for Rome. None of you need fear anything: ye have my assurances; I am here by the permission of the noble Festus. And now that ye have learnt from me the hazard that cast me among you I will tell you that I am a Jew like yourselves: one born in Tarsus, a great city of Cilicia; a Roman citizen as ye have heard from me, a privilege which was not bought by me for a great sum of money, nor by any act of mine, but inherited from my father, a Hebrew like yourselves, and descended from the stock of Abraham like yourselves. And by trade a weaver of that cloth of which tents are made; for my father gave me that trade, for which I thank him, for by it I have earned my living these many years, in various countries and cities. At an early age I was a skilful hand at the loom, and at the same time learned in the Scriptures, and my father, seeing a Rabbi in me, sent me to Jerusalem, and while I was taught the law I remember hearing of the Baptist, and the priests of the Temple muttering against him, but they were afraid to send men against him, for he was in great favour with the people. Afterwards I returned to Tarsus, where I worked daily at my loom until tidings came to that city that a disciple of John was preaching the destruction of the law, saying that he could destroy the Temple and build it up again in three days. We spoke under our breaths in Tarsus of this man, hardly able to believe that anyone could be so blasphemous and reprobate, and when we heard of his death upon a cross we were overjoyed and thought the Pharisees had done well; for we were full of zeal for the traditions and the ancient glory of our people. We believed then that heresy and blasphemy were at an end, and when news came of one Stephen, who had revived all the stories that Jesus told, that the end of the world was nigh and that the Temple could be destroyed and built up again, I laid my loom aside and started for Jerusalem in great anger to join with those who would root out the Nazarenes: we are now known as Christians, the name give to us at Antioch.

I was telling that I laid aside my loom in Tarsus and set out for Jerusalem to aid in rooting out the sect that I held to be blasphemous and pernicious. Now on the day of my arrival in that city, while coming from the Temple I saw three men hurrying by, one whose face was white as the dead, with a small crowd following; and everyone saying: Not here, not here! And as they spoke stones were being gathered, and I knew that they were for stoning the man they had with them, and this was Stephen himself, they said, who had been teaching in the Temple that Jesus was born and died and raised from the dead, and that since his death the law is of no account. So did I gather news and with it abhorrence, and followed them till they came to an angle, at which they said: This corner will do. Stephen was thrown into it, and stones of all kinds were heaped upon him till one spattered his brains along the wall, after which the crowd muttered: We shall have no more of them. That day I was of the crowd, and the stone that spattered the brains of Stephen along the wall seemed to me to have been well cast: I hated those who spoke against the law of our fathers, which I held in reverence, as essential and to be practised for all time; and the mild steadfastness in their faces, and the great love that shone in their eyes when the name of our Lord Jesus Christ was mentioned, instead of persuading me that I might be persecuting saints, exasperated me to further misdeeds. I became foremost in these persecutions, and informed by spies of the names of the saints, I made search in their houses at the head of armed agents and dragged them into the synagogue, compelling them to renounce the truth that the Messiah had come which had been promised in the Scriptures. Nor was I satisfied when the last Nazarene had been rooted out of Jerusalem, but cast my eyes forward to other towns, into which the saints might have fled, and, hearing that many were in Damascus, I got letters from the chief priests and started forth in a fume of rage which I strove to blow up with the threats of what we would put the saints to when we reached Damascus. But while the threats were on my lips there was in my heart a mighty questioning, from which I did not seem to escape, perhaps because I had not thrown a stone but stood by an approving spectator merely. I know not how it was, but as we forded the Jordan the cruelties that I had been guilty of, the inquisitions, the beatings with rods, the imprisonment — all these things rose up in my mind, a terrible troop of phantoms. Gentle faces and words of forgiveness floated

328

past me one night as we lay encamped in a great quarry, and I asked myself again if these saints were what they seemed to be; and soon after the thought crossed my mind that if the Nazarenes were the saints that they seemed to be, bearing their floggings and imprisonments with fortitude, without complaint, I was guilty of persecuting God, since all goodness comes from God.

I had asked for letters from Hanan, the High Priest, that would give me the right to arrest all ill thinkers, and to lead them back in chains to Jerusalem, and these letters seemed to take fire in my bosom, and when we came in view of the town, and saw the roofs between the trees, I heard a voice crying to me: Saul, Saul, why persecutest thou me? It is hard for thee to kick against the pricks; and trembling I fell forward, my face upon the ground, and the Lord said: I am Jesus whom thou persecutest. Arise, and go into the city and it shall be told to thee what thou must do; by these words appointing me his apostle and establishing my rights above those of Peter or John or James or any of the twelve who walked with him whilst he lived as a man in Galilee. My followers, who were merely stricken, but not blinded as I was, took me by the arm and led me into Damascus, where I abode as a blind man till Ananias laid his hands upon me and the scales fell from my eyes, and I cried out for baptism, and having received baptism, which is spiritual strength, and taken food, which is bodily, I went up to the synagogue to preach that Jesus is the son of God, and continued till the Jews in that city rose up against me and would have killed me if I had not escaped by night, let down from the wall in a basket. From Damascus I went into Arabia, and did not go up to Jerusalem for three years to confer with the apostles, nor was there need that I should do so, for had I not received my apostleship by direct revelation? But after three years I went thither, hearing that the persecutions had ceased, and that some of those whom I had persecuted had returned. The brother of Jesus, James, had come down from Galilee and as a holy man was a great power in Jerusalem. His prayers were valued, and his appearance excited pity and belief that God would hearken to him when he knelt, for he was naked but for a coarse cloth hanging from his neck to his ankles. Of water and cleanliness he knew naught, and his beard and hair grew as the weeds grow in the fields. Peter, too, was in Jerusalem, and come

329

into a great girth since the toil of his craft, as a fisher, had been abandoned, as it had to be, for, as ye know, it is dry desert about Jerusalem, without lakes or streams. But he lived there better than he had ever lived before, by talking of our Lord Jesus Christ, of whom it was no longer a danger to talk, for James had made his brother acceptable in Jerusalem by lopping from him all that was Jesus, making him according to his own image; with these Christians he no longer stood up as an opponent of the law, but as one who believed in it, who had said: I come not to abolish the law but to confirm it. So did his brother James interpret Jesus to me who had heard Jesus speak out of the spirit, and when I answered that he had said too that he had come to abolish the law, James answered only that his brother had said many things and that some were not as wise as others. Peter, who was called upon to testify that Jesus wished the Jews to remain Jews, and that circumcision and all the observances were needed, answered that he did not know which was the truth, Jesus not having spoken plainly on these matters, and neither one nor the other seemed to understand that it was of no avail that Jesus should have been born, should have died and been raised from the dead by his Father if the law were to prevail unchanged for evermore. To James and to Peter Jesus was a prophet, but no more than the prophets, and unable to understand either Peter or James, I returned to Tarsus broken-hearted, for there did not seem to be on earth a true Christian but myself, and I knew not whom to preach to, Gentiles or Jews. Only of one thing was I sure, that the Lord Jesus Christ had spoken to me out of the clouds and ordained me his apostle, but he had not pointed out the way, and I mourned that I had gone up to Jerusalem, and abode in Tarsus disheartened, resuming my loom, sitting at it from daylight till dark, waiting for some new sign to be given me, for I did not lose hope altogether, but, knowing well that the ways of Providence are not immediate, waited in patience, or in such patience as I might possess myself of. Barnabas I had forgotten, and he was forgotten when I said that I had met none in Jerusalem that could be said to be a follower of the Master.

It was Barnabas who brought me to James, the brother of the Lord, and to Peter, and told them that though I had persecuted I was now zealous, and had preached in many synagogues that Christ

330

Jesus had died and been raised from the dead. But whether they feared me as a spy, one who would betray them, or whether it was that our minds were divided upon many things, I know not, but Barnabas could not persuade them, and, as I have said, I left Jerusalem and returned to Tarsus, and resumed my trade, until Barnabas, who had been sent to Antioch to meet some disciples, said to them: But there is one at Tarsus who has preached the life and death of our Lord Jesus Christ and brought many to believe in him. So they said to him: Go to Tarsus for this man and bring him hither. And when they had seen and conferred with me, and knew what sort of man I was, Barnabas said: With your permission and your authority, Paul and I will start together for Cyprus, for that is my country, and my friends there will believe us when we tell them that Jesus was raised from the dead and was seen of many: first by Martha and Mary, the sisters of Lazarus, and afterwards by Peter and by the apostles and many others. As the disciples were willing that we should go to preach the Gospel in Cyprus, we went thither furnished with letters, and received a kindly welcome from everybody, as it had been foretold by Barnabas, and many heard the Gospel; and if my stay among you Essenes could be prolonged beyond this evening and for several days, I could tell you stories of a great magician and how he was confuted by me by the grace of God working through me; but as everything cannot be told in the first telling I will pass from Cyprus back to Antioch, where we rested awhile, so that we might tell the brethren of the great joy with which the faith had been received in Cyprus, of the churches we founded and our promise to the Cyprians to return to them. And so joyful were the brethren in Antioch at our success that I said to Barnabas: Let us not tarry here, but go on into Galatia. We set out, accompanied by John Mark, Barnabas's cousin, but he left us at Perga, being afraid, and for his lack of courage I was unable to forgive him, thereby finding myself estranged later on from Barnabas, a God-fearing man. But to tell you what happened at Lystra. We found the people there ready to listen to the faith, and it was given to me to set a cripple that had never walked in his life straight upon his feet, and as sturdy as any. The people cried out at this wonder: The gods have come down to us, and when the rumour reached the High Priest that the gods had come

331

to their city, he drove out two oxen, garlanded, and would have sacrificed them in our honour, but we tore our garments, saying : We are men like yourselves and have come to preach that ye should turn from vanities and false gods and worship the one true living God, who created the earth, and all the firmament. The people heard us and promised to abjure their idolatries, and would have abjured them for ever if the Jews from the neighbouring cities had not heard of our preaching and had not gathered together and denounced us in Lystra, where there were no Jews, or very few. Nor were they content with denouncing us, but on a convenient occasion dragged Barnabas and myself outside the town, stoned us and left us for dead, for we, knowing that God required us, feigned death, thereby deceiving them and escaping death. We returned to the town by night and left it next day for Derbe.

Now, Essenes, this story that I tell of what happened to us at Lystra has been told with some care by me, for it is significant of what has happened to me for twenty years, since the day, as you have heard, when the Lord Jesus himself spoke to me out of the clouds and appointed me to preach the Gospel he had given unto me, which, upheld by him, I have preached faithfully, followed wherever I went by persecution from Jews determined to undo my work. But undeterred by stones and threats, we returned to Lystra and preached there again, and in Perga and Attalia; from thence we sailed to Antioch, and there were great rejoicings in Saigon Street, as we sat in the doorways telling of the churches that we founded in Galatia, and how we flung open the door of truth to the pagans, and how many had passed through. But some came from Jerusalem preaching that the uncircumcised could not hope for salvation, and that there could be no conversion unless the law be observed, and the first observance of the law, they said, is circumcision. We answered them as is our wont that it is no longer by observances of the law but by grace, through our Lord Jesus Christ, that men may be saved; and we being unable to yield to them or they to us, it was resolved that Barnabas and Titus, a Gentile that we brought over to the faith, should go to Jerusalem. And on the way thither we preached that the Saviour promised to the Jews had come, and been raised from the dead, and the Samaritans hearkened and were converted in great numbers, and the

332

tidings of these conversions preceding us, the joy among the brethren was great; ye that are learned in Scripture know that the conversion of the Gentiles was always in the Lord's mind; and it was not till we began to talk about the abrogation of the law that James and the followers of James rose up against us. We wondered, and said to each other: Were ever two brothers as unlike as these? Though myself had never seen the Lord in the flesh, I knew of him from Peter, and we whispered together with our eyes fixed on the long, lean man whose knees were reported callous from kneeling in the Temple praying that God might not yet awhile destroy the world. It was sufficient, so it was said, for him to hold up his hand to perform miracles, and we came to dislike him and to remember that he had always looked upon Jesus our Lord with suspicion during his lifetime. Why then, we asked, should he come into power derived from his brother's glory? He seemed to be less likely than any other Jew to understand the new truth born into the world. So I turned from him to Peter, in whom I thought to find an advocate, knowing him to be one with us in this, saying that it were vain to ask the Gentiles to accept a yoke which the Hebrews themselves had been unable to bear; but Peter was still the timid man that he had ever been, and myself being of small wit in large and violent assemblies said to him: Thou and I and James will consult together in private at the end of this uproar. But James could not come to my reason, saying always that the Gentiles must become Jews before they became Christians; and remembering very well all the trouble and vexation the demand for the circumcision of Titus had put upon me (to which I consented, for with a Jew I am a Jew so that I may gain them), and how he had submitted himself lest he should be a stumbling-block, I said to Timothy, my own son in the faith: Thy mother and grandmother were hearers of the law, and he answered: Let me be a Jew externally, and myself took and circumcised him. A good accommodation Peter thought this to be, and I said to Peter: Henceforth for thee the circumcised and for me the uncircumcised. Against which Peter and James had nothing to say, for it seemed to them that the uncircumcised were one thing in Jerusalem and another thing beyond Jerusalem. But I was glad thus to come to terms with them, thinking thereby to obtain from them the confirmation of my apostleship, though there was no need

333

for any such, as I have always held, it having been bestowed upon me by our Lord Jesus Christ himself; and holding it to be of little account that they had known our Lord Jesus in the flesh, I said to their faces : It were better to have known him in the spirit, thereby darkening them. It might have been better to have held back the words.

Myself and Barnabas and Titus returned to Antioch and it was some days after that I said to Barnabas : Let us go again into the cities in which we have preached and see if the brethren abide in our teaching and how they do with it. But Barnabas would bring John Mark with him, he who had left us before in Perga from cowardice of soul. Therefore I chose Silas and departed. He was our warrant that we were one with the Church of Jerusalem, which was true inasmuch as we were willing to yield all but essential things so that everybody, Jews and Gentiles, might be brought into communion with Jesus Christ. . . . We went together to Lystra and Mysia, preaching in all these towns, and the brethren were confirmed in their faith in us, and leaving them we were about to set out for Bithynia and would have gone thither had we not been warned one night by the Holy Breath to go back, and instead we went to Troas, where one night a vision came to me in my sleep : a man stood before me at the foot of my bed, a Macedonian I knew him to be, by his dress and speech, for he spoke not the broken Greek that I speak, but pure Greek, the Greek that Mathias speaks, and he told me that we were to go over into Macedonia. But to tell of all the countries we visited and the towns in which we preached, and the many that were received into the faith, would be a story that would carry us through the night and into the next day, for it would be the story of my life, and every life is long when it is put into words; nor would the story be profitable unto you in any great measure, though it be full of various incidents. But it behoves me to tell that wherever we went the persecution that began in Lystra followed us. As soon as the Jews heard of our conversions they assembled either to assault us or to lay complaints before the Roman magistrates, as they did at Philippi, the chief city of Macedonia. Among my miracles was the conversion of a slave, a pythonist, a teller of fortunes, a caster of horoscopes, who brought her master good money by her divinations, and seeing that he would profit thereby no longer, he drew myself and Silas into the market-place and calling for help of others had us brought before
334

the rulers, and the pleading of the man was, and he was upheld by others, that we taught many things that it was not lawful for them, being Jews, to hearken to, and the magistrates, wishing to please the multitude, commanded us to be beaten, and when many stripes had been laid on us we were cast into prison, and the jailer being charged to keep us in safety thrust our feet into the stocks. And side by side myself and Silas prayed and sang praises unto God despite our wounds, and in response there was a great earthquake, and the prison was shaken and all the doors opened, on seeing which the keeper of the prison drew his sword and would have fallen upon it, believing that the prisoners had fled, if I had not cried to him in a loud voice: There is no reason to kill thyself, for thy charges are here. What may I do to be saved? he said, being greatly astonished at the miracle, and we answered: Believe in the Lord Jesus Christ. Thereupon he invited us into his house and set food before us, and he was baptized and bidden to have no fear, for we confided to him that we were Romans, and that the magistrates would tremble when they heard that they had ordered a citizen of Rome to be beaten and him uncondemned. Why, he asked, did ye not declare yourselves to be Romans? Because, we answered, we were minded to suffer for our Lord Jesus Christ's sake, at which he wondered and gave thanks. He was baptized by us, and when he had carried the news of their mistake to the ears of the magistrates they sent sergeants saying that we were to be allowed to go. But we refused to leave the prison, saying: We are Romans and have been beaten uncondemned. Let the magistrates come to fetch us. Which message being taken to them they came beseeching us to go, and not to injure them, for they had done wrong unwittingly, and taking pity on them for the sake of our Lord Jesus Christ we passed into Thessalonica, where I preached in the synagogues for three Sabbaths and reasoned with the Jews, showing them passages in the Scriptures confirming all that we said to them about the Christ that had suffered and been raised from the dead. Some believed, and others assaulted the house of Jason, in which we were living, and the Romans were perplexed to know how to keep order, for wherever we went there were stirs and quarrels among the Jews, the fault being with them and not with us. In Corinth too the Jews pleaded against us before the Roman magistrates and ——

335

CHAPTER XXXV.

A SUDDEN dryness in Paul's throat prevented him from finishing his sentence, and he asked for a cup of water, and having drained it he put down the cup and said, looking round : I was speaking to you about Corinth. The moment seemed a favourable one to Mathias to ask why Paul had passed on to Corinth without stopping at Athens. I made stay at Athens, Paul answered, and I thank thee, Mathias, for having reminded me of Athens, for the current of my discourse had borne me past that city, so eager was I to tell of the persecutions of the Jews. We are all Jews here! I speak of the Hierosolymites, who understand only that the law has been revealed and should be followed, though it leads no farther than the grave. Athens is a city of images and statues and altars to gods. On raising my eyes I always saw their marble deities — effigies, they said, of all the spirits of the earth and sea and the clouds above the earth and the heavens beyond the clouds. Whereupon I answered that these statues that they had carved with their hands could in no wise resemble any gods even if the gods had existence outside of their images, for no man sees God. Moses heard God on Mount Sinai, but he saw only the hinderparts; which is an allegory, for there are two covenants, and I come to reveal —— Whereat they were amused and said : If Moses saw the hinderparts why should we not see the faces, for our eyes see beauty, whereas the Hebrews see but the backside ? At which I showed no anger, for they were not Jews, but strove, as it is my custom, to be all things to all men. The Jews require a miracle, the Greeks demand reason, and therefore I asked them why they set up altars to the unknowable God. And they said : Paul, thou readest our language as badly as thou speakest it : we have inscriptions to unknown gods, but not to the unknowable God. Didst go to school

336

at Tarsus, yet canst not tell the plural from the singular? To which I answered : Then you are so religious-minded that you would not offend any god whose name you might not have heard, and so favour him by the inscription to an unknown God? But some of your philosophers, Athenians, call God unknowable. I knew this before I learnt how superstitious ye are. Ye are all alike ignorant since God left you to your sins for your idolatry; God, unknown or unknowable, has been made manifest to us by our Lord Jesus Christ, who was born like us all for a purpose, his death, which was to save the world from its sins; whereupon, greedy for a story, they began to listen to me, and I had their attention till I came to these words : And was raised by his Father from the dead. Paul, they answered, we will listen another day to the rest of this story of thy new divinity — a frivolous people, Mathias, living in a city of statues in the air, and in the streets below a city of men that seek after reason, and would explain all things in the heavens above and the earth beneath by their reason, and only willing to listen to the story of a miracle because miracles amuse them. A race much given to enjoyment, like women, Mathias, and among their mountains they are not a different race to what they are in the city, but given to milking goats and dancing in the shade to the sounds of a pipe, and dreaming over the past glories of Athens, that are dust to-day though yesterday they were realities, a light race that will be soon forgotten; and convinced of their transience I departed for Corinth, a city of fencing masters, merchants, slaves, courtesans, yet a city more willing to hearken to the truth than the light Athenians, perhaps because it has much commerce and is not slothful in business, a city wherein I fortuned upon a pious twain, Aquila and Priscilla, of our faith, and of the same trade as myself, wherefore we set up our looms together in one house and sold the cloths as we weaved them, getting our living thereby and never costing the faithful anything, which was our just pride, and mine always, for I have travelled the world over, gaining a living with my own hands, never taking money from any, though it has been offered to me in plenty by the devout, thinking it better to be under no obligation, for such destroys independence. . . .

Once only was this rule broken by me. In Macedonia, a dyer of purple —— But Lydia's story concerns you not, therefore I will leave her story untold and return to Corinth, to Priscilla and Aquila, weavers like myself, with whom I worked for eighteen months, and more than that, preaching the death and resurrection of our Lord Jesus Christ to all who would hear us when our daily work was done, until the same fate befell us — the intervention of the Jews, who sought to embroil us, as beforetimes, with the Romans. We preached in the synagogues on the Sabbath and I upheld the faith I had come to preach : that the Messiah promised to the Jews had lived and had died for us. Whereupon there was a great uproar among the Jews, who would not believe, and so I tore my garments and said : Then I will go forth to the Gentiles, and find believers in our Lord Jesus Christ, and leave you who were elected by God as his chosen people, who were his by adoption, a privilege conferred upon you throughout the centuries, the race out of whom came the patriarchs, and Jesus Christ himself in the flesh. I will leave you, for ye are not worthy and will perish as all flesh perishes; will drift into nothingness, and be scattered even as the dust of the roads is scattered by the winds. My heart is broken for you, but since ye will it so, let it be so. So did I speak, but my heart is often tenderer than my words, and I strove again to be reconciled with the Jews, and abode in Corinth proving their folly to them by the Scriptures till again they sought to rid themselves of me by means of the Romans, saying before Gallio : This fellow persuadeth men to worship God contrary to the law. But Gallio, understanding fully that his judgment seat had not been set up for the settling of disputes of the spirit, but of the things of this world, drove the Jews out of his court, and there was an uproar, and Sosthenes, a God-fearing man, was beaten. Yet for the sake of the race of the patriarchs, the chosen people of God, I abode in Corinth till the close of the second year, when news reached me of the many dissensions that had arisen in Jerusalem. The old questions were always stirring : whether the Gentiles should be admitted without circumcision and if the observances of the law were sufficient; if salvation could be obtained by works without faith, and many other matters that I thought had long been decided; in the hope of putting an end to these discussions, which could end only in schism, I bade the brethren good-bye on the wharf, and, shaving my head as a sign of my vow to keep the Feast

338

of Pentecost, I set sail with Aquila and Priscilla for Syria and left them at Ephesus, though there were many Christians there who prayed me to remain and speak to them; but pointing to my shaved head, I said : My vow! and went down to Jerusalem and kept the Feast of Pentecost and distributed money among the poor, which had been given to me by the churches founded by me in Macedonia, in Greece and Syria.

I had hoped to escape from discussion with James, the brother of the Lord, for of what good could it be to discuss once again things on which it is our nature to think differently? but upheld by hope that the Jews might be numbered among the faithful at the last day, I told him that the Jews were the root of the olive-trees whose branches had been cut, and had received grafts. But let not the grafts, I said, indulge in vainglory; it is not the branches that bear the root, but the root that bears the branches. And many other things of this sort did I say, wishing to be in all things conciliatory; to be, as ever, all things to all men; but James, the brother of the Lord, answered that Jesus had not come to abrogate the law but to confirm it, which was not true, for the law stood in no need of confirmation. James could do that as well as his brother and better, and Peter not being there to bear witness of the teaching of Jesus (he too had gone forth upon a mission with John Mark as an interpreter, for Peter cannot speak Greek), Silas, who was with me, was won over by James, and easily, for Silas was originally of the Church of Jerusalem; as I have already told you, he had been sent with us to Antioch. But I would not weary you with such small matters as Silas's desertion of me to join Peter, who was preaching in Syria, and whose doctrine he said was nearer to Jesus's than mine, it having been given to him by Jesus, whom he had known in the flesh. So be it, I said to Silas, and went without him to Antioch, a city dear to me for that it was there the word Christian was spoken for the first time; my return thither was fortunate, for there I met Barnabas, whom it was pleasant after these many years to meet again; all memory of our dissension was forgotten, which was according to reason, it having arisen out of no deeper cause than my refusal to travel with John Mark, his cousin. Titus was there too, and we had much to tell each other of our travels and the conversions we had made, and all was joy amongst us;

and our joy was increased by Peter, who appeared amongst us, bringing Silas with him, who must have been grieved though he said nothing to me of it; but who must have seen that the law to which he was attached was forgotten at Antioch, not by us only, but by his new leader, Peter, who mixed like ourselves with the Gentiles and did not refuse to eat with them. A moment indeed of great joy this was, but it did not last longer than many other moments of the same kind with which my life has been sprinkled. James, the brother of the Lord, sent up agents to Antioch with letters signed by himself. They had come to tell the people that I had not authority to teach, and could not be considered by anybody as a true apostle, for I had not known the Christ, it was said: and when I answered them that my authority came straight from him, they began to make little of my revelation, saying: Even if thou didst hear the Christ on the road to Damascus, as thou sayest, it was but for a few minutes, and he couldn't teach thee all his doctrine in a few minutes. A year or more would be required. Thou wast deceived. No vision can be taken as of equal evidence to the bodily senses. Those that we see in a vision may be but the evil spirits that, if it were possible, would fain deceive the very elect. If we question an apparition it answers anything that we wish. The spectre shines for an instant and disappears quickly before one has time to put further questions; the thoughts of the dreamer are not under his control. To see the Son of God outside of the natural flesh is impossible. Even an angel wishing to be seen has to clothe himself in flesh. Nor were they satisfied with such sayings as these, but mentioned the vision of infidels and evil livers, and to support their argument they quoted Scripture, proving that God sent visions when he was irritated. As in Numbers, murmured Eleazar. And likewise in Exodus, said Manahem, and he turned over the quires before him. These emissaries and agents asked me how it was that even if Jesus had appeared to me he could not have instructed me wrongly. If I wished to prove the truth of my vision it were better for me to accept the teaching of the apostles, who had received it directly from him; to which I made answer: My revelation was not from Jesus when he lived in the flesh, but from the spiritual Jesus; the spirit descended out of heaven to instruct me, and if God has created us, which none will

340

deny, he has created our souls wherewith to know him, and he needs not the authority of other apostles who speak as men, falling into the errors that men must fall into when they speak, for every man's truth is made known unto him by God.

One day we came out of a house heated with argument, and as we loitered by the pavement's edge regretting we had not said certain things whereby we might have confuted each other, we came upon Peter in a public inn, eating and drinking with the uncircumcised, whereupon the Hierosolymites said: We see now what thou art, Peter, a Jew that eats with Gentiles and of unclean meats. Peter did not withstand them and say as he should have done: How is it that you call them that God has made unclean? but being a timid man and anxious always to avoid schism, he excused himself and withdrew, and was followed by Barnabas and Silas. It was for this that I withstood him before all in the assembly, reproaching him for his inconsequences, saying to him: If thou that art a Jew livest according to the manner of Gentiles, how is it that thou wouldst compel the Gentiles to live as the Jews do? and until this man came thou wert one with us, saying as we say, that none is justified by conforming to the law and practising it, but by the faith in Jesus Christ. But if we seek justification in Christ, and in him alone, and yet are found to be sinners, of what help is Christ then to us? Is he a minister of sinners? God forbid! By his life and death he abolished the law, whereby we might live in faith in Christ, for the law stands between us and Christ. I say unto thee, Peter, that if Christ was crucified for me I live in Christ; no longer my own life of the flesh, but the spiritual life that Christ has given me. I say unto thee likewise, that if we care only to know Christ through the law then Christ has died in vain. To which Peter answered nothing, but went his way, as is his custom, in silence, and my grief was great; for I could see that the many were shocked, and wondered at our violence, and could not have deemed other than that we were divided among ourselves, though they said it under their breath. Nor did peace come till the emissaries of James left us to go to the churches I had founded in Galatia and undo the work I had done there. Whereupon I collected all my thoughts for an epistle that would comfort those, and enable them to resist, saying: Though an angel from heaven tell you a different doctrine from the one that I have taught you, listen not to him. Copies of this letter were sent to the churches that I had founded, but the sending of the letter did not calm my anger. An angry soul I have been since God first separated me from my mother's womb, gaining something on one side and losing on the other side; but we make not ourselves; God makes us. And there is a jealousy still within me; I know it and have suffered from it, and never did it cause me greater suffering than in those days in Antioch. My jealousy was like a hungry animal, gnawing at my ribs till, unable to bear it any longer, and seeing in visions all that I had raised pulled down, I started with Titus and travelled all over Galatia and Phrygia to Bithynia, along the shores of Pontus, and returned back again, informing the kindly, docile souls, who loved us in their weakness, of Lystra, Derbe and other towns, setting up my loom and preaching every evening the coming of the Lord whither I went in Macedonia, Thessalonica, Iconium, Laodicea, not forgetful of Colossæ, for two years or more (I have forgotten); and then hearing that Apollos, an Alexandrian Jew of great learning, our most notable convert, of whom I have not spoken, for there is no time to speak of everything, had taken ship at Corinth for Ephesus, I returned the way I had come along the coast to meet him there, likewise many good friends, Aquila and Priscilla, who were working at their looms, gathering a faithful circle about them. We set up shop again as we had done at Corinth, Aquila, Priscilla and myself worked at our looms all day, and preached in the evening in and about the city, and on the Sabbath in the synagogue.

CHAPTER XXXVI.

IN Ephesus stands a temple said to be one of the wonders of the world, the Temple of Diana; pilgrims come to it from all countries, and buy statues of the goddess to set upon their tables (little silver statues), and as the making of these is the principal industry in that city, the silversmiths raised cries against me in the theatre, where once I stood up to address the people. Great is Diana, goddess of the Ephesians! they cried out, and would have thrown me to the beasts. Yea, I fought with the beasts, for they were nothing else, and had not Aquila and Priscilla risked their lives to save me I should have perished that day. That day or another day; it matters not; we all perish sooner or later. My life has never been my concern, but God's, a thing upheld by God for so many years that I shun danger no longer. It has even come to pass that I am lonely in security, withdrawn from God in houses, and safe in his arms when clinging to a spar in the dark sea. God and our Lord Jesus Christ, his beloved son, have walked on either side of me in mountain passes where robbers lie in wait. We are nearer to God in hunger and thirst than when the mouth is full, in fatigue rather than in rest, and to know oneself to be God's servant is good cheer for the traveller, better than the lights of the inn showing over the horizon, for false brethren may await him in the inn, some that will hale him before rulers, but if he knows that he is God's servant he will be secure in his own heart, where alone security abides. It may have been my sin to weary too often at the length of the journey, and to cry out to the Lord Jesus to make an end of it. It may have been that I was often too eager to meet my death and to receive the reward of all my labour, but who shall judge me? Our Lord Jesus Christ is the only judge and his reign shall endure over this world till the last man has vanished into death. And when the last man has perished? Mathias asked. Paul answered: Jesus shall pass into his Father's keeping and again there shall be but one God. But, Paul, Mathias rejoined, if I understand thee rightly, there are now two Gods, and our hope is that in time to come the twain may turn to one. Paul was about to answer, but his lips were parched, and he raised the cup of water to his lips, and when he had drunk he was about to answer Mathias, but Hazael said: Mathias, we are all eager to hear the story of Paul's own life. There will be time afterwards to discuss his doctrine. Mathias waved his hand, a sign that Paul might continue his story, which he did.

From Ephesus we returned to Corinth and to Macedonia, and dreams began to take hold on us of longer journeys than any we had yet undertaken; we dreamed of Rome, and then of Spain, for all should hear the joyful tidings that there is salvation for all, and we live in dread that the judgment may come upon the world before the distant countries have heard that the Christ has been born and has died and been raised by his Father from the dead, thereby abolishing the law, which was no longer needed, faith in Christ being sufficient. But if the judgment comes before all men have heard of the Christ, then is God unjust. God forbid: our sloth and tardy feet are responsible. Our fear is for the Jews that have closed their ears to the truth, and, therefore, we were warned not to leave Palestine without a last effort to save them. Once more my soul said unto me: Paul, go to Jerusalem, for the last time enter the Temple and comply with all the law, for these things matter not whether they be done or left undone; all that matters is that Jerusalem should accept Jesus. Be all things, once more, to all men. And it was after this command, given to me in the silence of the night, that I took leave of the brethren at Ephesus, saying to them: Brethren, ye knew from the first day that I came unto Asia what manner of man had come among you, directing you only towards repentance towards God, and faith in our Lord Jesus Christ. I would indeed remember all I said on that occasion, for I spoke well, the Holy Ghost being upon me, putting the very words of the leave-taking into my mouth that I should speak, words which I cannot find again, but which were written by me afterwards, as I wished them to be preserved for the use of the faithful. They shall be sent to you. But in this moment I'm too tired to remember them,

344

and will continue my story, telling how when the sails of the ship were lifted we came with a straight course unto Coos, and the day following unto Rhodes, and thence to Patara, and finding a ship about to start for Phœnicia, we went aboard and set forth again. We left Cyprus on the left, and were landed at Tyre, where there were many disciples who said to me that I must not go to Jerusalem. We kneeled on the shore and prayed; and when we had taken leave of one another, and I had said : My face ye shall see no more, we took ship, and they returned home. Next day we were at Cæsarea and went to the house of Philip the Apostle (him of many daughters, and all prophetesses), and lived with him, tarrying till there came from Judea Agabus, who, when he saw me, took my girdle and bound his own hands and feet, and said : So at Jerusalem shall the Jews bind him that owns this girdle, and they shall deliver him into the hands of the Gentiles. At which all my disciples there wept, and I said : Why do ye weep? for your weeping breaks my heart. Think not of what this man has said, even if he has spoken the truth, for I am ready to die for the name of the Lord Jesus Christ. I comforted them and went up to Jerusalem, and was received by the brethren. James and all the elders were present, and after having heard from me how widely the name of our Lord Jesus Christ had been made known to the Gentiles and to the Jews that lived among the Gentiles, they answered : Brother, there are a great many believers among the Jews, and all here are ardent followers of the law, and these have heard that thou teachest the Jews in exile that Moses may be forsaken, and that they need not circumcise their children and may set aside our customs. Now, Paul, they asked, what favour dost thou expect from us if these things be as they have been reported to us? And being sure within myself that it was not counsel they sought from me, but words out of my own mouth whereby they might stir up the people against me, I answered only : Upon whose testimony do ye say these things? There are, they said, four holy men, who are under a vow; go with them and purify thyself and pay the money they need for the shaving of their heads and all other expenses. Whereupon I was much angered, seeing the snare that they were laying for me, but, as I have told you, my rule is always to be all things to all men, and remembering that though Jesus Christ our

Lord has set us free from the law, it would be better to forgo this
liberty than to scandalise a brother, I said : I will do, brethren, as
you ask, and went with the four poor men to the Temple and remained there with them for five days, abstaining from wine, and
yielding my pate to the shearer for him to take from it the few locks
that time had spared.

All went well during the first days, but the emissaries and agents
of James, seeing that my devotion in the Temple might win over
the Jews to me, laid another snare, and I was accused of having
held converse with Trophimus, an uncircumcised Greek, in the
street the day of my arrival in Jerusalem, and this not being a
sufficient offence to justify them in stoning me as they had stoned
Stephen before my eyes, it was said that I had brought him into
the Temple, and the agents of the priests came on the fifth day to
drag me out and kill me in some convenient byway, the sacristans
closing the doors of the Temple behind me. We will make an end of
this mischief, the hirelings said, and began to look around for stones
wherewith to spatter out my brains ; they cast off their garments
and threw dust into the air, and I should have met my death if
the noise had been any less, but it was even greater than the day
Stephen died, and the Roman guard came upon the people and
drew me out of their hands, saying : What is the meaning of this ?
The Jews could not tell them so great was their anger. We'll take
him to the castle, the centurion said, and the crowd followed, pressing upon us and casting stones at me till the soldiers had perforce
to draw their swords so as to get me to the castle alive. We were
thrown hither and thither, and the violence of the crowd at the
foot of the stairs and the pressure obliged the soldiers to carry me
up the steps in their arms. So I turned to the Chief Captain, who
was trying in vain to calm the rioters, and said to him in Greek :
May I speak to them ? So thou canst speak Greek ? he answered,
surprised, and gave me leave to speak, and I said : Hebrews, listen
to a Hebrew like yourselves, and I told of the vision on the road
to Damascus, to which they listened, but as soon as the tale was
over they cried : Remove him from this world, he is not fit to live.
At these words the centurion, who was anxious to appease the
people, signed to his apparitors to seize me, and before I had time
to make myself heard these strapped me to the whipping-post, my
346

hands above me. But is it lawful to scourge a Roman and he un-condemned? I said to the centurion next to me. Whereupon the lictors withdrew and the centurion turned to the Chief Captain, who looked me up and down, for, as you see, my appearance did not command respect. Is it true that thou'rt a Roman citizen? he asked, and I answered: Yes; and he was astonished, for he had paid a great deal of money for the title. But I was born free, I answered him, confusing and perplexing him and putting a great fear in his heart that belike his office might be taken from him for having tied a Roman citizen to the whipping-post, merely that and nothing more. It was to gain my favour that he promised to sum-mon a council (the Sanhedrin), and on the day appointed, ordering my chains to be unlocked, introduced me to the Jews as a free man, saying he would remain to hear the discussion. Brothers, I began, I have lived till to-day in good conscience before God. On that the High Priest ordered those that stood by him to strike me on the face. God shall strike thee, thou whited wall, I answered him, for thou sittest to judge me according to the law, and breaking the law thou orderest me to be struck. Those that were present said: So that is how thou revilest the High Priest. I did not know he was the High Priest, I answered; if I had, I should not have spoken as I spoke, for is it not written: thou must not insult the chief of thy people?

As I spoke these words I saw that the assembly was divided into two parts, that each part was inspired by different ideas, and that one part, the Sadducees, were determined upon my death. There-fore my words were: Brothers, I am a Pharisee and the son of a Pharisee; do you know of what they accuse me? Of saying that the dead will be raised out of their graves for judgment, a thing which ye all believe. So did I divide my enemies, persuading the Phari-sees thereby to defend me, and they, believing the story I told of my vision on the road to Damascus, said: Let us hear nothing against him, a spirit or angel may have spoken to him. But the Sadducees were the stronger party, and dividing the Pharisees with their arms many rushed to kill me, and they would have done this if the Captain of the Guard had not sent soldiers to my assist-ance, who with difficulty rescued me from the Jews and brought me back to the castle. I was sorry for the Captain of the Guard,

347

who came to me and said : I know not how this will end or what to do with thee, and I answered him : There are knots in every business, and the clever man unties them, and thou'lt find a way of untying this knot in thy sleep to-night. . . . And I likewise, which was true, for a vision came to me that night, Jesus himself, and he said : Thou hast testified of me in Jerusalem and thou shalt testify of me in Rome, and Jesus having said this much, I knew that I should go to Rome; how I should go I knew not, but I knew that I should go and had no fear when my sister's son, my nephew, came to me next day and said : Forty of the Jews have banded together to kill thee, Uncle, and this is how they will do it. They will present a petition to the Chief Captain to have thee down among the council again so that they may question thee regarding some points of the law which they affirm thou hast transgressed. Thou must not go down to them, Uncle, for they have knives concealed under their cloaks, and are upon oath neither to eat nor to drink until they have killed thee. So they are base enough for this, I answered, but I'll outwit them, and calling to the centurion said : Take this young man to the Chief Captain of the Guard; he has matter to relate which the Chief Captain should hear at once; and when he had told the plot Chief Captain Lysias said : They have sworn in vain. Thou shalt go with me to Cæsarea and under a strong guard, two hundred soldiers, seventy horsemen, and two hundred spearmen; these will be able to resist any attack that the Jews may attempt even should they hear of thy departure. At nine o'clock to-night I shall put into thy hand a letter to Felix, the Governor, telling him that I know nothing against thee that merits death or prison. The orders of the Captain of the Guard were carried out punctually; we marched all night, arriving at Antipatris in the morning, which is about half-way between Jerusalem and Cæsarea, and all danger of surprise being now over the escort divided, the four hundred men returning to Jerusalem, myself going on to Cæsarea with the horsemen, to be judged by Felix, who said : I shall sit in judgment as soon as thine accusers arrive from Jerusalem. And it was five days afterwards that my accusers began to come into Cæsarea, Ananias arriving first with some of the elders and with one named Tertullus, who began his speech against me with many coaxings of the Governor, saying that it was through him that
348

Palestine enjoyed its great peace and prosperity and for these gifts he was truly thankful, and though he feared he might prove tedious, still he would hope that Felix in his great clemency might allow him to say a few further words about a pestilential fellow, an agent of sedition among the Jews throughout the world, and a ringleader of the sect known as the Nazarenes, one who came to Jerusalem but to profane the Temple. And wishing, he said, to judge him for his blasphemy according to our law, we laid hands upon him, but the Captain, Lysias, came upon us and with great violence took him out of our hands, and after hearing him disputing with us in the council said : I find no fault with him but will send him to the noble Felix. And thou, most noble Felix, hast sent for us, and we have come, and feel right well that we have not come in vain, for thy knowledge and thy justice are known in all the world. He said these things and many more of this sort till he feared that his first words were coming true and that he was beginning to weary Felix, which was the truth, for Felix raised his hand for me to speak, whereupon without cozenage and without preamble I told Felix that I had gone to Jerusalem with alms collected from all parts of the world for the poor and also for worship in the Temple. Why then, if I am the pestilential fellow that Tertullus says I am, is it that the Jews allowed me the Temple to abide therein for five days and that they have not brought witnesses to testify that they found me disputing therein or stirring the people to riot in the synagogue and in the city? And I see none here to bear witness that I do not believe in all that is written in the law and in the prophets; only that I believe with a great part of the citizens of Jerusalem that the dead will be raised from their graves for judgment at the last day. If I am guilty of heresy so are many others here. But you Essenes do not hold with the Pharisees that the corruptible body is raised from the dead, you believe that the soul only is immortal; I believe that there is a spiritual body also which is raised; and Paul turned his searching eyes on Mathias, in whose mind an answer was forming, but before he had time to speak it the brethren grew impatient for Paul to continue his story.

Felix after hearing me bade the Jews return to Jerusalem. I will deliver no sentence until I have conferred with Lysias, he said. The Jews returned discomfited, and Felix said to my jailer: Let him be relieved of his chains and be free to see his friends and disciples and to preach what he pleases. Nor was this all : Felix came with his wife, Drusilla, who was a Jewess, and she heard me tell Felix that there would be a judgment, and he answered : Speak to me again of this, and they came to me many times to hear of the judgment, and to hint at a sum of money which would be easy for me to collect; my disciples would pay for my liberty and the money would enable him to risk the anger of the Jews, who, he said, desired my death most savagely. But I was of no mind to ask my disciples to pay for my release; and then Felix, desirous of obtaining the good will of the Jews, put chains upon me again, and so left me for two years, till Festus was appointed in his place. It was three days after Festus had disembarked at Cæsarea that he went up to Jerusalem, and no sooner had he arrived there than the High Priest asked for audience and besought him to send for Paul that he might be judged in Jerusalem ; the intention of the High Priest being that I should be waylaid and killed by a highwayman among the hills. But Festus thought it was unnecessary to bring me to Jerusalem, for he was about to return to Cæsarea. Come, he said, with me, and accuse this man ; and they agreed. And it was ten days afterwards that Festus returned to Cæsarea and commanded me to be brought before his judgment seat. The Jews that had come with him sat about, and with many voices complained against me of blasphemy, but their accusations were vain, for I answered : I have not offended against the law of the Jews nor against Cæsar, and they answered : So thou sayest, but wilt thou come to Jerusalem to be judged by us? And Festus, who now only thought to avoid trouble and riot, said to me : Wilt thou go to Jerusalem that I may hear thee? But, Lord Festus, I answered, thou canst hear me here as well as in Jerusalem, and these men desire but my death and ask that I shall be brought to Jerusalem to kill me secretly ; therefore I appeal to Cæsar. Whereupon Festus answered that he had no fault to find with me, but since I had appealed to Cæsar I must go by the next ship, and as there would be none for some weeks Festus — who had said to King Agrippa and Berenice, when they came to pay a visit to the new governor, and, being Jews, were curious about my gospel : I find no fault with this man and would have set him at liberty, but he has appealed to Cæsar and by the

350

next ship he goes to Rome — permitted me my liberty to go whither I pleased and to preach as I pleased in the city and beyond the city if I pleased. Whereupon I notified to Festus I would go to Jericho, a two days' journey from Cæsarea, and he said: Go, and in three weeks a ship will be here to take thee to Rome. But he said: If the Jews should hear of thee thou'lt lose thy life; and he offered me a guard, which I refused as useless, knowing well that I should not meet my death at Jericho. Why cherish a love for them that hate thee? he said, and I answered: They are my own people, and my heart was filled again with the memory of the elect race that had given birth to the prophets. Shall these go down dead into their graves never to rise again, God's chosen people? I asked myself, and set out with Timothy, my son in the faith, for Jericho, a city I had never seen, nor had I seen the banks of Jordan down which Jesus went for John's baptism. But for these things I had little thought, but was as if thrust onwards by some force that I could not understand nor withstand; and a multitude collected and hearkened to the story of my conversion on the road to Damascus, but discontent broke out among them when I said that Jesus had come neither to confirm nor to abolish the law, that the law was well while we were children, but now we could enter into eternal life only through faith in Jesus Christ our Lord. . . . The rest of my story you know: how we fled into the hills for our lives' sake, and how Timothy in the dark of the evening kept to the left, whereas I came round the shoulder of the hill and was upheld in the path by God, who has still need of me. His ways are inscrutable, for, wishing to bring me to you, he sent me to preach in Jericho and urged the Jews to threaten me and pursue me into the hills, for he wished you holy men who live upon this ridge of rock in piety, in humility, in content, in peace one with the other, fearing God always, to hear of Jesus and his resurrection from the dead and the meaning thereof, which is that Christ came to redeem us from the bondage of the law and that sense of sin which the law reveals unceasingly and which terrifies and comes between us and love of Jesus Christ, who will (at the sound of the last trump) raise the incorruptible out of the corruptible. Even as the sown grain is raised out of its rotten grave to flourish and rejoice again at the light, so will ye flourish again in the fields of heaven, never again to sink into old age and death if ye have faith in Christ, for ye have all else, fear of God, and charity, piety and humility, brotherly love, peace and content in the work that the day brings to your hands, and the pillow that the night brings to your head for reward for the work done. God that knows all knew you were waiting on this margin of rock for the joyful tidings, and he sent me as a shepherd might send his servant out to call in the flock at the close of day, for in his justice he would not have it that ten just men should perish. He sent me to you with a double purpose, methinks, for he may have designed you to come to my aid, for it would be like him that has had in his heart since all time my great mission to Italy and Spain, to have conceived this way to provide me with new feet to carry the joyful tidings to the ends of the earth; and now I stand amazed, it being clear to me that it was not for the Jews of Jericho that I was sent out from Cæsarea but for you.

Paul waited for one of the Essenes to answer, and his eyes falling on Mathias's face he read in it a web of argument preparing wherein to catch him, and he prayed that God might inspire his answers. At last Mathias, in clear, silvery voice, broke the silence that had fallen so suddenly, and all were intent to hear the silken periods with which the Egyptian thanked Paul for the adventurous story he had related to them, who, he said, lived on a narrow margin of rock, knowing nothing of the world, and unknown to it, content to live, as it were, immersed in God. Paul's narrative was full of specious reasoning, and he regretted that Paul was leaving them, for he would have liked to have given longer time to the examination of the several points, but his story contained one thing of such great moment that he passed over many points to ask Paul to tell them why the resurrection of Jesus Christ should bring the law of Moses to an end. If the law was true once, it was true always, for the law was the mind and spirit and essence of God. That is, he continued, the law spiritually understood; for there are those among us Essenes who have gone beyond the letter. I, too, know something of that spiritual interpretation, Paul cried out, but I understand it of God's providence in relation to man during a certain period; that which is truth for the heir is not truth to the lord. Mathias acquiesced with lofty dignity, and continued his interrogation in measured phrases; that if he understood Paul
352

rightly, and he thought he did, his teaching was that the law only served to create sin, by multiplying the number of possible transgressions. Thy meaning would seem to be that Jews as well as Gentiles sin by acquiring consciousness of sin, but by faith in Jesus Christ we get peace with God and access unto his grace. Upon grace, Paul, we see thee standing as on a pedestal crying out: Sin abounds, but grace abounds; fear not sin. The words of my enemies, Paul cried, interrupting: sin so that grace may abound — God forbid! Those that are baptized in Christ are dead to sin, buried with him to rise with him again and to live a new life. The old man (that which we were before Christ died for us) was crucified with Christ so that we might serve sin no longer. Freed from the bondage of the law and concupiscence by grace we are saved through faith in our Lord Jesus Christ from damnation. It is of this grace that we would hear thee speak. Do we enter into faith through grace? Mathias asked, and, having obtained a sign of assent from Paul, he asked if grace were other than a free gift from God, and he waited again for a sign of assent. Paul nodded, and reminded him that God had said to Moses: I will have mercy on whom I will have mercy, and I will have compassion on whom I will have compassion. Then, Mathias said, the law of Moses is not ended; thou leanest upon it when it suits thy purpose to lean, and it is put aside when it pleases thee to reprove us as laggards in tradition and among the beginnings of things. It was lest some mood of injustice might be imputed to God in neglecting us that we were invited to become thy disciples, and to carry the joyful tidings into Italy and Spain. But we no longer find those rudiments in the law. We read it with the eyes of the mind, and we receive not from thy lips that God is like a man — a parcel of moods, and obedient to them. It is true that God justifies whom he glorifies, Paul answered, but for that he is not an unjust God. If he did not spare his son, but delivered him to death that we might be saved, will he not give us all things? Who shall accuse God's elect? He that chose them? Who will condemn them? Christ that will sit on the right hand of his Father, that intercedes for us? Neither death nor life nor angels can separate me from the love of our Lord Jesus Christ, and if I came hither it is for the sake of my brothers, my kinsmen that might be saved. God has not broken his promise to his chosen people. A man may be born an Israelite and not be chosen; we are true Israelites, not by birth but by election. God calls whom he pleases, and without injustice. But, Brethren, Mathias would ask of me : Why does God yet find a fault though none may resist his will? We dare not reason with God or ask him to explain his preferences. Does the vase ask the potter : Why hast thou made me thus? Had not the potter power over the clay to make from the same lump two vases, one for noble and the other for ignoble use? Not in discourse of reason is the Kingdom of God, but in its own power to be and to grow, and that power is manifested in my gospel.

The approval of the brethren whitened Mathias's cheek with anger, and he answered Paul that his denial of the law did not help him to rise to any higher conception of the deity than to compare him to a potter, and he warned Paul that to arrive at any idea of God we must forget potters, rejecting the idea of a maker setting out from a certain moment of time to shape things according to a pattern out of pre-existing matter. And I would tell thee before thou startest for the end of the earth that the Jesus Christ which has obsessed thee is but the Logos, the principle that mediates between the supreme God and the world formed out of matter, which has no being of its own, for being is not in that mere potency of all things alike, which thou callest Power, but in Divine Reason. I have heard men speak like thee in Athens, Paul answered slowly and sadly, and I answered them that the wisdom of man is but foolishness in God's sight. But thy stay was brief, and thou art without knowledge of my country, Egypt, Mathias replied, and rising from his seat he left the table and passed out on to the balcony like one offended, and, leaning his arms on the rail, he stood looking into the abyss. A Jew of Alexandria, Manahem whispered in Paul's ear, but he holds fast by the law in his own sense, and in telling of this Christ thou —— We would hear of Peter, Saddoc interrupted, the fisherman thou didst find eating unclean meat with the Gentiles. Have I not said, Paul answered, that what is eaten and what is drunk finds neither favour nor disfavour in God's eyes — that it is not by observance we are saved, but by faith in our Lord Jesus Christ that died to redeem us from the law, was raised from the dead by his Father, and appeared to the twelve
354

and to five hundred others, some of whom are dead, but many are still alive? But this Christ, who was he when he lived upon this earth? Manahem inquired. Son of the living God, Paul answered, that took on the beggarly raiment of human flesh at Nazareth, was baptized by John in Jordan, and preached in Galilee, went up to Jerusalem and was crucified by Pilate between two thieves; the third day he rose from the dead, that our sins —— Didst say he was born in Nazareth? Hazael asked, the word Nazareth having roused him from his reveries, and was baptized by John in Jordan, preached afterwards in Galilee, and suffered under Pilate? Was crucified, Paul interjected; then you have heard, he said, of the resurrection? Not of the resurrection; but we know that our Brother Jesus was born in Nazareth, was baptized in Jordan by John, preached in Galilee and suffered under Pilate. Pilate condemned many men, Paul answered, a cruel man even among the Romans. But born in Nazareth and was baptized by John didst say? I said it, Hazael answered. Which among you, Paul asked, looking into every face, is he? Jesus is not here, Hazael replied, he is out with the flock. He slept by thy side on this balcony last night. We've listened to thy story with interest, Paul; we give thee thanks for telling it, and by thy leave we will return to our daily duties and to our consciences.

CHAPTER XXXVII.

ONE of the Essenes had left some quires of his Scriptures upon the table; Paul picked them up, but, unable to fix his thoughts he walked out on to the balcony, and when he could bear no longer the murmur of the brook he returned to the domed gallery and walked through it with some vague intention of following the rubble path that led out on to the mountains, but remembering the Thracian dogs chained under the rocks, he came back and stood by the well, and in its moist atmosphere fell into argument with himself as to the cause of his disquiet, denying to himself that it was related in any way to the story he had heard from the Essenes — that there was one amongst them, a shepherd from Nazareth, who had received baptism from John and suffered under Pilate, the very one whom he had heard talking that morning to Jacob about yoes and rams. At last he attributed his disquiet to his anxiety for the safety of Timothy. All the same, he said, it was strange that Pilate should have put one from the cenoby on the cross, another Jesus of Nazareth. . . . It might be that this Essene shepherd and his story were but a trap laid for him by the Jews! But no —— Paul had written a long epistle to the Galatians reproving them for lack of faith, and now he found himself caught in one of those moments to which all flesh seems prone. But no; the cause of his disquiet was Timothy; Jesus had promised him news of Timothy, else he would not have delayed so long among these clefts. He might start at once; but he would not be able to find the way through these hills without a guide, and he could not leave till he heard from this Essene why Pilate had ordered him to be scourged. What crime was he guilty of ? A follower he was, no doubt, of Judas the Gaulonite, else Pilate would not have ordered him to be crucified. But the reason for his having left the wilderness ? There must be one, and
356

he sought the reason through the long afternoon without finding one that seemed plausible for more than a few minutes. The drone of the brook increased his agitation and the day was well-nigh spent when the doors of the cells opened and the brethren began to appear in their white garments; and when they had found seats about the table Paul related that he was waiting for Jesus to return from the hills. At last he heard one say: Here is Jesus, and at the sound of the familiar name Paul started up to meet him, and speaking the first words that came to his lips he asked him if it were true that he was from Nazareth, and had received baptism from John and suffered under Pilate. I was born in Nazareth, but what of that? Why dost thou look into my face so steadfastly? Because this noon, Paul answered, while thou wast with thy flock, I was moved to tell the brethren of Jesus of Nazareth, who died on the cross to redeem us, for I would that all you here should join with us and carry the joyful tidings to Italy and Spain. The doors are open —— Hazael coming from his cell at that moment stayed the words that had risen up in Paul's mind, and he looked at the president as if he expected him to speak, but Hazael sank into his chair and soon after into his own thoughts.

So thy name is Jesus and thou'rt from Nazareth? Paul said, turning to the shepherd, and Jesus answered: I was born in Nazareth and my life has been lived among these hills. Our guest, Saddoc said, interrupting, has told us the story of his life, and he hopes to persuade us to leave this gorge and go with him to Italy and on to Spain. To Spain? Jesus asked. To carry the joyful tidings that the doors of salvation are now open to all, Saddoc answered. He has told us that he was once a great persecutor of Christians. Of Christians? Jesus repeated. And who are they? The Christians are they that believe the Messiah promised to the Jews was raised by God from the dead, Saddoc replied, and our guest would have us go with him to Spain, for on the road to Damascus he had a vision, and nearly lost his sight in it. And ever since he has been preaching that the doors are open to all. He is the greatest traveller the world has ever known. Christ is a Greek word, Manahem said, for it seemed to him that Saddoc was speaking too much, and that he could give Jesus a better account of Paul's journeyings, his conversions of the Gentiles and the persecutions that followed

357

these conversions : For the Jews, Manahem said, have been on his track always, and his last quarrel with them was yester evening, by the Jordan, where he was preaching with Timothy. They lost each other in the hills. Of Timothy I have news, Jesus answered. He met a shepherd in the valley who pointed out the way to Cæsarea to him, and it may be that he is not far from that city now. Then I will go to Cæsarea at once, Paul cried. I have promised to put thee on the direct road, Jesus said, but it is for thee to choose another guide, he added, for Paul's face told him the thoughts that were passing in Paul's mind : that he would sooner that any other of the brethren should guide him out of the wilderness. After looking at Paul for some time he said : I've heard from Manahem and Saddoc that thou wast a persecutor of Christians, but without understanding, so hurried was the story. And they tell me, Paul said, that thou'rt from Nazareth and suffered under Pilate. More than that they do not seem to know; but from what they tell me thy story resembles that of our Lord Jesus Christ who was betrayed in a garden and was raised from the dead. At the words, who was betrayed in a garden, a light seemed to break in Jesus's face and he said : Some two years of my life are unknown to anybody here; even Hazael does not know them, and last night I was about to tell them to him on the balcony. You all remember how he was carried out of the lecture-room on to this balcony by Saddoc and Manahem, who left him with me. I had just returned from the mountain, having left my flock with Jacob, our new shepherd, and Hazael, who recovered his senses quickly in the evening air, begged me to tell him of Jacob's knowledge of the flock, and I spoke to him highly of Jacob. . . . Hazael, have I thy permission to tell the brethren here assembled the story I began to tell thee last night, but which was interrupted? The old man raised his head and said : Jesus, I hearken; go on with thy story.

Brethren, yester evening I returned from the hills after having left our flock in charge of Jacob. You know, Brethren, why I confided the flock to him. After fifty (I am fifty-three) our steps are no longer as alert as they were : an old man cannot sleep in a cavern like a young man nor defend himself against robbers like a young man, and yesternight was the first night I spent under a roof for many a year, and under that roof I am to live henceforth with you

358

here, tending on our president, who needs attention now in his great age. These things were in his mind and in mine while we sat on the balcony last night taking the air. Hazael had spoken his fear that the change from the hills to this dwelling would irk me at first, and our talk turned upon the life I have led since boyhood. Our president seemed to think that the better life is under the sky and the sure way to happiness is solitude, for he had fallen to admiration of my life spent among the hills, and had spoken to me of the long journeys it was his wont to undertake in his youth over Palestine, seeking for young men in whom he foresaw the making of good Essenes; many of you here are his discoveries, myself certainly. We indulged in recollection, and listening to him my thoughts were back in Nazareth, and I waited for him to tell me how one night he met my father, Joseph the carpenter, returning home after his day's work, and seeing in him a native of the country, he begged him to point out the road to Nazareth. My father answered: I am going thither, and the two fared on together, talking of a lodging for the night, my father fearing that no house would be open to a stranger, which was the truth. They knocked at many, but received only threats that the dogs would be turned upon them if they did not hasten away. My father said: Never shall it be rumoured of Nazareth that a stranger was turned away and had to sleep in the streets. Thou shalt have my son's bed; and taking Hazael by the hand my father urged him and forced him into our house. Thou shalt sleep in my house, my father said, and shook me out of my sleep, saying: Jesus, thy bed is wanted for a stranger; and to this day I remember standing in my smock before Hazael, my eyes dazed with sleep. Next day Hazael was teaching me, and it pleasing him to see in me the making of a good Essene, and my father being willing that I should go (a good carpenter he did not see in me), he took me away with him through Samaria into Jerusalem, and we struck across the desert, descending the hills into the plain of Jericho, and crossed the Jordan.

After a year's probation I was admitted into the order of the Essenes and was given choice of a trade, and it was decreed that I should follow that of my father or work amid the fig-trees along our terraces, but my imagination being stirred by the sight of the shepherds among the hills, I said: Let me be one. And for fifteen

359

years I led my flock, content to see it prosper under my care, until one day, spying two wolves scratching where I knew there was a cave, an empty one I thought, the hermit having been taken by wolves not long before, I couched my spear and went forward; at sight of me and my dogs the wolves fled, as I expected they would, and the hermit that had come to the cave overnight came out, and after thanking me for driving off the wolves asked me if I could guide him to a spring of pure water. Thou'rt not far from one, I said, for the cave he had come to live in was situated in the valley of the leopard's den, which is but half-a-mile from our brook. I will go thither with thee this evening, but first drink from my water-bottle, I said, for I could see he needed water. I spoke to him of the number of hermits we had lost lately from wild animals, and when he had soothed his parched mouth with my water-bottle he began to tell me that he had come from the shores of the Dead Sea and was about to begin to preach the baptism of repentance for the remission of sins, and that we must not indulge in hope of salvation because we have Abraham for our father. His words seemed to be true words, and I pondered on them, and along the Jordan everybody was asking whether he was the promised Christ. I walked miles to hear him, leaving my flock in another's charge, or waited for him to return to his cave, and often spent the night watching over him lest a wild beast should break in upon him while he slept. I had known none but my brethren, nor any city, and John had travelled through all Judea, and it was from him I learned that the world was nearing its end, and that if man did not repent at once God would raise another race out of the stones by the wayside, so needful was the love of man to God; and though God was always gentler in my mind than John's prophesying, yet John's teaching suddenly seemed right to me. I got baptism from him in Jordan and went into the wilderness to read the Book of Daniel, in which he said all had been foretold, and, having read, at his advice I bade farewell to the brethren. Manahem, Saddoc, Mathias, Caleb and Eleazar remember my departure; ye regretted it and sought to dissuade me, but I answered you, saying that God had called me to preach in my own country, Galilee, that whosoever has two coats should give one to the poor; for it is the poor that will intercede for us on the last day; and, carrying John's doctrine further, I declared that it were easier for a sword to pass through an eye of a needle than for a rich man to go to heaven, which may be true, but such judgments should be left to God, and, carrying it still further, I said it was as hard for a rich man to go to heaven as for a cow to calve in a rook's nest. I wandered beyond our doctrines and taught that this world is but a mock, a shame, a disgrace, and that naught was of avail but repentance. John's teaching took possession of me, but I would not have you think that I am about to lay my sins at John's door, for sin it is for a man to desire that which God has not given, and I should have remained an Essene shepherd following my flocks in the hills, but John did well to come out of the desert to preach the end of the world, for God had willed him to preach it. His teaching was true when he was the teacher, but when I became his disciple his teaching became false; it turned me from my natural self and into such great harshness of mind that in Nazareth when my mother came with my brothers and sisters to the synagogue, I said : Woman, I have no need of thee; and when Joseph of Arimathea returned to me after a long attendance by his father's bedside (his father had lain in a great sickness for many months; it was through Joseph's care that he had been saved from death, Joseph was a good son), I told him he must learn·to hate his father and his mother if he would become worthy to follow me. But my passion was so great in those days that I did not see that my teaching was not less than blasphemy against God, for God has created the world for us to live in it, and he has put love of parents into our hearts because he wishes us to love our parents, and if he has put into the heart of man love of woman, and into the heart of woman love of man, it is because he wishes both to enjoy that love.

I fear to think of the things I said at that time, but I must speak of them. One man asked me before he left all things to follow me if he might not bury his father first. I answered : Leave the dead to bury their dead, and to another who said : My hand is at the plough; may I not drive it to the headland? I answered : Leave all things and follow me. My teaching grew more and more violent. It is not peace, I said, that I bring to you, but a sword, and I come as a brand wherewith to set the world in flame. I said, too, that I came to divide the house; to set father against mother, brother

361

against brother, sister against sister. I can see that my remembrance of him who once was wounds the dear brethren with whom I have lived so long; I knew it would be hard for you to hear that an Essene had broken the rules of a holy order, and it is hard for me to stand before you and tell that I, who was instructed by Hazael in all the pious traditions of our race, should have blasphemed against God's creation and God's own self. Ye will thrust me through the door as an unworthy brother, saying: Go, live in the wilderness, and I shall not cry out against my expulsion through the hills and valleys, but continue to repent my sins in silence till death leads me into silence that never ends. Ye are perhaps asking yourselves why I returned hither; was it to hide myself from Pilate and the Jews? Nay, it was to repent of the evil seed I had sown that I returned to Kerith; and it was for that God wished me to repent that he took me down from the cross and cured me of my wounds in Joseph's house and sent me to lead sheep over the hills, and it was he who put this last confession into my mouth. . . . It seems to me that in telling this story, Brethren, I am doing but the work of God; no man strays very far from the work that God has decreed to him. But in the time I am telling I was so exalted by the many miracles which I had performed by the power of God or the power of a demon, I know not which, that I encouraged my disciples to speak of me as the son of David, though I knew myself to be the son of Joseph the carpenter; and when I rode into Jerusalem and the people strewed palms before me and called out: The son of David, and Joseph said to me: Let them not call thee the son of David, I answered in my pride: If they did not call it forth the stones themselves would. In the days I am telling pride lifted me above myself, and I went about asking who I was: Moses, Elijah, Jeremiah or the Messiah promised to the Jews —— A madman! A madman! or possessed by some evil spirit! Paul cried out, and rising to his feet he rushed out of the cenoby, but nobody rose to detain him; some of the Essenes raised their heads, and a moment after the interruption was forgotten.

A day passed in great exaltation and hope, and one evening I took bread and broke it, saying I was the bread of life come down from heaven and that whosoever ate of it had everlasting life given to him. After saying these words a great disquiet fell upon me,

and calling my disciples together I asked them to come to the garden of olives with me. And it was while I was asking God's forgiveness for my blasphemies that the emissaries and agents of the priests
came and took me prisoner. At the touch of their hands the belief
that I was the Messiah promised to the Jews rose up in my heart
again, and when the priests asked me if I were the Christ, the Son
of the Blessed, I answered: I am, and ye shall see the son of man
sitting on the right hand of God; and it was not till hanging on the
cross for upwards of two hours that the belief I had come down
from heaven to do our Father's will faded; again much that I had
said seemed to me evil and blasphemous, and feeling myself about
to die I called out to my Father, who answered my call at once,
bringing Joseph of Arimathea to the foot of the cross to ask the
centurion for my body for burial. But the centurion could not
deliver me unto him without Pilate's order, and both went to Pilate,
and he gave me to Joseph for burial. Nor did our Father allow the
swoon to be lifted till Joseph entered the tomb to kiss me for the
last time. It was then he opened my eyes and I saw Joseph standing by me, a lantern in his hand, looking at me . . . for the last
time before closing the tomb. He lifted me on to his shoulder and
carried me up a little twisting path to his house, and an old woman
named Esora attended to my wounds with balsam, and when they
were cured Joseph began to tell me that my stay in his house was
dangerous to him and to me, and he spoke to me in turn of Cæsarea
and Antioch as cities in which I should be safe from the Jews.
But my mind was so weak and shaken that his reasons faded and I
sat smiling at the sunlight like one bereft of sense. Strive as he
might, he could not awaken me from the lethargy in which I was
sunken, and every day and every week increased his danger and
mine; and it was not till the news came that my old comrades
had come to live above the Brook Kerith that my mind began to
awaken and to move towards a resolution. I said: I have led my
sheep over the hills yonder many a time; and I was tempted to
speak of you till the desire arose in me to see you again. Ye remember our arrival one morning at daybreak and my eagerness to see
the flock? Brother Amos was glad to see me back again, and in
talking of the flock Joseph was almost forgotten, which shows
how wandering my mind was at the time. . . . He left without
363

seeing me, but not without warning Hazael not to question me, else my mind might yield to the strain, saying that it hung on a thread, which was true, and I remember how for many a year every cliff's edge tempted me to jump over. Joseph was gone for ever, and the memories of my sins were as tongues of flame that leaped by turns out of the ashes. But the fiercest ashes grow cold in time; we turn them over without fear of flame, and last night I said to Hazael as we sat together : There is a sin in my life that none knows of; it is buried fathoms deep out of all sight of men; and Hazael having said there was little of the world's time in front of him, I was moved to conceal from him no longer the sin that Joseph had not dared to tell him — how I had once held myself to be a forerunner of the Messiah even as many had that came before me, nay, that unlike any other I began to believe myself to be the incarnate word.

A soft, vague sound, the gurgle of the brook, rose out of the stillness, as it flowed down the gorge from cavern to cavern, and the Essenes listened to it; and after a little while Hazael called to Manahem and bade him relate Paul's story, and when Jesus had heard the story he was overtaken with a great pity for Paul. But will he believe thee ? Hazael asked, lifting his chin out of his beard, and the calm of Jesus's face was troubled by the question and he sank upon a stool close by Hazael's chair. What may we do ? he muttered, and the Essenes withdrew, for they guessed that the elders had serious words to speak together. Thou hast heard my story, Hazael; nothing remains now but to bid farewell to thy old friend. To say farewell, Jesus? Hazael repeated; why should we say farewell? Hazael, the rule of our order forbids me to stay, Jesus answered; those who commit crimes like mine are cast out and left to starve in the desert. But, Jesus, Hazael replied, thou knowest well that none here would put thee beyond the doors. Thy crimes, whatever they may have been, are between thee and God. It is for thee to repent, and from hill-top to hill-top thou hast prayed for forgiveness, and through all the valleys. All things in the end rest with him. Speak to us not of going. But if God had forgiven me, Jesus answered, and my blasphemies against him, he would not have sent this man hither. And what wouldst thou do ? Hazael asked, raising his head from his beard and looking Jesus in

364

the face. I would go to Jerusalem, Jesus answered, to tell the people that I was not raised from the dead by God to open the doors of heaven to Jews and infidels alike. But who will believe thee to be the Jesus that Pilate condemned to the cross? Hazael asked. Twenty years have gone over and they will say : A poor, insane shepherd from the Judean hills. Be this as it may, my repentance will then be complete, Jesus muttered. But thou hast repented, Hazael wailed in his beard. But, Jesus, all religions, except ours, are founded on lies, and there have been thousands, and there will be thousands more. Why trouble thyself about the races that cover the face of the earth or even about thine own race? Let thy thoughts not stray from this group of Essenes whom thou hast known always or from me who found thee in Nazareth and took thee by the hand. Why think of me? It is enough to remember that all good and all evil (that concern us) proceed from ourselves. Hast not said to me that God has implanted a sense of good and evil in our hearts and that it is by this sense that we know him rather than through scrolls and miracles? Abide by thine own words, Jesus. Be not led away again by an impulse, and go not forth again, for it is by going forth, as thou knowest, that we fall into sin. Wouldst try once more to make others see and hear and feel as thou dost see and hear and feel? but such changes may not be made by any man in another. We may not alter the work of God, and we are all the works of God, each shaped out of a design that lay in the back of his mind for all eternity. We cannot reshape others nor ourselves, and why do I tell things thou knowest better than I? The thoughts that I am teaching now are thine own thoughts related to me often on thy return from the hills and stored by me in faithful memory. Hast forgotten, Jesus, having said to me : The world cannot be remoulded; all men may not be saved, only a few, by the grace of God? I said these things to thee, Hazael, but what did I say but my thoughts, and what are my thoughts? Lighter than the seed of dandelion floating on the hills. It is not to our own thoughts we must look for guidance, but God's thoughts, which are deep in us and clear in us, but we do not listen and are led away by our reason. My sin was to have preached John as well as myself. I strayed beyond myself and lost myself in the love of God, a thing a man may do if he love not his fellows. My sin was

365

not to have loved men enough. But we are as God made us, and must do the best we can with ourselves.

Jesus waited for Hazael to answer him, but Hazael made no answer, but sat like a stone, his head hanging upon his chest. Why dost thou not answer, Hazael? he said, and Hazael answered: Jesus, my thoughts were away. I was thinking of last night, of our talk together in that balcony — I was thinking, Jesus, how sweet life is in the beginning, and how it grows bitter in the mouth; and the end seems bitter indeed when we think of the gladness that day when we walked through the garlanded streets of our first day together in Nazareth. It was in the springtime of our lives and of the year. How delightful it was for me to find one like thee so eager to understand the life of the Essenes; so eager to join us. Such delight I shall not find again. We spoke last night of our journey from Nazareth to Jerusalem and across the Jordan. Thou wouldst not follow thy father's trade, but wouldst lead flocks from the hills, and becamest in time the best shepherd, it is said, ever known in the hills. No one ever had an eye for a ram or yoe like thee, and of thy cure for scab all the shepherds are envious. We were proud of our shepherd, but he met John and came to me saying that God had called him to go forth and convert the world. Since God hath placed thee here, I said, how is it that he should come and call thee away now? And thou wast eager with explanation up and down the terraces till we reached the bridge. We crossed it and followed the path and under the cliffs till we came to the road that leads to Jerusalem. It was there we said farewell. Two years or more passed away, and then Joseph brought thee back. A tired, suffering man whose wits were half gone and who recovered them slowly, but who did recover them while leading his flock. How often have we talked of its increase, and now we shall never talk again of rams and yoes nor of thy meditations in the desert and on the hill-tops and in the cave at night. So sweet to me were these times of thy returning from the hills that my hope was that the dawn was drawing nigh when thou wouldst return no more to the hills, and yesternight was a happy night when we sat together on the balcony indulging in recollection, thinking that henceforth we should live within sight of each other's faces always. My hope last night was that it was for thee to close my eyes and
366

lay me in a rock sepulchre out of reach of the hyenas, but thou art about to leave me. Some of the brethren may linger on, but should all remain I shall die alone if thou art gone. But, Hazael, I may return safe from Jerusalem, Jesus answered. The Jews will welcome me. I am no longer the enemy; Paul is the enemy of Judaism and I am become the testimony. Judaism, he says, is the root that bears the branches, and if I go to Jerusalem and tell the Jews that the Nazarene whom Pilate put upon the cross still lives in the flesh they will rejoice exceedingly, and send agents and emissaries after him. Paul persecuted me and my disciples, and now it would seem that my hand is turned against him. Remain with us, Hazael cried. Forget the world, leave it to itself and fear not; one lie more will make no difference in a world that has lived upon lies from the beginning of time. The lie has spread, Hazael, and will run all over the world even as a single mustard seed, and that Paul was able to follow the path is certain testimony that he was sent by God to me, and that I am called to be about my Father's work. As thou sayest, things repeat themselves. Farewell, Hazael. Farewell, my father in the faith. So there is no detaining thee, my dear son ; and, rising from his seat, Hazael put a staff in Jesus's hand and hung a scrip about his neck. If thy business be done perhaps —— But no, let us indulge in no false hopes. Neither will look upon the other's face again. Jesus did not answer, and returning to the balcony Hazael said : I will sit here and watch thee for the last time. But Jesus did not raise his eyes until he reached the bridge, and then he took the path that led by the cenobies of other days, and walked hastily, for he was too agitated to think. A little in front of him, some hundred yards, a great rock overhung the path, and when he came there he stopped, for it was the last point from which he could have sight of the balcony. As he stood looking back, shading his eyes with his hand, he saw two of the brethren come and touch Hazael on the shoulder. As he did not raise his head to answer, they consulted together, and Jesus hurried away lest some sudden and impetuous emotion should call him back from his errand.

CHAPTER XXXVIII.

A SMALL black bird with yellow wings, usually met with along the brook flitting from stone to stone, diverted his thoughts from Jerusalem and set him wondering what instinct had brought the bird up from the brook on to a dry hill-top. The bird has sense of the coming rain, and he came hither to escape the torrent. On looking round the sky for confirmation of the bird's instinct, he saw dark clouds gathering everywhere and in a manner that to his shepherd's eye betokened rain. The bird seems a little impatient with the clouds for not breaking, he continued, and at that moment the bird turned sharply from the rock on which he was about to alight, and Jesus, divining a cause for the change of intention, sought behind the rock for it and found it in a man lying there with foam upon his lips. He seemed to Jesus like one returning to himself out of a great swoon, and helping him to his feet Jesus seated him on a rock. In a little while, Paul said, I shall be able to continue my journey. Thou'rt Jesus whom I left speaking in the cenoby. Give me water to drink. I forgot to fill the bottle before I left the brook, Jesus answered. A little is left, but water from overnight —— It matters not, Paul said, and having drunk a little, and bathed his temples, Paul asked Jesus to help him to his feet, but after a few yards he tottered into Jesus's arms and had to rest again, and while resting he said : I rushed out of the cenoby, for I felt the swoon was nigh upon me. I am sorry to have interrupted thy discourse, he added, but refrain from repeating any of it, for my brain is too tired to listen to thee. Thou'lt understand the weakness of a sick man and pardon me. Now I'm beginning to remember. I had a promise from thee to lead me out of this desert. Yes, Paul, I promised to guide thee to Cæsarea —— But I rushed away, Paul said, and thou hast followed me, knowing well that I should

368

not find my way alone to Cæsarea. I should have missed it and perhaps fallen into the hands of the Jews or fallen over the precipice and become food for vultures. Now my strength is coming back to me, but without thee I shall not find my way out of the desert. Fear nothing, Paul, I shall not leave thee till I have seen thee safely on thy way to Cæsarea or within sight of that city. Thou hast come to guide me? Paul asked, looking up. Yes, to guide thee, Paul, to accompany thee to Cæsarea, if not all the way the greater part of it, Jesus answered. Thou'lt sleep to-morrow at a village within two hours of Cæsarea, and there we shall part. But be not afraid. I'll not leave thee till thou'rt safe out of reach of the Jews. I must be at Cæsarea to-morrow, Paul said, else my mission to Italy and Spain will be delayed, perhaps forfeited. My mission to Spain — dost hear me? Do not speak of thy mission now, Jesus answered, for he was afraid lest a wrangle might spring up between him and Paul, and he was glad when Paul asked him if he had traced his footsteps in the sand, or if an angel had guided him. My eyes are not young enough to follow footsteps in the sand, Jesus replied, and I saw no angel, but a bird turned aside abruptly from the rock on which he was about to alight, and going to seek the cause of it I found thee. Now if thy strength be coming back we will try to walk a little farther. . . . I'll lean on thee. And then, just as if Paul felt that Jesus might tell him once again that he was Jesus of Nazareth whom Pilate had condemned to the cross, he began to put questions: was Jesus sure that it was not an angel disguised as a bird that had directed him? Jesus could only answer that as far as he knew the bird was a bird and no more. But birds and angels are alike contained within the will of God; whereupon Paul invited Jesus to speak of the angels that doubtless alighted among the rocks and conversed with the Essenes without fear of falling into sin, there being no women in the cenoby. But in the churches and synagogues it was different, and he had always taught that women must be careful to cover their hair under veils lest angels might be tempted. For the soiled angel, he explained, is unable to return to heaven, and therefore passes into the bodies of men and women and becomes a demon, and when the soiled angels can find neither men nor women to descend into they abide in animals, and become arch demons. And Paul, who now seemed to Jesus to

369

have recovered a great part of his strength, spoke with great volu-
bility and vehemence, saying that angels were but the messengers
of God; to carry on the work of the world God must have messengers, but angels had no power to carry messages from man back to
God, for there was but one Mediator; and he was about to say
that this Mediator was Jesus Christ our Lord, but he checked himself, and said instead that the power to perform miracles was not
transmitted from God to man by means of angels. Angels, he
continued, were no more than God's messengers, and he related
that when he had shed a mist and darkness over the eyes of Elymas,
the soothsayer in Cyprus, he had received the power to do so direct
from God; he affirmed too, and in great earnestness, that it was
not an angel but God himself that had prompted him to tell the
cripple at Iconium to stand upright on his feet; he had been warned
in a vision not to go into Bithynia; and at Troas a man had appeared to him in the night and ordered him to come over to Macedonia, which was his country; he did not know if the man was a
real man in the flesh or the spirit of a man who had lived in the
flesh: but he was not an angel. Of that Paul was sure and certain;
then he related how he had taken ship and sailed to Samothrace,
and next day to Neapolis, and the next day to Philippi, and how in
the city of Thyatira he had bidden a demon depart out of a certain
damsel who brought her master much gain by soothsaying. And
for doing this he had been cast into prison. He knew not of angels,
and it was an earthquake that caused the prison doors to open and
not an angel. Peter had met angels, but he, Paul, had never met
one; he knew naught of angels, except the terrible Kosmokratores,
the rulers of this world, the planetary spirits of the Chaldeans, and
he feared angel worship, and had spoken to the Colossians against
it, saying: Remember there is always but one Mediator between
God and man, Jesus Christ our Lord, who came to deliver us from
those usurping powers and their chief, the Prince of the Powers of
the Air. They it was, as he had told the Corinthians, that crucified the Lord of Glory. But perhaps even they may be saved, for
they knew not what they did.

Jesus was afraid that Paul's vehemence would carry him on into
another fit like the one that he had just come out of, and he was
glad to meet a shepherd, who passed his water-bottle to Paul.
370

Fill thy bottle from mine, the shepherd said to Jesus, and there is half-a-loaf of bread in my wallet which I'd like thee to have to share with thy traveller in the morning, else he will not be able to begin the journey again. Nay, do not fear to take it, he said; my wife'll have prepared supper for me. Jesus took the bread and bade his mate farewell. There is a cave, Paul, Jesus said, in yonder valley which we can make safe against wolves and panthers. Lean on my arm. Thy head is still a trouble; drink a little more water. See, the shepherd has given me half-a-loaf, which we will share in the morning. Come, the cave is not far: in yon valley. Paul raised his eyes, and they reasoned with vague, pathetic appeal, for at that moment Jesus was the stronger. Since it must be so, I'll try, he said, and he tottered, leaning heavily on Jesus for what seemed to him a long way and then stopped. I can go no farther; thou wouldst do well to leave me to the hyenas. Go thy way. But Jesus continued to encourage him, saying that the cave in which they were to rest was at the end of the valley, and when Paul asked how many yards distant, he did not answer the exact distance, but halved it, so that Paul might be heartened and encouraged; and when the distance mentioned had been traversed and the cave was still far away he bore with Paul's reproaches and answered them with kindly voice: We shall soon be there; another few steps will bring us into it, and it isn't a long valley. Only a gutter, Paul answered, a way the rains have worn through the centuries. A strange desert, the strangest we have seen yet, and I have travelled a thousand leagues but never seen one so melancholy. I like better the great desert. I have lived all my life among these hills, Jesus replied, and to my eyes they have lost their melancholy. All thy life in these deserts, Paul replied eagerly, and his manner softened and became winning. Thou'lt forgive, he said, any abruptness there may have been in my speech; I am speaking differently from my wont; but to-morrow I shall be in health and able to follow thee and to listen with interest to thy tales of shepherding among these hills, of which thou must know a goodly number. My speech is improving, isn't it? Answer me. Jesus answered that he understood Paul very well; and could tell him many stories of flocks, pillaging by robbers and fights between brave Thracian dogs and wolves, and if such stories interested Paul he would relate them.

371

But here is our cave, he said, pointing to a passage between the rocks. We must go down on our hands and knees to enter it; and in answer to Paul, who was anxious to know the depth of the cave, Jesus averred that he knew the cave only through having once looked into it. The caves we know best are the vast caves into which the shepherd can gather his flocks, trusting to his dogs to scent the approach of a wild animal and to awaken him. Go first and I'll follow thee; and Jesus crawled till the rocks opened above him and he stood up in what Paul described as a bowel in the mountain; a long cave it was, surely, twisting for miles through the darkness, and especially evil-smelling, Paul said. Because of the bats, Jesus answered, and looking up they saw the vermin hanging among the clefts, a sort of hideous fruit — Measuring three feet from wing to wing, Paul muttered, and as large as rats. We shall see them drop from their roosts as the sky darkens and flit away in search of food, Jesus said. Paul asked what food they could find in the desert, and Jesus answered: We are not many miles from Jericho and these winged rats travel a long way. By Brook Kerith they are destructive among our figs; we take many in traps. Our rule forbids us to take life, but we cannot lose all our figs. I've often wondered why we hesitate to light bundles of damp straw in these caves, for that is the way to reduce the multitudes, which are worse than the locusts, for they are eaten; and Jesus told stories of the locust-eating hermits he had known, omitting, however, all mention of the Baptist, so afraid was he lest he might provoke Paul into disputation. See, he said, that great fellow clinging to that ledge, he is beginning to be conscious of the sun setting; and a moment after the bat flopped away, passing close over their heads into the evening air, followed soon after by dozens of male and female and many half-grown bats that were a few months before on the dug, a stinking colony, that the wayfarers were glad to be rid of. But they'll be in and out the whole night, Jesus said, and I know of no other cave within reach where we can sleep safely. Sometimes the wild cats come after them and then there is much squealing. But think no more of them. I will roll up my sheepskin for a pillow for thee, and sleep as well as thou mayst, comrade, for to-morrow's march is a long one.

372

CHAPTER XXXIX.

IT was as Jesus had said: the bats kept coming in and going out all the night through, and their squeakings as they settled themselves to sleep a little before dawn awakened Paul, who, lifting his head from the sheepskin that Jesus had rolled into a comfortable pillow for him, spied Jesus asleep in a corner, and began to ask himself if he should awaken Jesus or let him sleep a little while longer. But myself, he said, must escape from the stifle of this cave and the reek of the bats; and dropping on his hands and knees, he crawled into the air, and it was a great joy to draw the pure air into his lungs, to drink a deep draught, to look round for a wild cat. One may be lurking, he said, impatient for our departure, and as soon as we go will creep in and spring among the roosts and carry off the flopping, squeaking morsel. But if a cat had been there licking her fur, waiting for the tiresome wayfarers to depart, she would have remained undiscovered to Paul's eyes, so thick was the shadow, and it was a long time before the valley lightened and a path appeared between steep hills, twisting up the hillside among rocks that set Paul thinking of the marches undertaken and accomplished in the old days without a thought of failure; but to-day he doubted himself in a march of twelve or thirteen hours. A lively little breeze came up the valley, and snuffing it he walked encouraged, till recognising in it the smell of a wild animal, he stopped, saying to himself: A wolf! it cannot be else; and looking up the rocks he spied two not more than fifty yards distant. He watched the lolloping gait of the wolves till they were out of sight, and then descending from his rock he returned to the cave, thinking he had done wrong to leave it, for he had entrusted himself to Jesus, and perforce to clear his conscience he had to tell him he had been out in the valley and seen two wolves go by. But they did not scent me, the wind being unfavourable. If they had, and been

373

hungry, it might have gone hard with thee; and overlooking Paul
and seeing how weary he was already, Jesus added: Thy legs will
not take thee to Cæsarea to-night. And they resumed their journey,
Paul complaining that he had come by a more direct and better
way with Timothy, Jesus insisting that the way they were going
was not many miles longer than the way Paul had come by.
Moreover, it was a safer way. The Jews of Jericho have had many
hours in which to lay plans for thy capture, but believe in me and
thou'lt reach in safety a village where the Jews will not dare to
arrest a Roman prisoner. In Bethennabrio thou'lt be within a
few miles of Cæsarea, and canst look forward to seeing thy comrade Timothy the next day. And Jesus's words bringing comfort
to Paul's heart, helped him to forget his feet but not the long distance that would still have to be traversed; and his eyes wandered
over the outlines of the round-backed hills divided by steep valleys,
so much alike that he asked himself how it was that Jesus could
distinguish one from the other. But his guide seemed to divine the
way as by instinct, and Paul struggled on, encouraged by a promise
of a half-hour's rest as soon as they reached the summit of the hill
before them. But no sooner had they reached it than Jesus said:
Come behind this rock and hide thyself quickly. And when he was
safely hidden Jesus continued: Now peep over the top and thou'lt
see a shepherd leading his sheep along the hillside. But what concern of mine is a shepherd leading his sheep? Paul asked, and
Jesus answered: My concern, not thine, for I am thinking whether
it would be well to let him go his way without putting a question to
him, or whether it would be better to leave thee here while I go to
him with the intention of finding out from him if there be tidings
going about that one Paul of Tarsus, a spreader of great heresies, a
pestilential fellow, a stirrer-up of sedition, has been seen wandering,
trying to find his way back to Cæsarea. But on what pretext wilt
thou question him? The pretext will come to me on my way to
him; do thou abide here till I return; and Paul watched him running, lurching from side to side over the rough ground towards the
shepherd, still far away. Will he overtake him before he passes out
of sight and hearing? he asked himself.

The sheep were running merrily, and the breeze carrying the
sound of the pipe to Paul set him thinking of the Patriarchs and
374

then of his guide — Only mad, he said, in one corner of his brain, convinced that he returned to the Essenes because he had said in Jerusalem that he was the Messiah. A strange blasphemy, he muttered, and yet not strange enough to save the brethren from the infection of it. It would seem that they believe with him that he suffered under Pilate, without knowing, however, for what crime he was punished; and a terrible curiosity arose in Paul to learn the true story of his guide's life, who, he judged, might be led into telling it if care were taken not to arouse his suspicion. But these madmen are full of cunning, he said to himself, and he asked Jesus when he returned if he had heard of an order to seize two vagrant preachers on their way to Cæsarea. Jesus answered him that he had put no direct question to the shepherd; he had talked to him of the prospect of future rains. And we were both agreed, Jesus said, that the sky looked like rain, and he told me we should find water in the valley collected in pools among the rocks; he mentioned one by a group of fig-trees which we could not miss seeing. Thou art safe, Paul, have no fear for thy safe arrival at Cæsarea at midday to-morrow. If a search had been ordered to arrest two wayfarers my shepherd would have heard of it, for it is about here that they would try to intercept us, and we shall do well to turn into a path that they will overlook even if they have sent out agents in pursuit of thee and Timothy.

CHAPTER XL.

BY midday they reached a region more rugged than the one they had come out of. The path they followed zigzagged up steep ascents and descended into crumbling valleys and plains filled with split stones, rubble and sand — a desert truly, without sign of a living thing till the shadow of an eagle's wings passed over the hot stones. Jesus told Paul that the birds nested up among the clefts yonder and were most destructive in the spring when the yoes were lambing. Having to feed three or four eaglets, he said, the birds will descend on the flocks, the she-eagle, the larger, stronger and fiercer, attacking and driving off even the dog that does not fear a wolf; yet I have seen, he continued, a timid yoe, her youngling behind her in a coign in the hill, face the bird fiercely and butt it till she lost her eyes, poor yoe, for I came up too late with my staff. And the lamb? Paul inquired. Was far away, Jesus answered, aloft among the eaglets.

Jesus had stories of wolves and hyenas to beguile the journey, and he pointed with his staff to the narrow paths above them up which they would have to climb. But be not discouraged, he said, we shall be in a better country presently; as soon as we pass yon hill we shall begin to descend into the plain; another three leagues beyond it we shall bid each other farewell. Our parting indeed will be farewell, Paul answered. I shall never see Palestine again; I am on my way to Italy, and thence to Spain. But I am glad to have seen the Jordan, the river in which John baptized Jesus. Hast seen Galilee? Jesus asked. Paul answered carelessly that he had not. Then I will tell thee of Galilee; and Jesus continued talking, showing at every moment such an intimate and personal knowledge of Galilee that Paul could not doubt he was what he professed to be, a Nazarene. But what of that? There are hundreds of Naza-
376

renes, many of whom are called Jesus, and there is only one Jesus of Nazareth. He forbore, however, to speak these words to Jesus, looking upon him as one of demented mind, but when Jesus asked him how it was that he, who had travelled the world over, had never turned his steps towards Galilee, he replied that the human life of Jesus in Galilee concerned him not at all, and his teaching very little. Jesus taught all the virtues, but these were known to humanity from the beginning. They are in the law that God revealed to Moses, and the Greeks expound them excellently well. A teacher Jesus was, and a great teacher, but far more important was the fact that God had raised him from the dead, thereby placing him above all the prophets and near to God himself. Wherefore I have always taught that if Jesus were not raised from the dead our teaching is vain. A miracle! he said, and he looked into Jesus's face just as if he guessed him to be thinking that something more than a miracle was needed to convince the world that a man was raised from the dead into life again; and forgetful for the moment that he was talking to one whom he judged to be demented, he continued: To the truth of my doctrine more than five hundred have already testified. Jesus appeared to Mary and Martha, afterwards to Cleophas and to Khuza. On the way to Emmaus he stayed and supped with them and afterwards he appeared to the twelve. Hast met all the twelve and consulted with them? Jesus asked, and Paul answered that he had seen Peter and John and James and Philip but he knew not the others; and, of course, James, the brother of the Lord. Tell me about him, Jesus answered. He avows Jesus as a prophet among the others but no more, and observes the law more strictly than any other Jew, a narrow-minded bigot, one that has opposed my teaching as bitterly as the priests themselves. It was he who — Paul began, but Jesus interrupted and asked about Peter. Where is he? And what doctrine is he preaching? Paul answered that Peter was at Antioch: Though why he should choose to live there has always seemed strange to me, for he does not speak Greek. But what trade does he follow? Jesus asked. There are marshes and lakes about Antioch, Paul replied, and these are well stocked with fish, of a quality inferior, however, to those he used to catch in the lake of Gennesaret, but still fish for which there is some sale. He and John ply up and down the marshes drawing up a living in their nets, a poor and uncertain living I believe it to be, for they are often about telling stories to the faithful of our Lord Jesus Christ, who pay them for their recitals. One is always with them, a woman called Rachel. It is said that she poisoned a rival at a wedding, a girl called Ruth whom Jesus raised from the dead. Ruth went to her husband, but Rachel followed Jesus of Nazareth. . . . Thou'rt a Galilean, Paul said, and knowest these stories better than I. And as they walked on together, Paul's thoughts returned to the miracle of his apostleship: Received, he said, by me from Jesus Christ our Lord himself on the road to Damascus. Thy brethren have doubtless told the story to thee how in my journey from Jerusalem to Damascus, full of wrath to kill and to punish the saints, I was blinded by a great light from the skies, and out of a cloud Jesus Christ our Lord spoke to me: Paul! Paul! he cried, why persecutest thou me? Ever since that day I have preached that there is but one Mediator between God and man — Christ Jesus our Lord, and if I ran out whilst thou wast telling thy story, crying: He is mad! he is mad! it was because it seemed to me that thou wert speaking by order of the Jews who would ensnare and entrap me. None may divine men's desire of soul; unless an evil spirit has descended into thee I may not divine any reason for thy story. Some mistake there is in it that none would regret more than thou, for thou wouldst hear the truth from me this day, thereby gaining everlasting life. Why dost thou not answer me, Jesus? Because thou'rt waiting to hear from me the words that our Lord Jesus Christ spoke to me? My brethren have told it to me, Jesus answered. And thou believest it not? Paul cried. I believe, Jesus answered, that the Jesus which spake to thee out of a cloud never lived in the flesh; he was a Lord Jesus Christ of thy own imagining, and I believe, too, that if we had met in Galilee thou wouldst not have heeded me, and thou wouldst have done well, for in Galilee I was but a seeker; go thou and seek and be not always satisfied with what first comes to thy hand. And these words raising up a great rage in Paul, and believing Jesus to be an evil spirit come to tempt him, he turned fiercely upon him, threatening him with his staff, bidding him begone. But as he could not desert Paul in the wilderness Jesus dropped behind him and directed Paul's journey, bidding him tread here and not there, to

378

avoid the hill in front of him, and to keep along the valley side. And in this way they proceeded for about another hour, till Jesus cried out to Paul: Yonder are the fig-trees where the shepherd told me to look for a pool among the rocks after the late rains! Art overcome, Paul, with the long march and the heat? Rest. Let me untie thy sandals. Alas! they are worn through and will scarce carry thee into Bethennabrio. But they must carry me thither, Paul answered, and if there be water in the pool after we have drunken and filled our water-bottle, I'll loose the thongs and bathe my feet.

The season was advanced, but there were still leaves on the fig-trees, and among the rocks some water, and having drunk and filled the water-bottle, Jesus loosed the thongs of Paul's sandals and bound his feet with bandages torn from his own clothing. He broke the bread that the passing shepherd had given him, but Paul could eat very little, so overcome was he with fatigue. I shall try to eat after I have slept a little; and having made his head comfortable with his sheepskin, Jesus watched him doze away. And soon after the warm rocks brought sleep to Jesus's eyes, and he fell asleep trying to remember that he had nothing more explicit to rely upon than his own declaration (where should it be made — in the streets to the people or in the Sanhedrin to the priests?) that he was Jesus of Nazareth whom Pilate condemned to the cross, only his own words to convince the priests and the people that he was not a shepherd whom the loneliness of the hills had robbed of his senses! He could not bring the Essenes as testimony, nor could they if they came vouch for the whole truth of his story.

CHAPTER XLI.

HAST slept well, Paul, and hath sleep refreshed thee and given thee strength to pursue thy journey? Paul answered that he was very weary, but however weary must struggle on to Cæsarea. Thy strength will not suffer thee to get farther than Bethennabrio, and thy sandals will need mending even to reach the village. And seating himself on a smooth stone Paul watched Jesus's hand tying new thongs, wondering if the madman's mind was still set on Jerusalem and if he would go thither as soon as he (Paul) was safely out of the ways of the Jews. Each shut himself within the circle of his own mind, and the silence was not broken till Paul began to fear that Jesus was plotting against him; and to distract Jesus's mind from his plots, if he were weaving any, he began to compare the country they were passing through with Galilee, and forthright Jesus began to talk to Paul of Peter and John and James, sons of Zebedee, mentioning their appearances, voices, manner of speech, telling of their boats, their fishing tackle, the fish-salting factory at Magdala, Dan, and Joseph his son. He spoke a winning story of the fishing life round the lake, without mention of miracles, for it was not to his purpose to convince Paul of any spiritual power he might have enjoyed, but rather of his own simple humanity. And Paul listened, still believing his guide to be a madman. If thou hadst not run away crying: He is mad! he is mad! thou wouldst have heard how my crucifixion was brought about; how my eyes opened in the tomb and —— Interrupting Jesus, Paul hastened to assure him that if he cried out: He is mad! he is mad! he had spoken unwittingly, the words being put into his mouth by the sickness in which Jesus had discovered him. And the sickness, he admitted, might have been brought about by the shock of hearing thee speak of thyself as the Messiah. But, Paul, I did not speak of myself as the Messiah, but as an Essene who during some frenzied

380

months believed himself to be the Messiah. But shepherd, Paul answered, the Messiah promised to the Jews was Jesus of Nazareth, who was raised by his Father from the dead, and thou sayest that thou art the same. If thou didst once believe thyself to be the Messiah thou hast repented thy blasphemy. In the desert these twenty years, Jesus answered. But not till now did I know my folly had borne fruit, and that Joseph knew a story had been set going; or it may be that the story was not set going till after his death. Now it seems too late to go into the field thou hast sown with tares instead of corn. To which Paul answered: It is my knowledge of thy life among rocks that prompts me to listen to thee. The field I have sown like every other field has some tares in it, but it is full of corn ripening fast which will be ready for the reaping when it shall please the Lord to descend with his own son, Jesus of Nazareth, from the skies. As soon as the words: Jesus of Nazareth, had left his lips Paul regretted them, and upon a sudden resolve not to utter another word that might offend the madman's beliefs, he began to tell that he had brought hope to the beggar, to the outcast, to the slave; though this world was but a den of misery to them, another world was coming to which they might look forward in full surety. And many, he said, that led vile lives are now God-fearing men and women who, when the daily work is done, go forth in the evening to beseech the multitude to give some time to God. In every field there are tares, but there are fewer in my field than in any other, and that I hold to be the truth; and seeing that Jesus was listening to his story he began to relate his theology, perplexing Jesus with his doctrines, but interesting him with the glad tidings that the burden of the law had been lifted from all. If he had stopped there all would have been well, so it seemed to Jesus, whose present mind was not able to grasp why a miracle should be necessary to prove to men that the love of God was in the heart rather than in observances, and the miracle that Paul continued to relate with much unction seemed to him crude; yet he once believed that God was pleased to send his only begotten son to redeem the world by his death on a cross. A strange conception truly. And while he was thinking these things Paul fell to telling his dogma concerning predestination, and he was anxious that Jesus should digest his reply to Mathias, who had said that predestination conflicted with the doctrine of salvation for all. But Jesus,

381

who was of Mathias's opinion, refrained from expressing himself definitely on the point, preferring to forget Paul, so that he might better consider if he would be able to make plain to Paul that miracles bring no real knowledge of God to man, and that our conscience is the source of our knowledge of God and that perhaps a providence flourishes beyond the world. Meanwhile Paul continued his discourse, till, becoming suddenly aware that Jesus's thoughts were far away, he stopped speaking; the silence awoke Jesus from his meditation, and he began to compare Paul's strenuous and restless. life with his own, asking himself if he envied this man who had laboured so fiercely and meditated so little. And Paul, divining in a measure the thoughts that were passing in Jesus's mind, began to speak to Jesus of our life in the flesh and its value. For is it not true, he asked, that it is in our fleshly life we earn our immortal life? But, Paul, Jesus said, it seems unworthy to love virtue to gain heaven. Is it not better to love virtue for its own sake? I have heard that question many times, Paul answered, and believe those that ask it to be of little faith; were I not sure that our Lord Jesus Christ died, and was raised by his Father from the dead, I should turn to the pleasures of this world, though there is but little taste in me for them, only that little which all men suffer, and I have begged God to redeem me from it, but he answered : My grace suffices.

A great pity for Paul took possession of Jesus, and seeking to gain him, Jesus spoke of the Essenes and their life, and the advantage it would be to him to return to the Brook Kerith. Among the brethren thou'lt seek and find thyself; and it behoves every man, he continued, sooner or later to seek himself; and thyself, Paul, if I read thee rightly, hast always been overlooked by thee, which is a. fault. So thou thinkest, Jesus, that I have always overlooked myself? But which self? For there have been many selves in me. A Pharisee that went forth from Jerusalem with letters from the chief priests to persecute the saints in Damascus. The self that has begun to wish that life were over so that I may be brought to Christ, never to be separated again from him. Or the self that lies beyond my reason, that would hold me accursed from Christ, if thereby I might bring the whole world to Christ in exchange : which self of those three wouldst thou have me seek and discover in the caves of Kerith? He waited a little while for Jesus to answer, then he answered his own question: My work is my conscience made mani-
382

fest, and my soul is in the Lord Jesus Christ which was crucified
and raised from the dead by his Father. He lives in me, and it is
by his power that I live. . . . The men stopped and looked into
each other's eyes, and it seemed to them that no two men were so
irreparably divided. Thou must bear with me, Paul, Jesus said, a
little while longer, till we reach a certain hillside, distant about an
hour's journey from this valley. I must see thee to a place of safety,
and the thoughts in my mind I will consider while we strive up
these sand-hills. Now if thy sandals hurt thee tell me and I will
arrange the thongs differently. Paul answered that they were easy
to wear, and they toiled up the dunes in silence, Paul thinking how
he might persuade this madman to return to his cenoby and leave
the world to him. There are some, he said, as they came out of a
valley, that think the time is long deferred before the Lord will
come. Thou'rt Jesus of Nazareth, I deny it not, but the Jesus of
Nazareth that I preach is of the spirit and not of the flesh, and it
was the spirit and not the flesh that was raised from the dead. Thy
doctrine that man's own soul is his whole concern is well enough for
the philosophers of Egypt and Greece, but we who know the judgment to be near, and that there is salvation for all, must hasten with
the glad tidings. Wilt tell me, Paul, of what value would thy teaching be if Jesus did not die on the cross? Many times and in many
places I have said my teaching would be as naught if our Lord
Jesus had not died, Paul answered. Are not my hands and feet
testimony, Paul, that I speak the truth? Look upon them. Pilate
put many besides thee on the cross, Paul replied, and, as I have
told thee, my Christ is not of this world. If he be not of this world,
is he God or angel? Jesus asked, and Paul said: Neither, but God's
own son, chosen by God from the beginning to redeem the world,
not the Jews only, but all men, Gentiles and Jews alike. Thou hast
asked me to look into thy hands and feet, but what testimony may
be a few ancient scars to me that heard our Lord Jesus Christ
speak out of the clouds? Thou wast not in the cenoby when I told
my story, hoping thereby to get a dozen apostles to accompany me
to Spain — a wide and difficult country I'm told, a dozen would
not be too many; but thou wast not there to hear what befell
me on the road to Damascus, whither I was going to persecute the
saints; and again a great pity for Paul took possession of Jesus as
he listened to the story. Were I to persuade him that there was no

383

miracle, his mind would snap, Jesus said to himself, and he figured Paul wandering demented through the hills.

And when Paul came to the end of his story he seemed to have forgotten the man walking by his side. He is rapt, Jesus said to himself, in the Jesus of his imagination. And when they had walked for another hour Jesus said : Seest the ridge of hills over yonder? There we shall find the village, two hours' march from Cæsarea. The sea rises up in front of thee and a long meandering road will lead thee into Cæsarea. At yonder ridge of hills we part. And whither goest thou? Paul asked. Returnest thou to the Brook Kerith? I know not whither I go, but a great seeming is in my heart that it will not be to the Brook Kerith but to Jerusalem. To Jerusalem? Paul repeated. What persuasion or what desire would bring thee to that accursed city of men more stubborn than all others? I left the Brook Kerith, Paul, after listening to Hazael for a long while; he sought to dissuade me against Jerusalem, but I resisted his counsel, saying that now I knew thee to be preaching the resurrection of Jesus of Nazareth from the dead, thereby leading the people astray, I must return to Jerusalem to tell the priests that he whom they believed to be raised from the dead still lived in the flesh. However mad thou beest, the priests will welcome thy story and for it may glorify thee or belike put thee on the cross again. But this is sure : that emissaries will be sent to Italy and Spain, who will turn the people's mind from the truth; and the testimony of the twelve who saw Jesus and of the five hundred who saw him afterwards will be as naught; and the Jews will scoff at me, saying : He whom thou declarest was raised from the dead lives; and the Gentiles will scoff and say : We will listen to thee, Paul, another day; and the world will fall back into idolatry, led back into it by the delusions of a madman. The word of God is a weak thing, Paul, Jesus answered, if it cannot withstand and overcome the delusions of a madman, and God himself a derision, for he will have sent his son to die on the cross in vain. Of the value of the testimony of the twelve I am the better judge. Then thou goest to Jerusalem, Paul asked, to confute me? No, Paul, I shall not return to Jerusalem. Because, Paul interrupted, thou wouldst not see the world fall back into idolatry? Thou art a good man despite —— Despite my imaginations, Jesus said, interrupting Paul. So thou'rt afraid the world will fall back into idolatry? — yet Jesus of Nazareth has

384

been proclaimed by thee as the Messiah, a man above mankind.
A spiritual being, higher than the angels, therefore, in a way, part
and parcel of the Godhead though not yet equal to God. Thinkest,
Paul, that those who come after thee will not pick up the Messiah
where thou hast left him and carry him still further into deity?
It is not fear of idolatry, Paul, that turns me from Jerusalem. The
world will always be idolatrous in some sort of fashion. Bear that
well in mind whither thou goest. The world cannot be else than the
world. Let us sit here, Paul answered, for I would hear thee under
this rock in front of this sea; thou shalt tell me how thou camest
into these thoughts. Thou, a shepherd among the Judean hills.
Jesus answered him: The things that I taught in Galilee were not
vain, but I knew only part of the truth, that which thou knowest,
that sacrifices and observances are vain; and when I went to Jerusalem the infamy of the Temple and its priests became clear to me,
and I yielded to anger. Paul, it is better to love the good than to
hate the wicked. The Scribes and Pharisees conspired against me,
I was brought before the High Priest, who rent his garments ——
But, said Paul, we have little time to pass together, and rather
than that story I would hear thee tell the thoughts that came to
thee whilst thou wast leading thy flocks over the hills.

For many years, Paul, there were no thoughts in my mind, or
they were kept back, for I was without a belief; but thought returned to my desolate mind as the spring returns to these hills;
and the next step in my advancement was when I began to understand that we may not think of God as a man who would punish
men for doing things they have never promised not to do, or recompense them for denying themselves things they never promised to
forgo. Soon after I began to comprehend that the beliefs of our
forefathers must be abandoned, and that if we would arrive at any
reasonable conception of God, we must not put a stint upon him.
And as I wandered with my sheep he became in my senses not
without but within the universe, part and parcel, not only of the
stars and the earth, but of me, yea, even of my sheep on the hillside.
All things are God, Paul: thou art God and I am God, but if I
were to say thou art man and I am God, I should be the madman
that thou believest me to be. That was the second step in my advancement; and the third step, Paul, in my advancement was the
knowledge that God did not design us to know him but through our

consciousness of good and evil, only thus far may we know him. So thou seest, Paul, he has not written the utmost stint of his power upon us, and this being so, Paul — and who shall say that it is not so — it came to me to understand that all striving was vain, and worse than vain. The pursuit of an incorruptible crown leads us to sin as much as the pursuit of a corruptible crown. If we would reach the sinless state we must relinquish pursuit, which means that he who seeks the incorruptible crown starts out with words of love on his lips to persuade men to love God, and finding that men do not heed him he begins to hate them, and hate leads on into persecution. Such is the end of all worship. There is but one thing, Paul: to learn to live for ourselves, and to suffer our fellows to do likewise; all learning comes out of ourselves, and no one may communicate his thought; for his thought was given to him for himself alone. Thou art where I was once, thou hast learnt that sacrifices and observances are vain, that God is in our heart; and it may be that in years to come thy knowledge will be lengthened, or it may be that thou hast come to the rim of thy circle: we are all at tether, Paul. Wouldst thou have me learn, Jesus, that God is to be put aside? Again, Paul, thou showest me the vanity of words. God forbid that I should say banish God from thy heart. God cannot be banished, for God is in us. All things proceed from God; all things end in God; God like all the rest is a possession of the mind. He who would be clean must be obedient to God. God has not willed us to know him save through our conscience. Each man's conscience is a glimpse. These are some of the things that I have learnt, Paul, in the wilderness during the last twenty years. But seek not to understand me. Thou canst not understand me and be thyself; but, Paul, I can comprehend thee, for once I was thou. Whither goest thou? Paul cried, looking back. But Jesus made no answer, and Paul, with a flutter of exaltation in his heart, turned towards Cæsarea, knowing now for certain that Jesus would not go to Jerusalem to provoke the Jews against him. Italy would therefore hear of the life and death of our Lord Jesus Christ that had brought salvation for all, and Spain afterwards. Spain, Spain, Spain! he repeated as he walked, filled with visions of salvation. He walked with Spain vaguely in his mind till his reverie was broken by the sound of voices, and he saw people suddenly in a strange garb going towards the hillside on which he had left Jesus;

386

neither Jews nor Greeks were they, and on turning to a shepherd standing by he heard that the strangely garbed people were monks from India. And they are telling the people, the shepherd said, that they must not believe they have souls, and that they know they are saved. What can be saved but the spirit? Paul cried, and he asked the shepherd how far he was from the village of Bethennabrio. Not more than half-an-hour, the shepherd answered, and it was upon coming into sight of the village that Paul began to trace a likeness between the doctrines that Jesus had confided to him and the shepherd's story of the doctrines that were being preached by the monks from India. And he continued to unravel the skein of doubts and fears till he must needs ask the first passenger coming from the village to direct him to the inn, and it was good tidings to hear that there was one; for however meagre the food might be, it would be enough, he answered, and while he sat at supper he remembered Jesus again, and while thinking of his doctrines and the likeness they bore to those the Indians were preaching, some words of Jesus returned to him. He had said that he did not think he was going back to the Brook Kerith — And it may well be, Paul muttered, that in saying those words he was a prophet without knowing it. The monks from India will meet him in the valley, and if they speak to him they will soon gather from him that he divined much of their philosophy while watching his flock, and finding him to be of their mind they may ask him to return to India with them and he will preach there.

Sleep began to gather in Paul's eyes and he was soon dozing, thinking in his doze how pleasant it was to lie in a room with no bats above him. A remembrance of the smell kept him awake, but his fatigue was so great that his sleep grew deeper and deeper and many hours passed over, and the people in the inn thought that Paul would never wake again. But this long sleep did not redeem him from the fatigue of his journeys. He could not set out again till late in the afternoon, and it was evening when he passed over the last ridge of hills and saw the yellow sands of Cæsarea before him. The sky was grey, and the rain that Jesus had foreseen was beginning to fall, and it was through shades of evening that he saw the great mole covered with buildings stretching far into the sea. Timothy will be waiting for me at the gate if he have not fallen over a precipice, he said, and a few minutes after he caught sight of Timothy waiting for him. Paul opened his arms to him. Didst thou think that I was lost to thee for ever, Timothy? God whispered in my ears, Timothy answered, that he would bring thee back safely, and the ship is already in the offing. It would be well to go on board now, for at daybreak we weigh anchor. Thou'lt sleep better on board. And Paul, who was too weary even to answer, allowed himself to be led. And, too weary to sleep, he lay waking often out of shallow sleeps. He could hear Timothy breathing by his side, and when he raised his eyes he saw the stars that were to guide them along the coasts; but the beauty of the stars could not blot out of his mind the shepherd's face: and Paul's thoughts murmured: He who believed himself the Messiah and still thinks he is Jesus of Nazareth which was raised by his Father from the dead. Yet without his help I should not have reached Cæsarea. It then seemed to Paul that the shepherd was an angel in disguise sent to his aid, or a madman. A madman with a strange light in his eyes, he continued, and fell to thinking if the voice that spoke out of the cloud bore any likeness to the voice that had compelled his attention for so long a term on the hillside. But a bodily voice, he said, cannot resemble a spiritual voice, and it is enough that the Lord Jesus spoke to me, and that his voice has abided in me and become my voice. It is his voice that is now calling me to Rome, and it is his voice that I shall hear when my life is over, saying: Paul, I have long waited for thee; come unto me, faithful servant, and receive in me thy gain and the fruit of all thy labour. He repeated the words so loudly that Timothy awoke, and at the sight of the young man's face the present sank out of sight and he was again in Lystra, and on looking into the young man's eyes he knew that Timothy would remind him always of the woman in Lystra whom he would never see again. Of what art thou thinking, Paul? The voice seemed to come from the ends of the earth, but it came from Timothy's lips. Of Lystra, Timothy, that we shall never see again nor any of the people we have ever known. We are leaving our country and our kindred. But remember, Timothy, that it is God that calls thee Romeward. And they sat talking in the soft starlight of what had befallen them when they separated in the darkness. Timothy told that he remembered the way he had come by sufficiently not to fall far out of it, and that at daybreak he had met shepherds who had directed him. He had walked and he had rested and in that way had managed to reach Cæsarea the following evening. A long journey on foot, but a poor adventure. But thou hast been away three days, three days and three nights. . . . How camest thou hither? Thy eyes are full of story. A fair adventure, Timothy; and he related his visit to the Essenes and their dwelling among the cliffs above the Brook Kerith. A fair adventure truly, Timothy. Would I'd been with thee to have seen and heard them. Would indeed that we had not been separated —— He was about to tell the shepherd's story but was stopped by some power within himself. But how didst thou come hither? Timothy asked again, and Paul answered: The Essenes sent their shepherd with me. Timothy begged Paul to tell him more about the Essenes, but the sailors begged them to cease talking, and next day the ship touched at Sidon, and Julius, in whose charge Paul had been placed, gave him the liberty to go unto his friends and to refresh himself.

The sea of Cilicia was beautifully calm, and they sailed on, hearing all the sailors, who were Greek, telling their country's legends of the wars of Troy, and of Venus whose great temple was in Cyprus. After passing Cyprus they came to Myra, a city of Cilicia, and were fortunate enough to find a ship there bound for Alexandria, sailing from thence to Italy. Julius put them all on board it; but the wind was unfavourable, and as soon as they came within sight of Cnidus the wind blew against them and they sailed to Crete and by Salome till they came to a coast known as the Fair Havens by the city of Lasea, where much time was spent to the great danger of the ship, and also to the lives of the passengers and the crew, as Paul fully warned them, the season, he said, being too advanced for them to expect fair sailings. I have fared much by land and sea, he said, and know the danger and perils of this season. He was not listened to, but the Haven not being safe in winter they loosed for Phœnice; and the wind blew softly, and they mocked Paul, but not long, for a dangerous wind arose known as Euroclydon, against which the ship could not bear up, and so the crew let her drive before it till in fear of quicksands they unloaded the ship of some cargo. And next day, the wind rising still higher, they threw overboard all they could lay hands upon, and for several days and nights the wrack was so thick and black overhead that they were driven on and on through unknown wastes of water, Paul exhorting all to be of good cheer, for an angel of God had exhorted him that night,

389

telling that none should drown. And when the fourteenth day was spent it seemed to the sailors that they were close upon land. Upon sounding they found fifteen fathoms, and afraid they were upon rocks, they cast out anchors. But the anchors did not hold, and the danger of drowning became so great as the night advanced that the sailors would have launched a boat, but Paul besought them to remain upon the ship; and when it was day they discovered a certain creek in which they thought they might beach the ship, which they did, and none too soon, for the ship began to break to pieces soon after. But shall our prisoners be suffered to swim ashore? the soldiers asked, and they would have killed the prisoners, but the centurion restrained them, for he was minded to save Paul's life, and all reached the shore either by swimming or by clinging to wreckage which the waves cast up upon the shore. They were then upon the Island of Melita, where Paul was held to be a murderer, for a viper springing out of a bundle of sticks fastened on his hand. But he shook off the beast into the fire and felt no harm, and the islanders waited for him to swell and fall down suddenly; but when he showed no sign of sickness they would have it he was a god, and fearing lest they might offer sacrifices in his honour, as the priests of Lystra had wished to do when he bade the cripple stand straight upon his feet, he told them that he was a man like themselves; he consented, however, that they should bring him to Publius, the chief man of the island, who lay sick with fever and a flux of blood, and he rose up healed as soon as Paul imposed his hand upon him. And many other people coming, all of whom were healed, the island folk brought him presents.

After three months' stay they went on board a ship from Alexandria, which had for sign Castor and Pollux. A fair wind took them to Syracuse, where they tarried three days, and a south wind arose at Rhegium and carried them next into Puteoli, where Paul found the brethren, who begged the centurion Julius to allow him to remain with them for a few days, and on account of his great friendship and admiration of Paul he allowed him to tarry for seven days. From Puteoli Paul and Timothy and Aristarchus went forward towards Rome with the centurion, and the news of their journey having preceded them the brethren came to meet them as far as The Three Taverns. . . . With great rejoicing they all

390

went on to Rome together, and when they arrived in Rome the centurion delivered the prisoners to the Captain of the Guard, but Paul was permitted to live by himself with a soldier on guard over him, and he enjoyed the right to see whom he pleased and to teach his doctrine, which he did, calling as soon as he was rested the chiefs of the Jews together; and when they were come together he related to them the story of the persecutions he had endured from the Jews from the beginning, and that he had appealed to Cæsar that he might escape from them. He expounded and testified the Kingdom of God, persuading them on all matters concerning Jesus, his birth, his death and his resurrection, enjoining them to look into the Scriptures and to accept the testification of five hundred, many of whom were still alive, while some were sleeping. He spoke from morning to evening.

The rest of his story is unknown.